Science in Schools

Exploring the Curriculum

This book is one of a series designed to assist teachers to review practice in schools and classrooms. The series has been prepared by members of the Open University team for the course: *Applied Studies in Curriculum and Teaching*. Each volume follows a common sequence of issues relating to the nature of an area of specialization, its place in contemporary society, its treatment in schools, particular features of its teaching and learning, and consequences for organization and evaluation.

The titles in the series are:

J. Brown, A. Cooper, T. Horton, F. Toates and D. Zeldin (Eds.): *Science in Schools*
A. Cross and R. McCormick (Eds.): *Technology in Schools*
V. J. Lee (Ed.): *English Literature in Schools*

Science in Schools

edited by
Joan Brown, Alan Cooper, Tim Horton,
Frederick Toates and David Zeldin
at the Open University

Open University Press
Milton Keynes ● Philadelphia

Open University Press
Open University Educational Enterprises Limited
12 Cofferidge Close
Stony Stratford
Milton Keynes MK11 1BY, England

and
242 Cherry Street
Philadelphia, PA 19106, USA

First published 1986

British Library Cataloguing in Publication Data
Science in schools.—(Exploring the curriculum)
1. Science—Study and teaching—Great Britain
I. Brown, Joan II. Series
507'.1041 LB1585.5.G7

ISBN 0-335-15982-6
ISBN 0-335-15981-8 pbk

Library of Congress Cataloging in Publication Data
Science in schools

(Exploring the curriculum series)
Includes index.
1. Science—Study and teaching (secondary)
I. Brown, Joan (Joan E.)
Q181.3.S35 1986 507'.12 86-16336
ISBN 0-335-15982-6
ISBN 0-335-15981-8 pbk

Text design by Carlton Hill
Typeset by Getset (BTS) Ltd, Eynsham, Oxford
Printed in Great Britain by Butler and Tanner Ltd, Frome and London

Contents

Acknowledgements

The editors and publisher gratefully acknowledge the following for permission to reproduce the articles in this collection:

CHAPTER 1: The Open University (1981) *S101 Science: A Foundation Course*, Unit 1 *Science and the Planet Earth 1*, pp. 6–12, and the Open University (1976) S335 *Case Studies in Earth Science: Surface and Sedimentary Processes: Methods and Consensus in the Earth Sciences*, pp. 8–19, Milton Keynes, The Open University Press.

CHAPTER 2: J. Donnelly (1979) 'The work of Popper and Kuhn on the nature of science', *School Science Review*, March 1979, pp. 489–500.

CHAPTER 3: R.A. Lyttleton (1977) 'The nature of knowledge', in R. Duncan and M. Weston-Smith (eds) *The Encyclopedia of Ignorance*, Pergamon Press, pp. 9–17.

CHAPTER 4: P.B. Medawar (1979) 'Is the scientific paper a fraud?', BBC Publications.

CHAPTER 5: O.R. Frisch (1977) 'Why?' in R. Duncan and M. Weston-Smith (eds) *The Encyclopedia of Ignorance*, Pergamon Press, pp. 2–4.

CHAPTER 6: Albert Einstein, Foreword to M. Jammer (2nd edn, 1969) *Concepts of Space*, Cambridge Mass., Harvard University Press, pp. xi–xv.

CHAPTER 7: C.P. Snow (1965) *The Two Cultures: A Second Look*, Cambridge University Press, pp. 1–21.

CHAPTER 8: H. Collins and S. Shapin (1984) 'Uncovering the nature of science', *The Times Higher Education Supplement*, 27 June 1984, p. 13.

CHAPTER 9: T. Roszak (1970) *The Making of a Counter Culture*, London, Faber and Faber, pp. 205–38.

CHAPTER 10: S.P.R. Rose and L. Appignanesi (1986) *The Limits of Science*, Oxford, Blackwell.

CHAPTER 11: D. Layton (1982) 'Science education and values education – an essential tension?', in The British Council, *UK-USA Seminar: Science Education for the Citizen*, London, The British Council, pp. 101–8.

CHAPTER 12: N.J. Selley (1981) 'The place of alternative models in school science', *School Science Review*, December 1981, pp. 252–9.

CHAPTER 13: J. Ziman (1980) *Teaching and Learning about Science and Society*, Cambridge University Press, pp. 5–17.

CHAPTER 14: J. Soloman (1981) 'STS for schoolchildren', *New Scientist*, 8 January 1981, pp. 121–3.

CHAPTER 15: P. Uzzell (1978) 'The changing aims of science teaching', *School Science Review*, 60(210), pp. 7–20.

CHAPTER 16: D. Hodson and R.B. Prophet (1983) 'Why the science curriculum changes – evolution or social control?', *School Science Review*, September 1983, pp. 5–18.

CHAPTER 17: M.F.D. Young 'The schooling of science', in G. Whitty and M. Young (eds) *Exploration in the Politics of School Knowledge*, Driffield, Nafferton Books, pp. 47–61.

CHAPTER 18: W.J. Sherratt (1982) 'History of science in the science curriculum: an historical perspective. Part 1: Early interest and roles advocated', *School Science Review*, December 1982, pp. 225–36.

CHAPTER 19: R.H. Millar (1981) 'Curriculum rhetoric and social control: a perspective on recent science curriculum development', *European Journal of Science Education*, 3(3), pp. 272–84.

CHAPTER 20: M. Waring and B. Schofield (1981) 'Core science – educational necessity or academic pipe dream?' *School Science Review*, December 1981, pp. 215–25.

CHAPTER 21: R.W. West (1981) 'A case against the core', *School Science Review*, December 1981, pp. 226–36.

CHAPTER 22: R.W. West (1983) 'Purpose and values in science education', *School Science Review*, March 1983, pp. 407–17.

CHAPTER 23: R. Driver (1983) *The Pupil as Scientist*, The Open University Press, pp. 73–85.

CHAPTER 24: J. Gilbert (1982) 'Pupils' learning in science – issues in cognitive development', in The British Council, *UK-USA Seminar: Science Education for the Citizen*, London, The British Council, pp. 27–36.

CHAPTER 25: R. Driver (1981) 'Pupils' alternative frameworks in science', *European Journal of Science Education*, 3 (1), pp. 94–101.

CHAPTER 26: J.K. Gilbert, R.J. Osborne and P.J. Fensham (1982) 'Children's science and its consequences for teaching', *Science Education* 66(4), John Wiley and Sons Inc, pp. 623–33.

CHAPTER 27: R.J. Osborne, B.F. Bell and J.K. Gilbert (1983) 'Science teaching and children's views of the world', *European Journal of Science Education*, 5(1), pp. 1–14.

CHAPTER 28: W. Beasley (1983) 'Teacher actions and student task involvement in high school science classrooms', *European Journal of Science Education*, 5 (4), pp. 403–14.

CHAPTER 29: J. Head (1982) 'Personality and attitudes to science', in The British Council, *UK-USA Seminar: Science Education for the Citizen*, London, The British Council, pp. 57–60.

CHAPTER 30: B. Smail, J. Whyte and A. Kelly (1982) 'Girls into science and technology: the first two years', *School Science Review*, June 1982, pp. 620–30.

CHAPTER 31: G.J. Prickett (1982) 'Departmental self-evaluation in practice', *School Science Review*, December 1982, pp. 207–11.

CHAPTER 32: S. Brown and D. McIntyre (1982) 'Influences upon teachers' attitudes to different types of innovation: a study of Scottish Integrated Science', *Curriculum Inquiry*, 12 (1), pp. 35–51. Copyright 1982 The Ontario Institute for Studies in Education.

Editors' introduction

Science has had, until recently, an assured place in the curriculum of secondary schools. Now its contribution to the totality of the education of young people of all ages is under debate. At the same time, despite a plethora of schemes vying for attention, the place of science in primary education remains uncertain. We highlight some fundamental issues about science teaching in schools, examining both intentions and practice in the field. Our own view is that the future of science depends both on its integration within a 'seamless' curriculum and the identification of the unique contribution scientific understanding and awareness can give to pupils and students. Here there is a tension – perhaps an essential one – that ought not to be masked by a casual acceptance of slogans.

Many of the changes in science curriculum result from wider innovations in education and the allocation of resources to education. In secondary schools, general comprehensive reorganization has not been followed by significant changes in 'sixteen-plus' assessment. These add new emphasis to the nurturing of process skills and understanding, rather than the accumulation of scientific knowledge. At first glance this may provide for common ground with the primary tradition of 'discovery'. Yet the debates on pedagogy concerning, for example, scientific methods and frameworks are still in their infancy. In addition, science remains a high resource element in the curriculum. Innovative work, and even conventional work, on syllabuses and schemes has become under tremendous pressure in schools. Change is rarely cheap or self-sustaining. It requires investment and management to avoid disappointment and disillusionment.

The contributions in this volume are therefore intended to give much practical guidance to teachers who might also better appreciate the case for altering practice. The question 'what science should we teach?' requires some explanation of how science education is as it is and begs an understanding of science and scientific activity itself. The philosophy of science and the role of science in our technological society have rarely been major elements in the preparation of science teachers. Yet the experience of teaching, particularly as the demands within the timetables of schools grow, forces the practitioner towards rethinking their role.

There is no lack of evidence concerning 'grass roots' movements for change. Teachers of science support the largest subject association in the country in the *Association for Science Education* and, in local and regional networks, they explore the capacity of schools to develop practice. For the present, movement is in several directions simultaneously. Attention is focused on children's framing of scientific concepts, on science education in the service of 'Big Science' and technology, and its contribution to moral understanding and action. The movement for change is not without its contradictions, therefore, and we have selected articles that reveal, and may help resolve, these tensions.

The first section entitled *Science and Scientific Activity* refers to some major theories in the philosophy of science. In articles by Lyttleton and Medawar, we find that uncertainty in the mode of 'professional' activity in science is no less than in the pedagogy of schools. In the second section, concerning *Science in a Technological Society*, there are four articles, different in their messages, but each concerned with the interplay between scientific activity and wider society. A return to the classical lecture by C. P. Snow, *The Two Cultures* is rewarding, particularly for its contrast with the radical political and psychological ideas in the contributions by Roszak and Rose.

In the third section, *Science in Education*, the debate on the 'place of science' is examined for its implications at the school level. The attention to 'Science, Technology and Society' (STS) is considered critically. Layton is sceptical about the claim that it must prove emancipating for young people. Selley suggests that schools should be less tied to 'relevance' in a technological world, and introduce more appropriate models and theories. The tension between relevance, utility and disciplined learning is further explored in the following section, *Science in the Curriculum*. First it emerges in the examinations of the history of the science curriculum by Uzzell, Hodson and Prophet, and Sharratt. Young and Millar, in critical reviews of more contemporary practice, seek to explain the shifts in school science in more ideological terms. The debates here are shown in practical relief through the discussion about 'essential' school science and the core curriculum.

The fifth section, *Teaching Methods in Science*, brings together several articles on recent work on pupils' alternative frameworks in science and also gives attention to sex bias in the science work in schools. Our final section on *Review and Evaluation: Science in Schools* contains two articles relevant to the collegiality of science teachers. Prickett proposes many practical ways in which staff can be given a common sense of purpose. Brown and McIntyre's research reveals some of the difficulties, and how and why responses vary within and between schools, when new programmes are introduced. We end with reviewing the science curriculum but in fact our concern with appraising programmes of science work in schools has been paramount in earlier selections too. If the debate about school science is not to lead to indecision, there is need to rekindle fundamental thinking about the intentions and practices of those who have interest in the field.

A number of people have helped us in forming this collection. We are particularly grateful to the E803 Course Team and tutors and students of the Open University, whose guidance and advice has been invaluable.

I SCIENCE AND SCIENTIFIC ACTIVITY

The first six chapters are concerned with the related questions of characterizing the nature of scientific knowledge, describing the process of its development and relating science to other forms of knowledge. Chapter 1 presents some consciously oversimplified ideas, and the other articles fill in some of the complexities and imperfections of real science. Can one define and delimit science, despite these complexities?

Like mathematics, science has a backbone of laws, but in the case of science they can be falsified, and so are constantly being refined or replaced. Like social science and technology, science uses models to set up working hypotheses — but in science the models are likely to be based on fundamental laws. As in many of the arts, science has guiding concepts — but only in science, according to Chapter 6, is nature itself, and not opinion and consensus, the arbiter of their validity.

Science is not only an activity of the mind, widening our horizons and sharpening our curiosity, it also finds many applications. The process is not direct; scientists are rarely successful inventors. But science stimulates technologies which have, on balance, vastly improved our well-being.

No single attribute or effect of science distinguishes scientific studies from other studies, and there are senses in which 'scientist' can be interpreted very widely. Nevertheless, science has a definite character. It is, in particular, possible to identify an (idealized) methodology of science, whereas a 'methodology of art' would be a very elusive idea.

The methodology of science consists of creating a framework of theories, encapsulated in laws, expressed in terms of concepts, valid in domains well-defined by logic or by measurement. Measurements can, by the same token, lead to the falsification of the laws. The value and prestige of a theory rises with its predictive power and width of application. How important is it to appreciate scientific methodology? If we look at the people traditionally called scientists, there is little evidence that those trained in methodology are more successful than those with little such training. Perhaps this is not surprising. The patterns discerned by Kuhn and Popper are patterns in the development of a subject by a body of scientists, not the working practice of an individual scientist faced with a particularly delicate measurement or stubbornly intractable equation. But it is disturbing if, as Medawar claims, the traditional structure of a scientific paper misrepresents the way science is normally done, and so perpetuates a myth.

Perhaps the greatest strength and value of a scientific methodology is at the most general level. After all, a democratic society can only operate successfully if a high proportion of all its voters can distinguish genuine patterns in development, and critically separate fair appraisals from misleading propaganda. Frisch distinguishes different types of answers that we may encounter when we ask 'why?', as we do very often in childhood, and not often enough later on. Science is very good at making one new solution raise two new questions. Maybe that is the most important thing of all.

1 What is science? An Open University perspective

The word 'science' refers to the activity of scientists, to the knowledge held (as published material) and to the institutions that practise science. Science is an extension of everyday observations on the nature of the world; it attempts to provide models and to theorize about how *things happen. It seeks consensus. It is not essentially good or evil, but can be used to either end. Systematic experimentation and reasoning, induction and deduction, form the core of the scientific method. Science seeks to represent nature in the form of* laws, *to which each of a number of different observations can be fitted. Science is not a static body of dogma. With time, models get replaced by new models that fit a wider range of phenomena. Such replacement may be gradual or the changes can be so radical that we speak of a* conceptual revolution.

In everyday use, the words 'science' and 'scientific' mean different things to different people. They can be used to describe the *activity* of individuals or teams leading to the discovery of new knowledge. They can also mean the sum of this knowledge, the *content* of scientific books and journals in which acquired knowledge is recorded for posterity. Some people would use the same terms in an *institutional* sense, emphasizing the existence and the activities of research institutions, cooperation between specialized teams of researchers, and the planning and funding of their activities.

In spite of all these nuances of terminology, it is possible to identify at least two common aspects in any human endeavour that can legitimately claim to be of a scientific nature:

1 The aim of science is the discovery, description and understanding of new facts about nature (whether on a large scale or a small one, about things living or lifeless).

2 The methods of scientific enquiry are based on a combination of observation, experiment and reasoning.

SCIENCE AS A SOCIAL ACTIVITY

Science plays an extremely important role in the life of industrialized societies. Food and clothing, health and leisure, means of transport and long-distance communications are all strongly influenced by the results of scientific research and by its applications. At the same time, the progress of science can also be linked with the production of more destructive weapons, with increased pollution of air, rivers and oceans, and with the squandering of some rare resources.

Should scientists alone be praised for all things good and pleasant that science brings to our lives, and blamed for all that is bad, destructive and terrifying? Would it be possible to devise some mechanism by which the only scientific research allowed to flourish would be that leading to obvious benefits to mankind? Perhaps scientists themselves should take the responsibility for stopping any research that might lead to the production of weapons or to the destruction of the natural environment?

There are no simple answers to these questions because they necessarily involve moral and ethical judgements. There are, however, some important objective aspects that anyone who considers these problems must keep in mind.

First of all, it is only within the last century that science has become recognized as an organized form of human activity. Before that it was regarded only as a hobby, a pastime for a few privileged enthusiasts. But people were perfectly capable of producing tools and goods and improving their quality without having any scientific background. Glass and metals were produced by our distant ancestors, and receptacles, tools and weapons made from them, without any knowledge of the physics and chemistry involved. The desire to improve one's life, and an ability to do so, existed before science. So did the evil streak in human nature that led to the destruction of life. Science did not create social problems, it merely made them more acute. Even if it were possible to stop and abolish science, they would not go away.

The next thing to consider is that it is no more possible to stop the development of science than it is to stop the development of man. The quest for knowledge is so much a part of human nature that it cannot be curbed without changing or destroying human nature itelf. The fact that individual curiosity has become interlinked with social organization makes the position of an individual scientist more difficult, more dependent on the society as a whole. But there is no way of stopping a man from being curious and wanting to know.

Last but not least, it must be realized that most scientific discoveries can be applied *either* for the benefit *or* to the detriment of humanity. For instance, recent research in genetics could have enormous utility in medicine, but it could also provide the basis for very dangerous biological warfare agents. Indeed, many biochemists feel greatly relieved that significant progress in genetic engineering has been made only since the adoption in 1972 of an international convention prohibiting biological warfare. The question of whether the results of scientific research will be used for good or for evil is not internal to science and cannot be solved by scientists. The answers to it must be sought in the social and political context in which science is practised.

You do not have to be a scientist to know that it is not advisable to touch an object that glows red. You have acquired this knowledge either from repeated unpleasant experience, or less painfully with the help of communication from your parents or other experienced people looking after you. To have such knowledge is undoubtedly very useful, if only because it enables you to keep out of harm's way. But it is not the same as understanding *why* a glowing object is hot and how the colour of the glow and the temperature of the object are related. In a similar way, your everyday experience tells you that the Sun never rises at the same place where it set the day before, but somewhere on the opposite side of the horizon. But this observation gives you no clues as to how the Sun got over there and what happened to it between sunset and sunrise.

One could say, somewhat crudely perhaps, that science begins when man tries to reach *beyond* his common observation and experience. The details of how this reaching beyond everyday experience is achieved may be different in different cases, but essentially there are two ways of going about it. One way is to organize new observations and experiences that are not readily available in everyday life. This activity can be broadly called *experimentation*. It usually involves some degree of control over the conditions in which observations are made, so that important relations between objects and their properties are not obscured by accidental, unimportant, interfering circumstances. The second way of reaching beyond everyday experience is by *reasoning*. This involves making a step from the analysis and evaluation of direct evidence, provided by observation and experiment, to a conclusion or statement that is not immediately obvious or observable.

In the development of science as a whole, observations, experiments and reasoning are inextricably intertwined. The results of observations and experiments provide a starting point for the formulation of hypotheses, models and theories by reasoning. But the outcome of such thought processes is again tested by new observations and experiments. So, a highly idealized scheme of a scientific method could be described by the following three steps:

1 Everyday experience is supplemented by *systematic observations* and *quantitative measurements*. Such observations and measurements involve the use of agreed *units* for comparing such things as the time intervals

required to complete different events or processes, distances between different places, volumes and weights of different objects, etc. In most cases there is a need for the use of *instruments*, to detect signals that human senses cannot detect at all or cannot properly analyse.

2 All evidence obtained in this way is carefully recorded (tables of data, graphs) and analysed. The aim is to discover regularities and patterns in the multiplicity of individual data and, if possible, to suggest a *theoretical model* that would explain all the observations. Moreover, such a model usually leads to *predictions* of new, as yet unobserved, effects or phenomena.

3 Predictions based on theoretical models are tested by *experiments*, that is by systematic observations and measurements designed specifically to check whether a predicted effect exists or not. The results of such test experiments sometimes necessitate the rejection of the theoretical model outright, but more often provide additional data for its further refinement or modification.

It would be naïve to think that each and every scientist has these three steps written down or programmed in his mind, and that unless all three steps can be clearly identified in his work he is not doing his science properly. In practice, there are scientists who excel in the collection of data and in the design and realization of experiments, but are not so good at proposing theoretical explanations. At the other end of the spectrum, there are fine theorists who, if put inside a laboratory, cannot tell a mouse from a rabbit or a voltmeter from an oscilloscope (to stretch the point just a bit). Similarly, there are whole branches of science where one or the other activity predominates. Thus biology and biochemistry produce a glut of detailed experimental results and rather few general theories, whereas in astronomy and cosmology experimental data are scarce compared with the level of theoretical activity. Hence the aspects or steps of the scientific method as listed above are an abstraction from science as a whole and not an actual recipe for becoming a scientist.

ASPECTS OF SCIENTIFIC REASONING: A VOCABULARY OF TERMS

ASSUMPTION: A statement about some important factor in an experimental situation or in a theoretical model that cannot be easily proven beyond doubt but can be reasonably expected to be true, or at least approximately true, in the given circumstances of the experiment or model.

Examples: It is sometimes assumed that light travels infinitely fast. This assumption is reasonable where small distances are involved, so that the time interval from the emission of light to its detection is extremely short (e.g. when getting one's bearings from a lighthouse). But it would be a wrong assumption when thinking about stars and planets. It can take millions of years for light to travel from one star to another.

Similarly, in most experiments within an Earthbound laboratory, it is perfectly reasonable to assume that light travels in a straight line. Indeed, our nearest real thing to an ideal straight line is a beam of light. But the same assumption would be wrong where light travels through different media (e.g. air of different densities in the atmosphere) or in close vicinity to very massive objects (e.g. stars).

These examples show how important it is to list any assumptions made in the process of analysing data and deriving conclusions from them.

HYPOTHESIS: A statement of expectation about the things being studied, which is put forward tentatively, usually on the basis of incomplete evidence, as a reasoned guess.

The formulation of a hypothesis takes into account all that is already known about the object or situation under investigation and tries to identify or predict as yet unknown but possible features and/or correlations between different parts or aspects of the object or situation.

Examples: 1 My new car will be better than the new one I've just sold.

2 Most people would stop smoking if the price of one cigarette were to be fixed at £1.00.

3 Changes of atmospheric pressure cause headaches.

Comments: 1 This is a hypothesis at the time of buying the car. You hope that it will be an established fact by the time you have driven it for a while. But there is also a possibility that future events may prove the hypothesis to be wrong.

2 There is evidence that increased cost discourages consumption of almost anything. Some people certainly would stop smoking, but how many is anybody's guess: very few – half – most – nearly all? Only an experiment could tell.

3 There is evidence of the simultaneous occurrence of headaches and pressure changes. But simultaneous (or consecutive) occurrence of two effects is not in itself a proof that one causes the other. There may be other factors involved in this coincidence that are less obvious but more important.

As can be judged from the description of hypotheses and from the examples, their main value is that they encourage, invite, initiate experimental activity for their rejection or justification.

INDUCTION (inductive statement, inductive inference) A statement about the properties, aspects or behaviour of a *whole group* (class) of objects or situations, formulated on the basis of direct evidence covering only a *part*

of the group (a limited sample of the objects or situations).
Examples: 1 *Observation*: The roses in my garden are red. *Induction*: All roses are red.

2 I am not going to like this piece of music by Schoenberg since I have never enjoyed any of his compositions before.

3 The consumption of electric power per household will double within the next ten years.

Comments: You will notice from these examples that inductive statements can have very different degrees of credibility and reliability.

1 This is a typical example of what is known in common parlance as jumping to conclusions on insufficient evidence.

2 This is a more subtle example of reasoning by induction. Because I have never enjoyed any composition by Schoenberg, I expect that I shall not like the next one I hear. Often, a similar induction is based on even less reliable foundations, such as information of other people. Most prejudices are examples of (unjustified) inductive thinking.

3 This induction is based on the fact that the consumption per household has doubled over the past ten years. An induction of this kind, where an *observed trend*, or rate of change of some quantity is *projected* into the future (or extended in any other way outside the scope of observation) is known as *extrapolation*.

It is important to note that an extrapolation always conceals a hidden *assumption*, namely that all factors that determined the observed trend will work in the same way in the future or in a different place. In this particular example, the hidden assumption is that the rate of acquisition of new consumer appliances will remain the same as it was over the past ten years. It is an unreasonable assumption, because most households are perfectly happy with one television set, one refrigerator and one washing machine.

Similar examples of unreliable extrapolations include estimates of population based on assumptions about birthrates.

DEDUCTION (deductive conclusion, deductive inference): A statement about the properties or behaviour of *one particular* object or situation (or a limited sample of objects or situations) that follows by simple rules of logical thinking from a statement covering the whole class of objects or situations to which the one under consideration belongs.

Examples: 1 Roses can have any possible colour. Hence some of the roses in my garden can be red.

2 Each sale item in this basket costs £5. Hence the green pullover I like (and which is in the basket) will cost me £5.

3 It is impossible to construct a triangle from three sticks of lengths 1 cm, 2 cm, and 4 cm.

Comments: First of all, notice that, in some ways, deduction is the opposite of induction (compare the first examples under both headings). However, there are important differences. Induction extends the applicability of a statement to *new* objects or situations. Deduction, on the other hand, only *specifies* or applies the consequences of a general statement to *one particular* object included in the whole class to which the general statement refers.

An inductive statement always involves an element of risk or doubt. It is possible to make a wrong induction from a true statement (for example by overlooking an assumption whose applicability is limited). On the other hand, only inductive reasoning opens new horizons and sets new problems.

Deductive reasoning is safer. Provided the initial general statement is true, the deduction from it is also true. But it does not offer anything new, it only elucidates the consequences of the initial general statement as they apply to one individual case (Examples 2 and 3).

LAW: A statement of relationship between things, covering results of observations and experiments over a wide range of individual cases, to which there are no known exceptions.
Examples: 1 The law of reflection says that when a beam of light hits a mirror the angle at which the light is reflected is the same as the angle at which it first arrived (for any angle and any mirror).

2 Heat does not flow spontaneously from a colder body to a warmer one.

3 If the temperature of a gas enclosed in a vessel of constant volume is increased, then its pressure against the walls of the container increases in the same proportion.
Comments: 1 No doubt you take into account the practical applications of this law when you cast the reflection of the Sun onto a wall or ceiling or onto the face of somebody whose attention you want to catch.

2 You may say, quite rightly, that this statement is no more than just plain commonsense truth. And yet, it is a manifestation of one of the most general and most important laws of nature, which restricts the convertibility of heat into other more useful forms of energy. (In the scientific jargon this law is known as the second law of thermodynamics.)

3 All gases obey this law within a wide range of temperatures and pressures. It is because of this law that you should not throw aerosol containers (such as from hairsprays, car paints and flykillers) into the fire: they still contain gas and its increased pressure may lead to the explosion of the container.

The important point is that laws are not based on assumptions or on hypotheses. They represent condensed formulations of what is actually observed. They are accepted as laws because they are supported by a great deal of experimental evidence and there are no known exceptions to them. Their value to science lies in the fact that whenever, in a new experimental situation, a law appears to be broken, it provides an incentive to search for new phenomena or new processes that would remove or explain the apparent discrepancy.

MODEL: An artificial construction invented to represent or to simulate the properties, the behaviour, or the relationship between individual parts, of the real object being studied.

Examples: 1 The structure and functions of the human heart are quite complicated. But for a simple description, quite adequate for an understanding of its main role, you could say that the heart behaves like a pump. Hence in this sense a pump in a central heating system is a model of the heart.

2 Before the age of space travel, no one could actually see that the Earth was round. Yet from many observations it was possible to conclude that it must be. Thus a sphere became a model for the shape of the Earth.

3 All grains of ordinary cooking salt have the same shape, namely a cube, even if their size is different. There must be some regularity in the internal structure of all grains, which cannot be seen directly, but can be deduced from chemical and physical experiments. In order to visualize this structure, it is useful to build a three-dimensional model. In this case the model will consist of an array of small cubes and of spherical balls of two different sizes, representing the two chemical constituents, chlorine and sodium. The balls will be arranged alternately at the corners and at the centres of the walls of each cube.

Comment: Notice that in none of the examples above does the term model stand for a scaled-down replica of the real thing. Here, we are not talking about balsa-wood or plastic miniatures of ships or planes.

Although there is usually some form of similarity or correspondence between the model and the thing it represents, they are not identical, nor are they mirror images of each other. The usefulness of models lies in their representing something new, unknown and complicated, by something else, simpler and already known to us.

THEORY: A set of very few general statements that correctly describe and explain all experimental observations about the behaviour and properties of a large variety of material objects or systems.

Examples: 1 Newton's theory of universal gravitation can be summed up in a single statement about how the attractive force between two bodies depends on their masses and on the distance between them. Yet this one formulation embraces an endless multiplicity of real individual situations, from falling apples to the motion of planets and satellites.

2 The propagation of radio waves, light and X-rays through empty space as well as through a variety of materials (glass, water, metals, etc.)

can all be summed up in the form of only four mathematical equations, first formulated by Maxwell (electromagnetic wave theory).

A PARADOX: A PROFESSION WITHOUT A METHODOLOGY

What is *The Scientific Method?* There are various views. Sir Peter Medawar (1969, p. 8), who won a Nobel prize for his work on immunology in 1960, explains these contrasting views as follows, starting with the layman's view.

> A scientist is a man who weighs the earth and ascertains the temperature of the sun; he destroys matter and invents new forms of matter, and one day he will invent new forms of life. But how has he achieved the understanding that makes this possible? What methods of inquiry apply with equal efficacy to atoms and stars and genes? What is 'The Scientific Method'? What goes on in the head when scientific discoveries are made?
>
> Rhetorical questions: and when we try to answer them a remarkable state of affairs is revealed. The scholarly discipline that might be expected to hold the answers is unpopular and in the main, in its larger ambitions, unsuccessful. If the purpose of scientific methodology is to prescribe or expound a system of inquiry or even a code of practice for scientific behaviour, then scientists seem to be able to get on very well without it. Most scientists receive no tuition in scientific method, but those who have been instructed perform no better as scientists than those who have not. Of what other branch of learning can it be said that it gives its proficients no advantage; that it need not be taught or, if taught, need not be learned?

And he continues (p. 12):

> You must admit that this adds up to an extraordinary state of affairs. Science, broadly considered, is incomparably the most successful enterprise human beings have ever engaged upon; yet the methodology that has presumably made it so, when propounded by learned laymen, is not attended to by scientists, and when propounded by scientists is a misrepresentation of what they do. Only a minority of scientists have received instruction in scientific methodology, and those that have, seem no better off.

But there might be some value in examining methodology, as Professor Jevons, Head of the Department of Liberal Studies in Science at the University of Manchester (1973, p. 46) suggests:

> Why consider methodology? Quite apart from sheer academic curiosity, various possible reasons present themselves for trying to describe and understand the nature of scientific method. First, there is the hope of improving the performance of practising scientists in research by giving them methodological rules to follow. Knowing something about the theory of what they are doing might help them to do it more effectively. It is on this kind of supposition that schoolteachers, for instance, as part of their training are taught something about educational theory, and the value of this, though not beyond all question, is at least widely accepted.

However, he continues in much the same vein as Medawar:

> The same cannot, however, be said of science. Most science students emerge from their formal education quite unscathed by philosophical consideration of methodology. How much of a pity this may be is a matter on which opinions vary.

We think it is a pity, for some consideration of methodology, in practical as well as intellectual terms, can guide the design of geological investigations. However, we are not advocating a *rigid* adherence to a particular method, such as the inductive or deductive approaches, for imagination and even luck make a large contribution to the advance of science.

THE HYPOTHETICO-DEDUCTIVE APPROACH

Examination of geological literature, or questioning of geologists will reveal that induction, deduction and the hypothetico-deductive approach are all used, but it is fair to say that fundamental advances in the subject have almost always been achieved by the last of these. And usually the expected outcome of an investigation, the spark of imagination for the Earth scientist, is some kind of model. Before we look into this aspect further in a geological context, to make quite sure you have grasped the significant difference between the inductive approach, and the hypothetico-deductive approach, consider the following extract from Medawar (1969, pp. 42–5):

> So much of what I have said has been abstract that I feel I should now make amends by entertaining you with a couple of methodological caricatures.
>
> Consider the act of clinical diagnosis. A patient comes to his physician feeling wretched, and the physician sets out to discover what is wrong. In the inductive view the physician empties his mind of all prejudices and preconceptions and observes his patient intently. He records the patient's colour, measures his pulse rate, tests his reflexes and inspects his tongue (an organ that seldom stands up to public scrutiny). He then proceeds to other, more sophisticated actions: the patient's urine will be tested; blood counts and blood cultures will be made; biopsies of liver and marrow are sent to the pathology department; tubing is inserted into all apertures and electrodes applied to all exposed surfaces. The factual evidence thus assembled can now be classified and 'processed' according to the canons of induction. A diagnosis (e.g. 'It was something he ate') will thereupon be arrived at by reasoning which, being logical, could in principle be entrusted to a computer, and the diagnosis will be the right one unless the raw factual information was either erroneous or incomplete.
>
> Grossly exaggerated? Of course: as I said, a caricature; but, like a caricature, not exaggerated beyond all reason. It is obviously incomplete because no place has been found for flair and insight, and the enrichment that long experience brings to clinical skills. In Commencement Addresses and other uplifting declarations, clinicians who discourse upon the 'spirit of medicine' will always point out that, while there is a large and

profoundly important scientific element in the practice of medicine, there is also an indefinable artistry, an imaginative insight, and medicine (they will tell us) is born of a marriage between the two. But then (it seems to me) the speaker spoils everything by getting the bride and groom confused. It is the unbiased observation, the apparatus, the ritual of fact-finding and the inductive mumbo-jumbo that the clinician thinks of as 'scientific', and the other element, intuitive, and logically unscripted, which he thinks of as a creative art.

To see whether this apportionment of credit is a just one, let us turn to another clinician in the act of diagnosis. The second clinician always observes his patient with a purpose, with an idea in mind. From the moment the patient enters he sets himself questions, prompted by foreknowledge or by a sensory clue; and these questions direct his thought, guiding him towards new observations which will tell him whether the provisional views he is constantly forming are acceptable or unsound. Is he ill at all? Was it indeed something he ate? An upper respiratory virus is going around: perhaps this is relevant to the case? Has he at last done his liver an irreparable disservice? Here there is a rapid reciprocation between an imaginative and a critical process, between imaginative conjecture and critical evaluation. As it proceeds, a hypothesis will take shape which affords a reasonable basis for treatment or for further examination, though the clinician will not often take it to be conclusive.

This is a travesty too. The imagination cannot work in vacuo: there must be something to be imaginative about, a background of observation and Baconian experimentation, before the exploratory dialogue can begin. Nor have I explained the natural progression of thought that goes into clinical examination.

THE CONSENSUS OF SCIENCE

Ziman (1968) describes his concept of the consensus of science as follows (p. 9):

> Science is not merely *published* knowledge or information. Anyone may make an observation, or conceive a hypothesis, and, if he has the financial means, get it printed and distributed for other persons to read. Scientific knowledge is more than this. Its facts and theories must survive a period of critical study and testing by other competent and disinterested individuals, and must have been found so persuasive that they are almost universally accepted. The objective of Science is not just to acquire information nor to utter all non-contradictory notions; its goal is a *consensus* of rational opinion over the widest possible field. . . .
>
> The scientific enterprise is corporate. It is not merely, in Newton's incomparable phrase, that one stands on the shoulders of giants, and hence can see a little farther. Every scientist sees through his own eyes – and also through the eyes of his predecessors and colleagues. It is never one individual that goes through all the steps in the logico-inductive chain; it is a group of individuals, dividing their labour but continuously and jealously checking each other's contributions. The cliché of scientific prose betrays itself 'Hence *we* arrive at the conclusion that . . .'. The audience to which scientific publications are addressed is not passive; by its cheering or booing, its

bouquets or brickbats, it actively controls the substance of the communications that it receives.

The way in which this consensus is achieved has implications for education, since knowledge and hypotheses accepted into the consensus become established in textbooks, whereas authors preparing their research papers tacitly assume that their readers have an intimate knowledge of all the 'consensus concepts' they use. Hence research papers are difficult, if not impossible to comprehend by the beginning student; it is only after an early apprenticeship spent gaining knowledge of specific facts and hypotheses – *the vocabulary of the consensus* – that study of original literature can be rewarding.

But how do facts become accepted as such, and hypotheses become respectable within the consensus? This acceptance is not gained simply by publishing; there are hurdles to be crossed before, and after, this particular event.

Publication

Before a paper is published (and sometimes before a contribution is made in person at a conference), its author has probably prepared several drafts, which he has shown to a few colleagues for comment and criticism. Once the final typescript is completed, it is sent to the editor of a relevant scientific journal, who then submits it to referees (usually two), who report on whether the work is readable, accurate, logical, fair, balanced, original and concise.

On the basis of these reports, the editor will decide whether to publish the paper unaltered, or to refer it back to the author for revision in the light of the referees' comments, or to reject it. So, even *before* publication, the results of science are subject to a test of acceptability. And, when the work is in print, it is continually appraised by the scientific community, who may refer to it in future works, or consign it to oblivion by completely ignoring it. But how can one tell whether an individual's work is respected by his peers, so becoming part of the consensus?

Productivity and acceptability

The standing of an individual scientist is almost impossible to quantify, but within any discipline of science there are always a few names that slip easily from the tongue. The practising scientist can quite easily gauge for himself the standing of individuals within his field; he reads their publications, hears their lectures at conferences, and discusses their work with his colleagues. Thus as a member of a community, an individual has ample opportunity to judge his peers in a qualitative way.

There are two ways in which status can be quantified, albeit a little crudely. One method involves finding out how much an individual scientist has published during his career, and the other is to check on whether these publications are of any use to other workers by ascertaining how many times an individual publication is *cited* by other people.

The consensus of science and science education

The concept of the consensus of science permits the student to place his studies in the context of the process of science. The student is at the end of a long paper-chase that begins when the researcher poses a problem. Work then begins on its solution. After publication of a paper, the ideas it contains may, or may not, be accepted into the consensus. Such acceptance is manifested by citations by other authors in their papers, and eventually by the incorporation of ideas into review papers and textbooks. There may be a considerable time-lag between the formulation of a new idea and its first appearance in a textbook. There are, of course, short cuts that students can take to get a more up-to-date view of the consensus, such as reading original literature and consulting 'current-awareness' pages of journals such as *Nature*, *New Scientist* and *Science*. Teaching staff can pass on new ideas directly to their students during lectures and tutorials.

Most teaching staff in higher-education establishments argue strongly that an involvement in research is one of the essential prerequisites for them to be good teachers. They claim that such involvement is the *only* way to keep up with new developments and to 'sharpen' their intellectual capabilities.

SCIENTIFIC REVOLUTIONS

Paradigms

The set of fundamental beliefs to which a given scientist subscribes, and which he uses as a framework within which to conduct his research work, has been termed a *paradigm* by the historian of science Thomas Kuhn. Kuhn uses this term in a special way to mean more than the dictionary definition ('example', 'pattern'); in a sense it encompasses the set of beliefs that go to make up the consensus of science described in the preceding Section. Thus, adherence to a given set of paradigms identifies scientists as belonging to a certain discipline (e.g. geology), or even a sub-discipline (e.g. palaeontology, oceanography).

Such adherence to given paradigms influences the nature of scientific specialization, and hence communication, for as Kuhn (1962, p. 19–20) states:

> it is sometimes just its reception of a paradigm that transforms a group previously interested merely in the study of nature into a profession or, at least, a discipline. In the sciences (though not in fields like medicine, technology, and law, of which the principal *raison d'être* is an external social need), the formation of specialized journals, the foundation of specialists' societies, and the claim for a special place in the curriculum have usually been associated with a group's first reception of a single paradigm. At least this was the case between the time, a century and a half ago, when the institutional pattern of scientific specialization first developed and the very recent time when the paraphernalia of specialization acquired a prestige of their own.
>
> The more rigid definition of the scientific group has other consequences. When the individual scientist can take a paradigm for granted, he need no longer, in his major works, attempt to build his field anew, starting from first principles and justifying the use of each concept introduced. That can be left to the writer of textbooks. Given a textbook, however, the creative scientist can begin his research where it leaves off and thus concentrate exclusively upon the subtlest and most esoteric aspects of the natural phenomena that concern his group. And as he does this, his research communiqués will begin to change in ways whose evolution has been too little studied but whose modern end products are obvious to all and oppressive to many. No longer will his researches usually be embodied in books addressed, like Franklin's *Experiments . . . on Electricity* or Darwin's *Origin of Species*, to anyone who might be interested in the subject matter of the field. Instead they will usually appear as brief articles addressed only to professional colleagues, the men whose knowledge of a shared paradigm can be assumed and who prove to be the only ones able to read the papers addressed to them.
>
> Today in the sciences, books are usually either texts or retrospective reflections upon one aspect or another of the scientific life. The scientist who writes one is more likely to find his professional reputation impaired than enhanced. Only in the earlier, pre-paradigm, stages of the development of the various sciences, did the book ordinarily possess the same relation to professional achievement that it still retains in other creative fields. And only in those fields that still retain the book, with or without the article, as a vehicle for research communication are the lines of professionalization still so loosely drawn that the layman may hope to follow progress by reading the practitioners' original reports.

Having introduced the concept of the scientific paradigm, we can now examine the process by which the consensus of science may change, and expand, by a process that Kuhn (1962) terms 'scientific revolution'. Such revolutions may depend on a new idea – perhaps arrived at by imagination or inspiration – being accepted by other workers, or be stimulated by a new technological innovation. Thus we can speak separately of *conceptual revolutions* and *technological revolutions*, but one may be dependent on the other.

Conceptual revolutions

Kuhn (1962) divides scientific activity into two parts: *normal science* and *extraordinary science*. He likens normal science to 'puzzle-solving'; it is research firmly based on one or more past scientific achievements – achievements that a particular discipline acknowledges for a time as supplying the foundation for its continued practice. Extraordinary science, on the other hand, is preceded by a period of uncertainty, when investigators may divide into different schools of thought, so that there is no generally accepted consensus. Extraordinary science begins when a new paradigm takes over from a previously held one: a new consensus then prevails and the revolution has begun. New ideas suddenly enable a whole range of previously puzzling phenomena to be explained, and so a vigorous 'mopping-up' operation commences. As Kuhn states (1962, p. 24):

> Few people who are not actually practitioners of a mature science realize how much mop-up work of this sort a paradigm leaves to be done or quite how fascinating such work can prove in the execution. And these points need to be understood. Mopping-up operations are what engage most scientists throughout their careers. They constitute what I am here calling normal science.

Revolutions – or 'paradigm shifts' – need not be instantaneous; years of argument may precede the final conversion.

The recent appearance of plate tectonics into the consensus of Earth science is a case in point. The roots of the concept lie in the formulation of the hypothesis of continental drift by the German meteorologist Alfred Wegener in 1912. In the northern hemisphere the idea was scorned by the majority of scientists until the late 1950s, but it was accepted by many geologists in the southern hemisphere even before the Second World War, for in this region evidence for former links between continents are strong. However, the geological evidence was refuted by geophysicists, who ridiculed the idea of lateral movements on the scale envisaged by the 'drifters' on the grounds that the crust was too rigid. Paradoxically, it was the geophysicists who much later provided evidence in favour of drift, and developed the models of sea floor spreading and plate tectonics that explained great lateral movements of the lithosphere.

Finally, two points need emphasizing. Firstly, not all historians of science agree with Kuhn's ideas, saying that it is difficult to maintain two distinct kinds of science (normal, and extraordinary). Secondly, as

Jevons (1973, p. 69) suggests 'contributions form a continuous spectrum, with really major changes very rare, and minor ones most frequent, but with intermediate ones occurring with intermediate frequency.' Perhaps this is stating the obvious!

REFERENCES

Jevons, F. R. (1973) *Science Observed*, Allen and Unwin.

Kuhn, T. S. (1962) *The Structure of Scientific Revolutions* (2nd enlarged edition, 1970), University of Chicago Press.

Medawar, P. B. (1969) *Induction and Intuition in Scientific Thought*, Methuen.

Ziman, J. (1968) *Public Knowledge*, Cambridge University Press.

2 The work of Popper and Kuhn on the nature of science

J. Donnelly

Donnelly analyses the occasionally conflicting contributions of Karl Popper and Thomas Kuhn to the debate on the nature of science and scientific method. The work of these contemporary theorists is made more difficult to appreciate when knowledge is not only viewed as relative but as a tool used to secure social dominance by groups. Donnelly describes Popper's concepts of 'falsifiability', emphasizing two elements – the demarcation between science and metaphysics and the description of method. Kuhn's approach is seen to be based rather more on the social and psychological behaviour of scientists. Donnelly places emphasis on the distinctions between 'normal science' and 'revolutionary science'.

Donnelly devotes some attention to the consequences for education, and science teaching in particular, of these sets of theories. He notes Kuhn's rejection of extreme relativism and the stress both men place on the idea that facts are theory-laden.

I conclude that natural science as a form of thought exists and always has existed in a context of history and depends on historical thought for its existence. From this I venture to infer that no one can understand natural science unless he understands history . . .

'The Idea of Nature' R. G. Collingwood

WHAT IS SCIENCE?

Is this question of relevance to the teacher of science? Not at all, if we are to judge by its cursory treatment in schools, textbooks, examinations and syllabi. Commonly articles on science education take a similar view. Either they confine themselves to stating what science is not ('certain', 'absolutely right'[1]) or to suggesting some 'simple statement' which is 'adequate',[2], at least so far as methodology is concerned. In these comments occasional reference is made to the dominant modes of thought in the area, but never at more than footnote length, and attempts to state the 'scientific method' explicitly have the air of Baconian folklore[3]. Yet the intuitive answer to the question is an emphatic 'yes!'. This is not, indeed, to maintain an identity between 'science' and 'scientific education', which truism I will elaborate later. The function of the science teacher has been described as 'to retail . . . vulgarization of vulgarizations' and 'imparting basic craft skills rather than "understanding"'[4]. Even this refers to the teaching of future scientists. What of the remainder? The above depressing view notwithstanding, is it not reasonable to suggest that for both groups, some thought directed to an understanding of science might be of value in deciding what to teach and why? The irony is unintentional!

Any attempt to answer the question must be complex, a complexity increased by the fact that barriers between different facets of of the word science seem to be disappearing. Science's historical role, traditionally neutral, as a contribution to industrial innovation is being discussed as a mode of social domination[5], as is science's contribution to human thought[6]. The area known as 'sociology of science' is beginning to claim competence to treat science substantively. (Although a rearguard action is being fought. See Professor A. Huxley's address to the British Association, and a recent article by Professor N. Hammerton[7].) Neglecting the more radical approaches, two men have played a dominant role in recent discussions on the nature of science. These two are T. S. Kuhn and Sir Karl Popper. I propose to discuss the work of both men, in order to throw some light on current views on the nature of science, and because both approaches seem to have relevance on the nature of science education.

JUSTIFICATION OF SCIENTIFIC KNOWLEDGE

Knowledge was once what could be 'proven'. If science was to claim for itself the status of 'knowledge' then its statements must be provable. This view is no longer fashionable, but our forebears using an 'inductive' method derived from Bacon, suggested that it was possible to observe a sufficient number of particular cases and then to generalize, either to some simple lawlike statement, or to some theoretical entity. An early critic of these views was Hume[8], but they appear to have retained a strong hold on the scientific mind. (The term 'the inductive sciences' was common in the last century.) It ought to be clear that whatever the merits of the 'problem of induction' as a football for philosophers, induction as a method of justifying scientific knowledge will not do. Science as an activity is at once less clear cut, more variegated and more important than the process of induction implies. All are agreed that we cannot prove scientific knowledge, unless we give the word 'prove' a much weaker sense than is customary. Various responses are possible following this recognition. One is to assert that, although scientific knowledge cannot be proven, it can be made more 'probable'. Popper himself has shown that this concept of probability is psychological rather than referring to 'probability' in its normally accepted use in the mathematical sciences. Using the term in its latter sense all scientific 'hypotheses' have probability zero[9]. A more radical approach is necessary. Popper provides one based on the concept of 'falsifiability'. Kuhn provides another based, to a large extent, on his historical studies on the work of practising scientists.

POPPER AND FALSIFIABILITY

Popper's approach to science contains two elements:
1. Criteria for 'demarcation' between science and metaphysics.
2. A description (or possibly prescription) of the nature of scientific methodology.

Of these the first is frequently concerned with Popper's attempts to deny the status of 'science' to *Marxism* and certain types of social science. His approach to the second has been very influential, although his interpretation of 'scientific method' is unorthodox, concerned as it is with the scientist's treatment of his theoretical ideas, rather than their framing[10]. His views are often presented in an extreme distortion[11], resulting in him appearing to have the status of a 'straw man'. This extreme distortion may be termed 'dogmatic falsificationism'. It is reported as follows. Science proceeds by framing hypotheses, while hypotheses may be distinguished sharply from the observations on which they are based. The scientist then attempts to falsify these hypotheses. At any moment science consists of the body of, as yet, unfalsified hypotheses. The motivation for this type of approach is said to be the breakdown of the idea of induction, in so far as no number of singular statements (supposedly 'observations') e.g. 'this raven is black', can justify a universal statement e.g. 'all ravens are black'. On the other hand *one* singular statement can falsify a universal statement, or, to put it in the terms normally used, one observation can falsify a hypothesis. Apart from this as an argument in logic, it is simply not what Popper says. In his own words: 'In point of fact, no conclusive disproof of a theory can ever be produced . . .'[12]. The basis of this is that 'facts' cannot falsify statements and, so Popper believes, 'science is a system of statements'. Any given fact may be made consistent with any given theory (system of statements) by appropriate means such as introducing subsidiary hypotheses, or denying the 'fact' to be a fact at all (any teacher who has claimed 'the meter is faulty' has done this) or a variety of other methods. A good example of this type of approach was the 'discovery' of the neutrino. This particle was introduced in order to save the law of conservation of energy from anomalous data, obtained while studying β-decay. An alternative way of formulating the procedure is in terms of the 'ceteris paribus' (other things being equal) clause. Such a clause seems to be called for in most significant scientific theories, and observation-statements can only falsify theory and clause together. The scientist remains free to choose to deny that other things *are* equal and to look for some difference, or perturbing phenomenon, while retaining the given theory. We may relate this to the tendency of 'empirical' scientific laws to take on a definitional character[13]. Thus Newton's Second Law may be interpreted as defining the meanings of equal time and equal distance in observational terms. Then any deviation, far from being a falsification is a licence to look for the perturbing 'force'. (And of course its discovery is a 'verification' of Newton's Second Law.)

Popper's falsificationism is very much an aspect of his criterion of demarcation. Its correct application is in the requirement that scientific statements must be testable or falsifiable. But how can this be, in view of what has been said? Popper's answer is that a series of methodological decisions must be made. It is these decisions and their aim, which is characteristic of the scientist *qua* scientist. The aim is to state, in advance, under what conditions the scientist *will consider* his theory to be falsified. In principle this is done by deduction of consequences from the theory, which consequences have the form of singular statements ('observations'). A number of types of methodological decision are necessary. First, the 'basic statements' of the science in question must be identified. These are not the theoretically neutral observations, or even sense-data, of some theories of science. No observation can be theory-free: the 'observation' of reading a voltmeter is a theory-laden act, and all 'statements' in Popper's view of science are 'impregnated' with theories. So the basic statements will contain theoretical elements. By accepting these statements the scientist effectively makes them and their associated theories unfalsifiable. '. . .we are prisoners caught in the framework of our theories'[14]. This acceptance can however always be undone: the scientist is free to criticise the basic statements in the light of their performance. He is prisoner always of *some* theory, but is also free at any moment to seek a more effective theory. It is clear that any approach to scientific methodology which makes use of decisions made by the scientist must contain elements of 'conventionalism', whereby theories are accepted by agreement. While Popper recognizes this, he seeks strongly to limit the conventionalist element in his ideas[15]. Popper claims that there are objective criteria for judging between theories. (We shall see that this is one of the supposed areas of disagreement between Popper and Kuhn.) Of two given theories the one that is better 'corroborated' is to be preferred. The term 'corroborated' has at least a twofold meaning for Popper: '. . . it is not so much the number of corroborating instances which determines the degree of corroboration as *the severity of the various tests* to which the hypothesis in question can be, and has been, subjected'[16]. Other decisions beside those stated are required of the Popperian scientist. These include decisions concerning the use of probabilistic hypotheses. (Which are unfalsifiable, and therefore unscientific, to the dogmatic falsificationist.) Similarly, decisions concerned with when to accept a *ceteris paribus* clause are called for. Popper's views on these matters have developed, and continue to develop (see for example reference 17).

Enough has been said of Popper's views to deprive him of straw man status. He attempts to consider the logical and philosophical basis of science in a manner which retains its empirical basis and its theoretical character. The latter is important, because attempts to eliminate all but 'observational' or 'empirical' statements from science rapidly lead to a type of positivism which excludes from science many of its most fruitful and characteristic aspects[18]. It is at least arguable that it is not his detailed logical analysis of science which has been most influential, but his underlying attitude, or perhaps ideology. This involves an attack on all dogma and a belief that scientific statements 'must remain tentative for ever'. The scientist must always be searching to find more rigorous methods of testing the answers he supplies. It is, I think, undeniable that these views have had a strong influence on scientific education.

KUHN: 'NORMAL' AND 'REVOLUTIONARY' SCIENCE

Kuhn's approach is based, more than Popper's, on the social and psychological behaviour of scientists, especially the former. As such it is more open to the charges of 'irrationalism' and 'subjectivism', because he deals with these factors as they affect the substantive aspect of science. More traditional workers in the field have confined themselves to organizational aspects, for example Merton. Three terms dominate Kuhn's discourse: 'normal science', 'revolutionary science' and 'paradigm'. Normal science constitutes the bulk of scientific work done, and is notable for the acceptance by its practitioners of a system of concepts, methods and assumptions, any or all of which Kuhn calls its 'paradigm'. (The vagueness of this term has been commented on at length[19]; Kuhn uses it with such disparate meanings as: a type of instrumentation, a metaphysical speculation, a textbook.) The terms of the acceptance of what Kuhn once called 'dogma' is an important area of the approach, and one that has brought him into some conflict with Popperians and others. The history of the process by which a paradigm becomes dominant Kuhn sees as the 'pre-history' of the mature science. This prehistory was often a period when many paradigms had currency, in consequence of which each new worker in the field felt the need to construct it 'from scratch'. At some stage one of the early paradigms established itself as dominant, that is to say the group of observations which were incorporated by it successfully into a body of theory became accepted as the most important problems to be solved. Consequently the large body of anomalous observations which any paradigm must generate were relegated, in its case, to a secondary status[20]. Kuhn uses a number of historical examples to elaborate this approach, for example, the various theoretical approaches to the nature of electricity. Alongside the dominant paradigm, Kuhn sees another vital facet in the maturing of a science as the emergence of a specialist group competent to deal in the paradigm. The presence of a dominant group and paradigm allows later practitioners to 'articulate' the paradigm and study more esoteric problems. This is the process of normal science which Kuhn sees as a prerequisite for progress.

The activity of normal science is seen as akin to puzzle-solving, in which the nature of the solution, and that there is a solution, is guaranteed by the paradigm. Kuhn subdivides the activity into a number of areas:

(a) finding more, and more accurate, knowledge of 'facts' relevant to the paradigm;
(b) confirmation, or otherwise, of facts predicted by the paradigm;
(c) articulation of the paradigm: determination of physical constants, quantitative laws;
(d) prediction of intrinsically useful information;
(e) elaboration of the paradigm to produce results which may be compared with experiment.

When the existence of this type of work has been accepted by Kuhn's critics[21], they have called it 'hack science'. Others have maintained that it is 'crashingly obvious' that science is 'as Kuhn says it is'[22]. The functions of normal science, as Kuhn sees it, need to be stated carefully. He does not 'identify science with its periods of theoretical stagnation'[23]. He sees it as existing in a symbiotic relationship with revolutionary science (q.v.) in which both have a vital role to play. The role of normal science is to strive fiercely to produce a better fit between the dominant theory and its world. Only in this way can the power *and* limitations of the theory be established. Popper has, however briefly, made precisely the same point: '. . . if we give in too easily to criticism we shall never find out where the real power of our theories lies'[24]. When the limitations lie exposed, it is the function of revolutionary science to bring about the changes which will lead to a more powerful theory.

The major mechanism by which Kuhn sees normal science being replaced by revolutionary science is the breakdown of the puzzle-solving tradition. Thus any or all of the activities described as normal science will fail to produce consistent solutions. The problems thus posed will begin to occupy a more prominent place in the hierarchy of problems, and attract the attention of the most able men in the field. Continuing failure to find solutions results in the emergence of 'crisis'. Kuhn has described such a situation at length, in his capacity as a historian, for the demise of Ptolemaic cosmology[25], although he clearly does not intend the concept to apply only to such large scale crises as this[26]. He delineates three possible resolutions to crisis:

1 Incorporation of the anomalous results into the paradigm.
2 Total failure to resolve the anomalies: they are left for future generations.
3 Change to a new paradigm, into which the anomalies may be incorporated.

During times of crisis alternative paradigms proliferate and, in the last mode of resolution, one emerges with the allegiance of the specialist group competent in the field. While the crisis persists, the activities of the scientist resemble most closely those in the traditional picture of him. (It is not without significance that *Popper's* view of science has been described by him as one of 'revolution in permanence'.) Speculative theories, which do not have the emotional and intellectual commitment of the paradigm, are produced and may be readily discarded. The scientist studies the anomalies with a view to pushing the paradigm to its limits. New, in the sense of unexpected, results are obtained. In the event of the third mode of resolution occurring, Kuhn has noted the tendency for the 'paradigm-shift' to be brought about by a young man or one new to the field. He has also noted the depressing phenomenon that a new paradigm does not generally win converts, but that old scientists die. To summarize: for Kuhn, the combination of crisis and subsequent paradigm shift is what constitutes the phenomenon of 'scientific revolution'. We can highlight two deviations of Kuhn's view from a more traditional picture of science: the idea that most scientists are actively hostile to change in the theoretical structure of science, and the idea that scientific theories are, at least partly, 'incommensurable'. The first is partly a matter for the psychology of scientists, although far from irrelevant to the progress of science, as we have seen. The second we have not so far discussed, but, apart from the existence or otherwise of 'normal science', it is the point of greatest disagreement between Kuhn and his critics.

INCOMMENSURABILITY AND RELATIVISM

Kuhn's critics accuse him of subverting the objective character of science and replacing it by a kind of 'mob rule'. The establishment of one paradigm in preference to another cannot be done, he claims, using rules and involves the 'techniques of persuasion'. This follows from the incommensurability of paradigms or theories: the areas of prediction and explanatory powers of alternative paradigms may cover alternative areas of knowledge, especially before paradigms are fully developed. The use of one paradigm frequently involves the sacrifice of explanations based on another paradigm. (He cites the case of the demise of phlogistic chemistry, which removed the explanation of the similarities between metals.) This approach, his critics claim, is equivalent to destroying the essential character of science. What is that character? In this context the word that springs to mind is 'progressive'.

> The history of science is the only history which can illustrate the progress of mankind. In fact, progress has no definite and unquestionable meaning in other fields than the field of science[27].

Thus a change in the theoretical structure of science is to be seen as in some sense 'absolute'. Kuhn seems to be maintaining that it is only progress relative to some definite assumptions and problems. Hence the accusation that he is a 'relativist'. Kuhn has however made clear[28] that he believes there are criteria the application of which will show the advance in the character of science with time. (It is not clear how he reconciles the unambiguous use of such criteria in this context and their failure to be of use to the individual scientist attempting to judge between competing paradigms.) He does not then subscribe to the views of the extreme relativists who have occasionally come to his defence[29]. The sense in which Kuhn asserts himself to be a relativist is in denying the approach of scientific theories to some absolute truth. In this however we can see that his views are very close to those of Popper (see above). Moreover he maintains that there are 'good reasons' for choosing one theory in preference to another: 'accuracy, scope, simplicity' etc. What he denies is that this can be done in a 'rule-governed' fashion. He claims there are 'values', which are essential to any practising scientist, but will lead different men to different conclusions. In addition he suggests that this diversity is essential to the progress of science, preventing it entering blind-alleys when paradigms are first adopted.

Kuhn's image for the change from one paradigm to another is twofold: the '*Gestalt*-switch', and the learning of a language. The most significant aspect of these two images is the sense in which both imply that the scientist undergoes a change in world view, and in some sense a change in the world which he occupies. In the first case this is obviously so, and Kuhn elaborates the image by various examples. For example he cites the differing views taken by Galileo and an Aristotelian of the movements of a pendulum: for the first it was a body 'almost succeeding in repeating the same motion *ad infinitum*, for the second it was an example of 'constrained fall'[30]. In the case of learning a language Kuhn points out the parallel in the absence of a 'neutral language', in which the other two may be compared, to produce exact translation. The latter is impossible. So in science he maintains that there is no neutral 'observation language' to which different theories may be compared. We see the world 'in the light of' our theories. Again the similarity to Popper should be clear, but there is a difference of emphasis. Kuhn does not believe we can 'break out of our theories at any time'. This is, at least partly, due to the effort with which they are achieved during our scientific education.

EDUCATION IN SCIENCE

> I believe that all teaching on the University level (and if possible below) should be training and encouragement in critical thinking. (Popper[31])

> Of course (scientific education) is a narrow and rigid education, probably more so than any other except perhaps in orthodox theology. (Kuhn[32])

Both Popper and Kuhn have commented on, rather than discussed, education in science. This is more true of Kuhn, for whom the passing on of a paradigm is clearly of primary importance in science. We are, however, entitled to ask whether their discussions of the nature of scientific practice, couched in terms appropriate to the highest levels of the latter, are relevant to the practises in schools. At the moment this relevance might seem more obvious than in the past, the reason being the currently fashionable thesis that the best method of educating a child in science is to allow him to impersonate a scientist[33]. This, however, is a largely illusory relevance; if we consider Kuhn's picture of science for a moment we will see that it is contradictory to suggest that the process of internalizing a paradigm will bear much resemblance to the practise of a scientist exploiting that paradigm. Popper also implies that his 'revolution in permanence' is inappropriate to science education at least at the elementary level. Perhaps the views of science due to Kuhn and Popper (especially the former) provide us first with a platform from which to criticise some current ideology of scientific education. (I am aware of course that the following criticism is likely to be seen as directed at straw men. I think I have cited one source to show that such views do exist.)

In what manner is the child encouraged to impersonate a scientist? I think we can isolate two facets of this impersonation:

1. It is suggested that the child (indeed the scientist) justifies the theoretical structure he uses in some empirical manner.
2. A primary function of the child as proto-scientist is that of critic. He is to oppose 'theories' to 'facts', and the dominant epistemological role

is given to the latter. Favourite phrases of Nuffield texts are 'It looks as if . . .' and 'all we can say so far is . . .'[34].

I think we can criticise these views on two counts: as misrepresenting the mode of activity of the scientists meant to be impersonated, and as misrepresenting the activity of scientific education as akin to scientific practice, when it is closer to language learning, craft apprenticeship, indoctrination, indeed almost anything, before scientific practice. (By a coincidence which is seldom stated explicitly it is suggested that this approach is also the one most likely to interest and excite the child. Whether or not this is true, it is likely to have been the dominant motivation for the introduction of the approach.) The consequences of all this in terms of the implicit epistemology of science the child absorbs is likely to be the following:

1. Develops in the child a respect for the empirical basis of science. This however will be interpreted as justifying scientific theories, rather than relating them to laboratory operations. A subsidiary effect is the belief that 'observations' and collection of data is the primary stage in any scientific investigation.
2. Implies a dogmatic falsificationist picture of science, and engenders a belief in the subservient character of theory. In particular, theory is to be thought of as 'tentative' and never to be constructed in the face of anomalous facts.

If a procedure is followed which induces the sort of views I have stated (and I accept there are many alternative approaches, perhaps as many as there are teachers) then it seems likely to be a step back compared to older approaches.

Against 1 the force of the Humean argument is peculiarly strong at the trivial level. In the classroom, limitations of time and resources narrow the facts to a bare minimum: even simple generalizations can only be 'justified' in the most cursory fashion. There is, however, a more fundamental objection to 1. If the approaches of Popper and Kuhn tell us anything it is that in a mature scientific discipline 'facts' do not precede 'theory' temporally or epistemologically. All facts are theory-laden. All investigations proceed in the light of theory. What, then, is the nature and function of the activity known in school as an 'experiment'? By a strange insight the child recognizes this when he asks the question (disliked by protagonists of 'discovery methods') 'is this the right answer?' He is recognizing that 'experiments' are not experiments but exercises, whose purpose, among other things, is to give a definite operational content to theoretical concepts.

> Given the slightest reason for doing so, the man who reads a science text can easily take the applications to be the evidence for the theory, the

> reasons why it ought to be believed. But science students accept theories on the authority of teacher and text, not because of evidence. What alternatives have they, or what competence?[35]

We must be wary of giving the impression that the theoretical structure of science rests on any probative base, still less on the set of practical and theoretical exercises used in school to hand on a paradigm.

We can attack the dogmatic falsificationism of 2 with particular force in the classroom: the ratio of false to true 'facts' there must be very large. We have already pointed out that, far from being a dogmatic falsificationist, Popper sees his methodology as requiring decisions of a high order of sophistication. We may recall also Kuhn's description of the normal/revolutionary science dichotomy. He links the inevitability with which science generates revolutions with the skill and determination with which the practitioners of normal science attempt to mold that science to its world. In doing so they generate anomaly, and eventually, crisis. This crisis comes only as a result of their efforts and thorough knowledge of the fit between the normal science and its world. Rapid, over-enthusiastic criticism of theories, from an undeveloped understanding of them, is characteristic only of immature sciences. Any theory, however revolutionary, will contain anomalies when compared to recorded facts. The attitude likely to be generated by 'all we can say so far is . . .' is likely to be fatal for normal and revolutionary scientist alike. The willingness to see beyond the facts is essential in both cases: in the first it is the ability to hold to a particular theoretical picture, in the second the ability to make bold and imaginative leaps. In both cases the existence of anomalies must be tolerated.

These criticisms of some ideas implicit in modern approaches seem to be generating some positive requirements for scientific education. These requirements, however, seem to be contradictory. This contradictory character seems to be implied by the standpoint from which the criticism is launched. The Kuhnian normal and revolutionary scientist (probably the same man) needs to transcend and respect 'facts' in each case. The Popperian scientist needs to criticise and create theoretical frameworks. In each case the need to treat theories as dogma goes hand in hand with a respect for facts, and an acceptance of the need to jettison theories at regular intervals. This view is perhaps summed up by the anarchist philosopher of science Feyerabend:

> given any rule, however 'fundamental' or 'necessary' for science, there are always circumstances when it is advisable not only to ignore the rule, but to adopt its opposite.[36]

How are these contradictions to be resolved for scientific education? What approach are we to encourage in children, and what methods are we to use? Perhaps a clue to the answer lies in the quotation with which

I began this article. Perhaps only a genuine study of the historical bases of science, based on a modern historiography of science, will bring out the dialectic between the critical and the dogmatic role of the scientist.

REFERENCES

1 Neville, P., *Secondary Science Review* [S.S.R.], 1968, 169, **49**, 859.
2 Prestt, B., *S.S.R.*, 1976, 203, **58**, 204.
3 ibid., 205.
4 Ravetz, J. R., *Scientific Knowledge and its Social Problems* (Penguin, 1973) p. 207.
5 Marglin, S., 'What do bosses do?' in Gorz, A. (ed.) *The Division of Labour* (Harvester Press, 1975).
6 Marcuse, H., *One Dimensional Man* (Abacus, 1972).
7 Hammerton, N., *New Scientist*, 3 December 1977, 274.
8 Hume, D., *A Treatise on Human Nature* (Oxford University Press, 1968).
9 L.S.D.,[1] 257.'
10 ibid., 31.
11 Matthews, P., *S.S.R.*, 1975, 198, **57**, 157.
12 L.S.D.,[1] 50.
13 Nagel, E., *The Structure of Science* (Routledge and Kegan Paul, 1961).
14 Popper, K., 'Normal Science and its Dangers' in C.G.K.,[2] 56.
15 L.S.D.,[1] 82.
16 ibid, 267.
17 Popper, K., *Conjectures and Refutations* (Routledge and Kegan Paul, 1963).
18 L.S.D.,[1] 36.
19 Masterman, M. 'The Nature of a Paradigm' in C.G.K.,[2] 61.
20 T.S.S.R.,[3] 17.
21 Popper, K., 'Normal Science and its Dangers' in C.G.K.,[2] 51.
22 Masterman, M., op. cit., 60.
23 Watkins, J., 'Against ''Normal Science''' in C.G.K.,[2] 32.
24 Popper, K., 'Normal Science and its Dangers' in C.G.K.,[2] 54.
25 Kuhn, T.S., *The Copernican Revolution* (Vintage, 1959).
26 Kuhn, T.S., 'Reflections on my critics' in C.G.K.,[2] 251.
27 Sarton, G., *The Study of the History of Science* (Dover, 1965).
28 Kuhn, T.S., 'Reflections on my critics' in C.G.K.,[2] 264.
29 Feyerabend, P., 'Consolations for the Specialist' in C.G.K.,[2] 219.
30 T.S.S.R.,[3] 123.
31 Popper, K., 'Normal Science and its Dangers' in C.G.K.,[2] 52.
32 T.S.S.R.,[3] 166.
33 Nuffield Physics, *Teacher's Guide I* (Longmans/Penguin, 1966) p. 73.
34 Nuffield Chemistry, *Handbook for Teachers*, (Longmans/Penguin, 1968) p. 7.
35 T.S.S.R.,[3] 80.
36 Feyerabend, P., *Against Method* (New Left Books, 1976).

[1] L.S.D. = Popper, K. *The Logic of Scientific Discovery* (Hutchinson, 1972).

[2] C.G.K. = Lakatos, I. and Musgrave, A. (eds.) *Criticism and the Growth of Knowledge* (Cambridge University Press, 1974).
[3] T.S.S.R. = Kuhn, T.S. *The Structure of Scientific Revolutions* (University of Chicago Press, 1970).

3 The nature of knowledge

● R.A. Lyttleton

A complex and paradoxical interaction between theory building and experimentation is described. Scientists are urged to employ lateral thinking in their generation of hypotheses. As an analogy of a scientist's belief in a theory, a bead running on a wire is proposed. The bead can assume any position on the wire between 0 (complete disbelief) and 1 (complete belief). The scientist is urged to avoid the twin evils that can accompany a closed mind: total confidence in a theory (1) or absolute rejection (0). Rather, a position between the extremes is urged; the bead is moved with each new confirming (towards 1) or rejecting (towards 0) observation. The vagaries of the processes of theory generation and testing are discussed, with reference to the psychological make-up of the scientist.

> If most of us are ashamed of shabby clothes and shoddy furniture, let us be more ashamed of shabby ideas and shoddy philosophies.
>
> Albert Einstein

When asked where one would like to see scientific research directed, there springs to mind the question whether truly scientific research can be directed at all. It is true that once the principles of a subject have been laid down for us by geniuses such as Newton and Maxwell, then research could be directed to studying their consequences, though even here great ingenuity requiring a high order of mathematical skill and imagination to overcome difficulties may be needed to pass from the principles to accounting for known observations and also making future predictions. The theory of the motion of the Moon provides a case in point: deep problems of mathematics have arisen all along and have had to be surmounted with the outcome of increasing accuracy of prediction, though even today, three centuries after Newton, there still remain puzzling features of the lunar motion. Are these difficulties of importance, and how much effort should be devoted to understanding them sufficiently to tackle them with success? Who is to decide such questions, and how can those doing so come to a proper assessment of such matters? With the early work to achieve more accurate measures of atomic weights, considered to be necessarily in integer-ratios, one can imagine proposals for such research turned down as of unlikely value, yet hidden there was the superlative power of nuclear energy.

Before stating my view as to where I consider effort might best be put, let us notice that our educational systems provide instruction from infancy up to doctoral level on everything appertaining to science, mathematics pure and applied, chemistry, physics, and so on, in order that pupils may achieve familiarity and facility with a subject as it exists. But the ideal objective, if a subject is not to become moribund, should be to learn it so well as to be scientifically critical of it with the object of bringing about advances in it. Sums of money vaster than ever before are enabling huge numbers of people to be drafted into scientific research, with all concerned inspired by an earnest hope that important contributions in the shape of new discoveries and fundamental principles will be made thereby. But when it comes to novel ideas, to the proposal of new hypotheses for realms in which there may be insufficient or even no established principles at all to serve as a guide, then controversy can arise and acute differences of opinion emerge, not always expressed in terms that pay due regard to the amenities of proper scientific discussion. Indeed, so strongly may some believe in their ideas, and so desirable may they consider it to promulgate them widely, that resort may be made to inadmissible ways and means to shield and defend them. (If you, dear reader, have never had any experience of this sort of thing, then your case has been more fortunate than most.)

This having briefly been said, my answer would be that the prime need of science today, so urgent that the body-scientific may choke to death in some fields of endeavour if nothing is done, is for steps to be taken to inform all those working in science what Science is really about, what is its true objective. Of course every scientist thinks he knows this, and this is right – he thinks he does, yet it has to be admitted that many very serious-minded, solid, and knowledgeable people work hard in science all their lives and produce nothing of the smallest importance, while others, few by comparison and perhaps seemingly carefree and not highly erudite, exhibit a serendipity of mind that enables them to have valuable ideas in any subject they may choose to take up. Few of the former have ever stopped off from their industrious habits to consider the question of How does one know when one knows?! It is true that much has been written discussing the subject, but mainly by writers handicapped by lack of experienced appreciation of the technicalities of mathematics and science, and even lack of acquaintance with the very things they are talking about. It is reported that a somewhat pretentious hostess once asked Einstein what were the philosophical and religious implications of his theory of relativity, to which he replied, of course correctly, 'None as far as I know'. Occasionally a Karl Pearson may come along, leaving aside his regular work, to set down his considered views of the matter for the intended benefit of others, but praiseworthy as such excursions may be, they may do more harm than good if they misconceive the matter, as indeed Pearson did. The few that properly understand the nature and object of science are usually as a result so busy with the work created by their attitude, which leads them to unending fruitful research, that they have little time for anything but actually *doing* science. Just as, contrariwise, those that do not understand the real object of science gradually come to rest in it and perhaps take up administration wherein they may be a ready prey to non-scientific approaches, or they may go in for popular exposition and thereby attain great repute as scientists of eminence by writing for the nursery. The late H. F. Baker, a pure mathematician for whom no point was too fine, when asked his opinion of one of Sir James Jeans's famous popularisations of astronomy, said, 'I wish I really knew what he puts on one page'.

As best one can apprehend something essentially difficult to discover, the attitude of most of those attempting scientific research seems to be that they believe themselves to be trying to find out the properties of some real material world that actually has independent existence and works in some discoverable structured mechanical way that can be ascertained if only it is studied carefully enough, 'Observe, and observe, and observe', and that the 'explanation' will emerge of its own accord if only the matter is studied sufficiently long and laboriously. But it will seldom if ever do so: indeed too much in the way of observations can reveal so many seeming complications and contradictions that almost any hypothesis may appear to be ruled out. A new idea may be likened to a newborn babe: it is to be carefully nurtured and given every consideration rather than attacked with the choking diet of a multitude of so-called facts because it cannot prove at once that it will one day grow into a Samson. In this connection, it has been conjectured that had Newton known all the complex details of the lunar motion now known he might never have believed that so simple a law as the inverse-square could possibly explain them. Indeed, even after his death, the observed advance of the perigee (which Newton had in fact already solved) seemed so puzzling that it led to proposals that an inverse-cube term should be added to resolve the problem. It must also be recognised that it is often only when a theory of some phenomenon exists can new discoveries be made and new or improved theories be invented. The advance of the perihelion of Mercury could not even have been conceived or discovered till Newtonian theory was available, while the problem posed by what seems so simple a phenomenon resisted solution for over half a century awaiting the right interpretation, as many consider the general-relativity explanation to be.

But important as it is to examine and if possible measure every possible aspect of the phenomenon of interest, it may come as a surprise to some and perhaps even be received coldly if it is stated that such activity is only a preliminary to science and not science itself, any more than the manufacture of golf-courses and equipment is golf itself, to give a trifling parallel. The true purpose of science is to invent hypotheses upon which can be developed mathematical theories and formalisms that enable predictions to be made in response to recognised objectives. But the statement raises further questions. First as to where the objectives come from, which is a subjective matter that need not be discussed here if it is admitted that men do find themselves with desired objectives, and second, which will be discussed, is where do the hypotheses come from and how are they to be invented. Newtonian dynamics enables predictions to be made of the motions of the planets and in realms far beyond that, while Maxwell's equations do this for the domain of electricity and magnetism, and quantum-theory for the infinitesimal realm of atoms and molecules.

Now although it is an essential precursor for the formulation of scientific theories that the phenomena of interest are first of all observed and if possible experimented with to at least some extent, it is of the utmost importance to recognise that no secure meaning or interpretation can be given to any observations until they are understood theoretically, or at best in terms of some hypothesis and theory based on it whether right or wrong. And it is here that one comes up against the strangely paradoxical nature of science, for the observations of phenomena are first needed to inspire someone to imagine an appropriate theory, yet they (the observations) cannot be claimed to be properly understood until a formal theory of them is available, and especially is this so where new phenomena are concerned when there are no (theoretical) means whereby the relevance of observations or experiments can be safely assessed. There can be no 'facts', no reliable 'evidence', until there are hypotheses and theories to test out. Before the advent of gravitational theory, comets were firmly believed to be by far the most important of all heavenly objects, and the official (verbal) theory of the phenomenon was that they were immaterial aethereal portents sent by the gods to warn man of coming violence and pestilence. The railway-lines can be observed definitely to meet in the distance, and interpretation of the observation requires some theory of space, and the lines might even actually meet if some impish engineer decided to make them do so a mile or so away! But the prediction on either hypothesis, parallel or meeting, could be tested out, for example by walking along the track to find out, or making accurate local measurements suggested by either hypothesis and a theory of space (Euclidean in this case would be adequate). The great Newton himself fell into error in this way, for when he found that the theoretical extrapolation of gravity to the distance of the Moon, which necessarily involved the 'known' size of the Earth, gave an acceleration inadequate to account for the lunar motion, he abandoned his theory as contradicted by 'facts'. Six whole years were to go by, with the world the poorer, before it was discovered that the measured size of the Earth was considerably in error and not the gravitational theory. Observations are by no means always to be trusted as reliable guides.

But many 'theories' have been constructed and proffered as scientific theories that do not really qualify as such at all. Some amount to no more than a more or less ingenious narration redescribing, sometimes imperfectly and all too often selectively, the data as known, without adding anything to these data, themselves describable in terms of some established theory: the shape of the Earth, for instance, requires for its description the theory of the Euclidean geometry of space, though the hypothesis of its near-sphericity was not always examined by some with due scientific consideration. But unless such a theory can make some prediction of its own, or suggest some crucial experiment, itself a kind of prediction, and few if any verbal theories can do this, it is not a scientific theory in a proper sense. Yet much science-literature today abounds with verbal 'theories' wrapped as established stories round data susceptible to more than one interpretation than that proposed and omitting to include equally established data as irrelevant when this is not yet known. Chaucer knew about such verbal rationalisations when he wrote warningly, 'You can by argument make a place A mile broad of twenty foot of space'. Such theories can add nothing to the data and may even degrade them, and unless the story makes some verifiable prediction unique to the theory itself and does not conflict with other available data, one might just as well accept the data in their entirety. By means of verbal theory, the Moon could be held to the Earth with a piece of string if gravitation were to cease: the force is in the right direction, it would be possible to make a quarter of a million miles of string, and an astronaut could attach one end to the Moon, and so on. But when numbers (theory) are put in, the verbal theory collapses at once, and it is found that a cable of stoutest steel several hundred kilometres thick would be needed. Verbal descriptive theories are analogous to putting a curve through points (representing, say, a series of observations): given a number of points in a plane, say, a curve can be put through them with as great precision as one wishes mathematically, but unless the resulting curve can predict the next point and the next (not necessarily absolutely accurately), the curve is not a theory of the phenomenon and is valueless. The correct theory may not quite go through any of the points.

Before discussing how new ideas and new hypotheses, on which new theories may be built and tested, come to be invented, let us leave the theme for a moment and consider what attitude a scientist should adopt towards such novelties, or indeed towards existing ideas and theories. In a recent lecture Medawar dealt with this briefly by the piece of advice, 'Never fall in love with your hypothesis'. But controlled energy and enthusiasm are needed to work upon and examine a hypothesis sufficiently carefully, and these are qualities turned on as it were by emotional drive, and if one succeeds in not actually falling in love with one's ideas, which state notoriously weakens if not altogether disables a person's judgement and critical faculty, then how far should one go in relation to a new idea, whether one's own or someone else's? This is obviously a subjective question, but knowably or not, if an idea comes to the awareness of a scientist, he will begin to adopt some attitude to it. This will result from interaction of the idea with all his previous experience, remembered or not, and his character and temperament and so on, and these will combine of their own accord to determine an attitude.

The scientific attitude to adopt in regard to any hypothesis in my view (and we are talking of subjective things) can be represented schematically by means of a simple model of a bead that can be moved on a short length of horizontal wire (see diagram below). Suppose the left-hand end denoted by 0 (zero) and the right-hand end by 1 (unity), and let 0 correspond to complete disbelief unqualified, and the right-hand end 1 to absolute certain belief in the hypothesis. Now the principle of practice that I would urge on all intending scientists in regard to any and every hypothesis is:

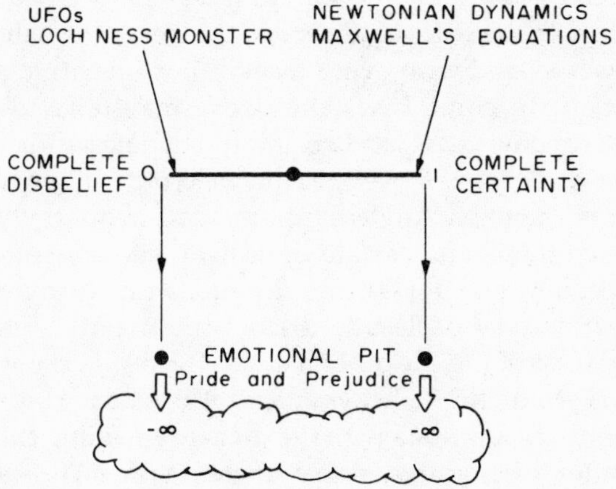

Never let your bead ever quite reach the position 0 or 1.

This is quite possible, for however close to the end one may have set it, there are still an infinite number of points to move the bead to in either direction in the light of new data or new arguments or whatever. If genuine scientific data reach your attention that increase your confidence in the hypothesis, then move your bead suitably towards 1, but never let it quite get there. If decreasing confidence is engendered by genuine data, then let your bead move towards 0, but again never let it quite reach there. Your changing confidence must be the result of your own independent scientific judgement of the data or arguments or proofs and so on, and not be allowed to result from arguments based on reputation of others, nor upon such things as numerical strength of believers or disbelievers. When Einstein heard that a book was being brought out entitled 'A Hundred Against Einstein', he merely said 'One would be enough!' My own beads for Newtonian dynamics and Maxwell's equations are very near to 1, and for flying-saucers and the Loch Ness monster very near to 0. But these it must be emphasised are my own subjective beads, and it seems there exist people whose beads for UFOs are near to 1 or even at it and beyond, the consequences of which we proceed to discuss.

It seems to be a common defect of human minds that they tend to crave for complete certainty of belief or disbelief in anything. Not only is this undesirable scientifically, but it must be recognised that no such state is attainable in science. However successful and reliable a theory may be up to any point of time, further data may come along and show a need for adjustment of the theory, while at the other extreme, however little confidence one has in a hypothesis, new data may change the situation. We come now to the reason why one should never allow a bead ever to get right to 0 or 1: it is that, if one does so, the bead will fall into a deep potential-well associated with every facet of non-scientific or even anti-scientific emotion. In some cases the depth may tend to infinity, especially with advancing years, and no amount of data conflicting with the certain belief or disbelief will ever get the bead out of the well back onto the even tenor of the wire. Any attempt to bring about the uplifting of a bead so situated, by means of data or reason, can sometimes lead the owner of the bead to manifest further attitudes unworthy scientifically. In some cases it may be useless to discuss the hypothesis or theory to which the bead relates. On the other hand, if the bead is kept somewhere on the wire *between* 0 and 1 always, it can if necessary be moved quite readily in response to new data with the owner remaining calmly tranquil rather than undergoing an emotional upset. With such reaction to hypotheses and theories, one can get genuine scientific pleasure from adjusting one's beads to take account of new data and new arguments. From the small sample that my experience has limited me to, it seems regrettably to be the case that few even among scientists are always capable of keeping their beads on the wire, and much tact may be needed if one wishes to help to restore them to a rational level on the wire, if indeed in some cases it is possible at all. In Nazi Germany, it would have been dangerous indeed to have one's bead on the wire even near to 1 as an attitude to the theory that theirs was a super-race destined to rule the world: 99.9 per cent of the beads were deep down the well and only violent efforts proved sufficient to move some of them. So one of the things I would like to see scientists directed to do is always to keep their beads safely on the wire, in order that their minds may be receptive to new ideas and advances. In the words of one Chan, 'Human mind like parachute: work best when open', and *open* means on the wire somewhere between 0 and 1.

When it comes to the question of how new ideas are to be arrived at, we meet up with the little-recognised fact that there is no such thing as '*the* scientific method'; there is no formal procedure, no fixed set of rules, whereby new problems can be tackled or the correct interpretation of data in a new area rigidly attained, or whereby the necessary ideas to establish new principles can be reached by logical induction. However, the history of science shows that certain types of mind can see into a problem more deeply than others by some inner light that enables such minds to imagine what the solution might be, or to see if only gropingly at first what the required theory may be. It is not a matter of random guesswork, though it can be a kind of inspired guess or a series of guesses that reveals what may prove to be a valid theory for explanation of some phenomenon and for prediction in its realm.

Advancement of a subject may require first and foremost the intrusion into it of minds that intuitively perceive the phenomena in an original way and approach the problem from an untraditional point of view. With hindsight, it can be seen quite clearly just how impossible it was to solve the problem of the excess motion of the perihelion of Mercury by any hypothesis within the scope of then-existing astronomy. The imaginative conceiving of new ideas and the developing of them into a rational workable theory for new predictions ranks as mental activity at least the equal of those brought to bear in any of the realms of so-called arts, but where science is concerned it may go much further and lead on to yield a power over nature, not to mention intellectual joy and satisfaction, that no other art gives or possibly can give. It is this that makes science the noblest work of all and the greatest of the Arts. It is essentially this capability of knowledge of the future that is the keynote of real science, and the marvellous quality that gives science its uniquely powerful importance.

Before attempting construction of any theory (verbal or otherwise) to account for some phenomenon, it is of primary importance to establish that the phenomenon under discussion is actually occurring and not some wishful process swamped by the associated noise of measurement, for example. For what is to become of the theory if the phenomenon turns out later to have been purely imaginary and non-existent? Science journals today abound with elaborate theories of alleged phenomena quite inadequately established other than by often intemperate asseveration, and before the prime requirement of any theory has been found, namely an engine or cause of the phenomenon. The main evidence usually disseminated to support such 'theory' often consists of no more than a sedulously conducted campaign of repetitious empty verbal propaganda assertively leading to the shallow conclusion that the theory is now 'generally accepted', a claim in itself always a clear warning to regard the validity of the theory with reserve and to examine its basis (if any) calmly and independently paying no heed to the alleged numerical strength of its adherents. It is an essential part of scientific investigation to bring every detail of assumption, approximation, method and all else to the surface, and have every component on the table, as it were, for examination and discussion: nothing should remain buried or left aside that any consideration suggests relevant until its importance or otherwise can be assessed. Equally so, in presenting scientific research publicly, it should be in such manner that a reader can recover for himself all the steps by which the results have been reached so that he can if necessary verify the conclusions for himself. In other words, none of the cards should remain face-down with assurances (or excuses) that this or that step is 'all right' and can be taken for granted, because it has been put on a machine for instance, or otherwise remains inaccessible to verification. Yet many papers are deficient in this respect.

It is imperative to realise that the test of any new hypothesis or theory cannot be made by any *prior* supposedly aesthetic considerations or by moral judgement of their seeming merits or demerits in terms of existing theories. This can only be done posterior, *after* the consequences have been correctly worked out to a stage at which comparison with properly interpreted observations can be made. A theory is to be judged acceptable solely to the extent both that its results accord satisfactorily with the existing data and that future observations predicted on the basis of the theory duly come to pass with pleasing accuracy. When continuous variables are concerned, which is the most frequent case, perfect accuracy of prediction is never attainable any more than perfect accuracy of observation is possible; only if pure counting in whole numbers is entailed could this be possible, and even then of course it may not be achieved if the theory is imperfect. How little this scientific attitude to new ideas is adopted reveals itself by the sort of absurd comments they have been known to provoke, criticisms springing from beads well off the wire, such as, 'The probability of the initial assumptions being true . . .', or the following unequalled gem: 'The author seems unaware that the problem may be conditioned by some effect as yet unknown to science.' These are just two samples from a great many that have come the way of this writer and sent out in all seriousness by chosen representatives of so-called learned societies, and if protest is made one may be informed, truthfully enough alas, that the opinions are from the most eminent referees in the field, not the most competent: the two are not always the same. It is axiomatic scientifically that no meaning attaches to such usage of the word 'true': only when the initially assumed ideas have been followed through to comparison with data or to verified predictions can the stage arrive for their truth to be assessed. And just how an author can be expected to make allowance for 'effects as yet unknown to science' requires an alchemy yet unknown to anyone.

Such absurdities would be avoided if the importance of keeping one's beads on the wire were sufficiently appreciated, and if it were also remembered that even though an idea should eventually turn out not to be true, in the sense that its predictions, properly evaluated of course, do not accord with observation, this alone does not constitute rigorous proof of the moral obliquity of the proposer. So reluctant are some scientists to bear such personal criticism that they shy away from the slightest risk of controversy, which new ideas frequently lead to, and devote themselves slavishly to the cloistered shelter of making routine measurements and observations, sometimes with no discernible objective. Some even make a virtue of the unimaginative collection of 'facts', which they regard as the real work of science, and deride the searching for valid hypotheses as mere airy-fairy speculation. To dash a pail of water on the floor, and then set about the tedious measurement of the size and shape of all the splashes, with extensive tabulation of these, and published at great expense, would not represent in smallest degree a contribution to hydrodynamics, and obviously could never suggest the Stokes-Navier equations. Indeed, if anything, such misguided effort would far more likely prove an obstacle to any such important theoretical advance. Yet much modern work is in this sort of vein, and woe betide the theorist whose work takes no account of the resulting well-established 'facts'.

Any dedicated scientist will continually strive to imagine new ideas even though he recognises that most of them will probably not prove fruitful, but for every nine failures, one real success will be more than adequate reward for his efforts. But he will take care to test them out for himself by thinking them through in private, or by informal discussion with colleagues, or by observation or experiment, or when possible by formal analysis. Should these steps so reduce confidence in an idea to a point making further work upon it seem no longer worth while, then he must start over and try to imagine some new or modified idea in the hope that it may bring the data into order and suggest an appropriate theory. However, so great is the incentive to publish nowadays, that many regard it as good 'scientific' practice to conduct this part of their education in public, mistakes and all. As a result, scientific literature becomes cluttered with inadequately ripe or even entirely erroneous material, which if subjected to open criticism is often, through faulty positioning of the relevant beads, quite invalidly defended, so great is the hurt to the pride of the authors and so unwilling are they admit to the slightest error.

By way of conclusion and emphasis of the theme of this essay may be quoted what Poincaré had to say more than fifty years ago concerning an attempt to explain away the so-called ultra-violet catastrophe by means of a 'theoretical' structure of matter more suggestive of poor-quality plumbing than the high-quality physical theory that eventually prevailed and revolutionised science: 'It is obvious that by giving suitable dimensions to the communicating tubes connecting the reservoirs and giving suitable values to the leaks, this "theory" could account for any experimental results whatever. But this (type of descriptive story) is not the role of physical theories. They should not introduce as many (or more) arbitrary constants as there are phenomena to be explained. They should establish connections between different experimental facts, and *above all they should enable predictions to be made*.' It is to precepts of this stamp, distilled from the wisdom of great thinkers, that I would wish to see the attention of research workers perennially and forcefully directed, for only by adherence to them and in no other way will science be advanced.

4

Is the scientific paper a fraud?

● P. B. Medawar

The traditional way of reporting scientific work, in the form of an academic paper, is a misrepresentation of the actual process of scientific discovery. Experimentation is not something guided by disinterested minds that finally, out of chaos, arrives at a conclusion. Rather, each experiment is guided by a hypothesis, an expectation about the outcome. As with our casual observations of the world, scientific observations are coloured by our expectations and prior experiences. It might be a good thing if scientific writing were to be a more accurate reflection of the true process of scientific discovery.

I have chosen for my title a question: Is the scientific paper a fraud? I ought to explain that a scientific 'paper' is a printed communication to a learned journal, and scientists make their work known almost wholly through papers and not through books, so papers are very important in scientific communication. As to what I mean by asking 'is the scientific paper a fraud?' – I do not of course mean 'does the scientific paper misrepresent facts', and I do not mean that the interpretations you find in a scientific paper are wrong or deliberately mistaken. I mean the scientific paper may be a fraud because it misrepresents the processes of thought that accompanied or gave rise to the work that is described in the paper. That is the question, and I will say right away that my answer to it is 'yes'. The scientific paper in its orthodox form does embody a totally mistaken conception, even a travesty, of the nature of scientific thought.

Just consider for a moment the traditional form of a scientific paper (incidentally, it is a form which editors themselves often insist upon). The structure of a scientific paper in the biological sciences is something like this. First, there is a section called the 'introduction' in which you merely describe the general field in which your scientific talents are going to be exercised, followed by a section called 'previous work', in which you concede, more or less graciously, that others have dimly groped towards the fundamental truths that you are now about to expound.

Then a section on 'methods' – that is O.K. Then comes the section called 'results'. The section called 'results' consists of a stream of factual information in which it is considered extremely bad form to discuss the significance of the results you are getting. You have to pretend that your mind is, so to speak, a virgin receptacle, an empty vessel, for information which floods into it from the external world for no reason which you yourself have revealed. You reserve all appraisal of the scientific evidence until the 'discussion' section, and in the discussion you adopt the ludicrous pretence of asking yourself if the information you have collected actually means anything; of asking yourself if any general truths are going to emerge from the contemplation of all the evidence you brandished in the section called 'results'.

Of course, what I am saying is rather an exaggeration, but there is more than a mere element of truth in it. The conception underlying this style of scientific writing is that scientific discovery is an inductive process. What induction implies in its cruder form is roughly speaking this: scientific discovery, or the formulation of scientific theory, starts with the unvarnished and unembroidered evidence of the senses. It starts with simple observation – simple, unbiased, unprejudiced, naïve, or innocent observation – and out of this sensory evidence, embodied in the form of simple propositions or declarations of fact, generalizations will grow up and take shape, almost as if some process of crystallization or condensation were taking place. Out of a disorderly array of facts, an orderly theory, an orderly general statement, will somehow emerge. This conception of scientific discovery in which the initiative comes from the unembroidered evidence of the senses was mainly the work of a great and wise, but in this context, I think, very mistaken man – John Stuart Mill.

John Stuart Mill saw, as of course a great many others had seen before him, including Bacon, that deduction in itself is quite powerless as a method of scientific discovery – and for this simple reason: that the process of deduction as such only uncovers, brings out into the open, makes explicit, information that is already present in the axioms or premises from which the process of deduction started. The process of deduction reveals nothing to us except what the infirmity of our own minds has so far concealed from us. It was Mill's belief that induction was the method of science – 'that great mental operation', he called it, 'the operation of discovering and proving general propositions'. And round this conception there grew up an inductive logic, of which the business was 'to provide rules to which, if inductive arguments conform, those arguments are conclusive'. Now, John Stuart Mill's deeper motive in working out what he conceived to be the essential method of science was to apply that method to the solution of sociological problems: he wanted to apply to sociology the methods which the practice of science had shown to be immensely powerful and exact.

It is ironical that the application to sociology of the inductive method, more or less in the form in which Mill himself conceived it, should have been an almost entirely fruitless one. The simplest application of the Millsian process of induction to sociology came in a rather strange movement called Mass Observation. The belief underlying Mass Observation was apparently this: that if one could only record and set down the actual raw facts about what people do and what people say in pubs, in trains, when they make love to each other, when they are playing games, and so on, then somehow, from this wealth of information, a great generalization would inevitably emerge. Well, in point of fact, nothing important emerged from this approach, unless somebody's been holding out on me. I believe the pioneers of Mass Observation were ornithologists. Certainly they were man-watching – were applying to sociology the very methods which had done so much to bring ornithology into disrepute.

The theory underlying the inductive method cannot be sustained. Let me give three good reasons why not. In the first place, the starting point of induction, naïve observation, innocent observation, is a mere philosophic fiction. There is no such thing as unprejudiced observation. Every act of observation we make is biased. What we see or otherwise sense is a function of what we have seen or sensed in the past.

The second point is this. Scientific discovery or the formulation of the scientific idea on the one hand, and demonstration or proof on the other hand, are two entirely different notions, and Mill confused them. Mill said that induction was the 'operation of discovering and proving general propositions', as if one act of mind would do for both. Now discovery and proof could depend on the same act of mind, and in deduction they do. When we indulge in the process of deduction – as in deducing a theorem from Euclidian axioms or postulates – the theorem contains the discovery (or, more exactly, the uncovery of something which was there in the axioms and postulates, though it was not actually evident) and the process of deduction itself, if it has been carried out correctly, is also the proof that the 'discovery' is valid, is logically correct. So in the process of deduction, discovery and proof can depend on the same process. But in scientific activity they are not the same thing – they are, in fact, totally separate acts of mind.

But the most fundamental objection is this. It simply is not logically possible to arrive with certainty at any generalization containing more information than the sum of the particular statements upon which that generalization was founded, out of which it was woven. How could a mere act of mind lead to the discovery of new information? It would violate a law as fundamental as the law of conservation of matter: it would violate the law of conservation of information.

In view of all these objections, it is hardly surprising that Bertrand Russell in a famous footnote that occurs in his *Principles of Mathematics* of 1903 should have said that, so far as he could see, induction was a mere method of making plausible guesses. And our greatest modern authority on the nature of scientific method, Professor Karl Popper, has no use for induction at all: he regards the inductive process of thought as a myth. 'There is no need even to mention induction,' he says in his great treatise, on *The Logic of Scientific Discovery* – though of course he does.

Now let me go back to the scientific papers. What is wrong with the traditional form of scientific paper is simply this: that all scientific work of an experimental or exploratory character starts with some expectation about the outcome of the inquiry. This expectation one starts with, this hypothesis one formulates, provides the initiative and incentive for the inquiry and governs its actual form. It is in the light of this expectation that some observations are held relevant and others not; that some methods are chosen, others discarded; that some experiments are done rather than others. It is only in the light of this prior expectation that the activities the scientist reports in his scientific papers really have any meaning at all.

Hypotheses arise by guesswork. That is to put it in its crudest form. I should say rather that they arise by inspiration; but in any event they arise by processes that form part of the subject-matter of psychology and certainly not of logic, for there is no logically rigorous method for devising hypotheses. It is a vulgar error, often committed, to speak of 'deducing' hypotheses. Indeed one does not deduce hypotheses: hypotheses are what one deduces things from. So the actual formulation of a hypothesis is – let us say a guess; is inspirational in character. But hypotheses can be tested rigorously – they are tested by experiment, using the word 'experiment' in a rather general sense to mean an act performed to test a hypothesis, that is, to test the deductive consequences of a hypothesis. If one formulates a hypothesis, one can deduce from it certain consequences which are predictions or declarations about what will, or will not, be the case. If these predictions and declarations are mistaken, then the hypothesis must be discarded, or at least modified. If, on the other hand, the predictions turn out correct, then the hypothesis has stood up to trial, and remains on probation as before. This formulation illustrates very well, I think, the distinction between on the one hand the discovery or formulation of a scientific idea or generalization, which is to a greater or lesser degree an imaginative or inspirational act, and on the other hand the proof, or rather the testing of a hypothesis, which is indeed a strictly logical and rigorous process, based upon deductive arguments.

This alternative interpretation of the nature of the scientific process, of the nature of scientific method, is sometimes called the hypothetico-deductive interpretation and this is the view which Professor Karl Popper in the *Logic of Scientific Discovery* has persuaded us is the correct one. To give credit where credit is surely due, it is proper to say that the first professional scientist to express a fully reasoned opinion upon the way scientists actually think when they come upon their scientific discoveries – namely William Whewell, a geologist, and incidentally the Master of Trinity College, Cambridge – was also the first person to formulate this hypothetico-deductive interpretation of scientific activity. Whewell, like his contemporary Mill, wrote at great length – unnecessarily great length, one is nowadays inclined to think – and I cannot recapitulate his argument, but one or two quotations will make the gist of his thought clear. He said: 'An art of discovery is not possible. We can give no rules for the pursuit of truth which should be universally and peremptorily applicable.' And of hypotheses, he said, with great daring – why it was daring I will explain in just a second – 'a facility in devising hypotheses, so far from being a fault in the intellectual character of a discoverer, is a faculty indispensable to his task'. I said this was daring because the word 'hypothesis' and the conception it stood for was still in Whewell's day a rather discreditable one. Hypotheses had a flavour about them of what was wanton and irresponsible. The great Newton, you remember, had frowned upon hypotheses. *'Hypotheses non fingo'*, he said, and there is another version in which he says *'hypotheses non sequor'* – I do not pursue hypotheses.

So to go back once again to the scientific paper: the scientific paper is a fraud in the sense that it does give a totally misleading narrative of the processes of thought that go into the making of scientific discoveries. The inductive format of the scientific paper should be discarded. The discussion which in the traditional scientific paper goes last should surely come at the beginning. The scientific facts and scientific acts should follow the discussion, and scientists should not be ashamed to admit, that hypotheses appear in their minds along uncharted by-ways of thought; that they are imaginative and inspirational in character; that they are indeed adventures of the mind. What, after all, is the good of scientists reproaching others for their neglect of, or indifference to, the scientific style of thinking they set such great store by, if their own writings show that they themselves have no clear understanding of it?

Anyhow, I am practising what I preach. What I have said about the nature of scientific discovery you can regard as being itself a hypothesis, and the hypothesis comes where I think it should be, namely, it comes at the beginning of the series. Later speakers will provide the facts which will enable you to test and appraise this hypothesis, and I think you will find – I hope you will find – that the evidence they will produce about the nature of scientific discovery will bear me out.

5 Why?

• O. R. Frisch

There are various possible ways of explaining a given phenomenon. The teleological method was once popular in both physics and biology. It has now been largely abandoned in physics, but in biology the process of evolution can give the strong impression of design with a purpose. Some explanatory problems arising in probability theory are discussed by Otto Frisch who in 1939 produced, in collaboration with Lise Meitner, the first definite identification and explanation of the phenomenon of 'nuclear fission', a term which he coined.

Some 15 years ago, WHY was a magic word, used by a small boy to keep Daddy talking.

'Daddy, why does the sun go down in the West?'

'Because West is what we call the place where the sun goes down.'

'But why does it go down?'

'It doesn't really; it's the Earth that turns round.'

'Why?'

'Because there is no friction to stop it.'

'Why' . . .'

But what do we mean when we say WHY? We expect some answer; what kind of answer? 'Why did Jones break his leg?'

'Because his tibia hit the kerb,' says the surgeon.

'Because some fool dropped a banana skin,' says Mrs Jones.

'Because he never looks where he goes,' says a colleague.

'Because he subconsciously wanted a holiday,' says a psychiatrist.

For any event there are several styles of answering the question why it happened. (For further confusion, see Schopenhauer's essay 'Die vierfache Wurzel des Satzes vom Grunde'.) But when we ask why something is so, then we are on different ground. It would be defeat for a scientist to accept the answer 'because God made it so'. But often there is another answer which perhaps comes to the same thing. To the question 'why do intelligent beings exist?' it seems legitimate to reply 'because otherwise there would be nobody to ask that question'. Many popular WHYs can be answered in that manner.

Let us try another question. In my car, why does the spark plug ignite the mixture at a particular instant? There are two answers:

(1) because the cam shaft causes a spark at just that instant;

(2) because a spark at that instant gives good engine efficiency.

Answer (1) is what a physicist expects. Still, he may ask why the cam shaft has been made to cause a spark at just that time; then (2) is the answer required. It introduces a new character: the designer, with intelligence and a purpose (in this case the design of an efficient car engine).

The teleological explanation, (2), is here certainly the more telling one (except to that mythical personage, the pure scientist). To the question 'why is John running?' the reply 'in order to catch the bus' is satisfactory; the reply 'because his brain is sending the appropriate messages to his leg muscles' (though basically correct) would be regarded as a leg-pull.

A couple of centuries ago, physical laws were often formulated in teleological language; that this was possible appeared to show that the laws had been designed to fulfil some divine purpose. For instance, a beam of light passing through refracting media (as in a telescope) was shown to travel along the path that requires the minimum time, according to the wave theory of light. But the basic law of refraction can be deduced without reference to that parsimonious principle and, moreover, allows light to travel equally on a path that requires not the least but the most time (at least compared to all neighbouring pathways).

Today such minimum (or maximum) principles are regarded merely as pretty (and sometimes useful) consequences of more basic laws, like the law of refraction; it was anyhow always obscure what divine purpose was served by making light go the quickest (or sometimes the slowest) way. Teleological explanations are not accepted nowadays; not in physics.

In biology it is otherwise; nobody doubts that many features of animals serve a purpose; claws serve to kill, legs to run, wings to fly. But is it a divine purpose? The great debate has not altogether ceased, but the large majority of scientists are agreed that natural selection can account for the appearance of purposeful design, even though some of them find it hard to imagine how such a marvellous instrument as the human eye (let alone the human brain) could have developed under the pressure of natural selection alone.

The power of artificial selection is, of course, well known to any plant or animal breeder. Admittedly, natural selection lacks the breeder's guiding hand. But it has acted through millions of years and on uncounted billions of individuals, and its power of favouring any improved adaptation to the life a species has to live is inexorable. The dug-up skeletons of horses show the development, over some millions of generations, of a rabbit-size creature to the powerful runner of today whose ancestors survived pursuit by ever faster predators. Natural selection still works today: of two varieties of moths of the same species, the darker variety predominates in smoky cities where it is well camouflaged, as his lighter cousins are in birchwoods where they in turn predominate.

As to the human eye, any light-sensitive organ, however primitive, is useful, and any improvement in sensitivity, resolution and mobility is strongly favoured by natural selection. But what about feathers? Even if a very unlikely mutation caused a reptile to have offspring with feathers instead of scales, what good would that do, without muscles to move them and a brain rebuilt to control those muscles? We can only guess. But let me mention the electric eel. It used to be a puzzle how his electric organ could have grown to its present size when in its early stages it would have been quite useless as a weapon. We now have an answer: even a feeble electric organ helps with navigation in muddy waters, and its gradual improvement has led, as it were, from a radar to a death ray.

Much about the process of evolution is still unknown; but I have no doubt that natural selection provides the justification for teleological answers.

Finally, let us go back to physics and ask a question to which, it seems, there is no answer: Why did a particular radium nucleus break up at a particular time? When the theory of atomic nuclei was young it was suggested that their complexity provided the answer: an alpha particle could escape only when all the others were in a particular configuration, as unlikely as twenty successive zeros in a game of roulette. Even with the configurations changing about 10^{20} times a second, it could take years before the right one turned up. That theory has been given up; for one thing there are much less complex nuclei with similar long lives.

Probability theory started as a theory of gambling. The apparent caprice of Lady Luck was attributed to our unavoidable ignorance of the exact way a dice was thrown; if we knew the exact way we could predict the outcome. Sure, we would have to know exactly how the dice was thrown and every detail of the surface on which it fell much more accurately than we could conceivably hope to achieve; but 'in principle' it would be possible.

From those humble beginnings in a gamblers' den, the theory of probability grew in power until it took over large parts of physics. For instance, the observable behaviour of gases was accounted for by the innumerable random collisions of its molecules. Just like computing the profitability of a gambling house or an insurance company, this could be done without predicting the behaviour of single molecules. It might still be possible in principle to predict where a given molecule would be one second later; but to do that we would have to know the positions and velocities of millions of other molecules with such precision that to write down, not those numbers themselves but merely the number of decimals required, would be more than a man's life work!

With that in mind, you might find it easier to accept that quantum theory uses the concept of probability without justifying it by ignorance. Today most physicists believe that it is impossible even 'in principle' to predict when a given radioactive nucleus will break up. Indeed it is only a few properties (such as the wavelength of light sent out by a given type of excited atom) for which the quantum theory allows us to calculate accurate values; in most other cases all we get is a probability that a particular event will take place in a given time.

To some people this idea of probability as a physical attribute of, say, an unstable atom seems distasteful; the idea of inexorable laws, even if we can never follow their work in detail, has not lost its appeal. Einstein felt it was essential; 'God does not play dice with the world', he said. Could not the seeming randomness of atomic events result from the activities of smaller, still unknown entities? The random movements of small particles (pollen grains, etc.) in a fluid, observed in 1827 through the microscope of a botanist, Robert Brown, were later understood as resulting from the impact of millions of molecules, whose existence was merely a matter for speculation in 1827. Perhaps we shall similarly explain the random behaviour of atoms, in 40 years or so?

Such entities, under the non-committal name of 'hidden variables', have been speculated on; so far they have remained hidden. Should they come out of hiding they would probably do no more than restore the illusion that the behaviour of atomic particles can be predicted 'in principle'. On the other hand, they may possibly predict new and unexpected physical phenomena, and that would be very exciting. I have no serious hope of that, but I can't foretell the future.

6 Concepts in physical science

• A. Einstein

In his foreword to Max Jammer's book Concepts of Space *(first published in 1953), Einstein argues that concepts are working tools to a physicist, but that he cannot choose them simply for his convenience, because they must be firmly rooted in reality. In other fields, one can expect a gradual clarification of concepts to emerge by discussion and mutual consensus, but in science only Nature is the arbiter. Should one think of space as delimited by the objects it contains (so that there can be no such thing as empty space) or does space have an absolute quality, a fixed stage for the play even when the players have left? Einstein does not see this as a matter of opinion. Modern physicists should take the first view, because without it general relativity and sub-nuclear physics would be closed books. Newton maintained the second view and could never have progressed beyond his own form of mechanics. Newton's contribution, however, was that he made clear a view that no one had seen before.*

In order to appreciate fully the importance of investigations such as the present work of Dr Jammer one should consider the following points. The eyes of the scientist are directed upon those phenomena which are accessible to observation, upon their apperception and conceptual formulation. In the attempt to achieve a conceptual formulation of the confusingly immense body of observational data, the scientist makes use of a whole arsenal of concepts which he imbibed practically with his mother's milk; and seldom if ever is he aware of the eternally problematic character of his concepts. He uses this conceptual material, or, speaking more exactly, these conceptual tools of thought, as something obviously, immutably given; something having an objective value of truth which is hardly ever, and in any case not seriously, to be doubted. How could he do otherwise? How would the ascent of a mountain be possible, if the use of hands, legs, and tools had to be sanctioned step by step on the basis of the science of mechanics? And yet in the interests of science it is necessary over and over again to engage in the critique of these fundamental concepts, in order that we may not unconsciously be ruled by them. This becomes evident especially in those situations involving development of ideas in which the consistent use of the traditional fundamental concepts leads us to paradoxes difficult to resolve.

Aside from the doubt arising as to the justification for the use of the concepts, that is to say, even in cases where this doubt is not in the foreground of our interest, there is a purely historical interest in the origins or the roots of the fundamental concepts. Such investigations, although purely in the field of history of thought, are nevertheless in principle not independent of attempts at a logical and psychological analysis of the basic concepts. But the limitations to the abilities and working capacity of the individual are such that we but rarely find a person who has the philological and historical training required for critical interpretation and comparison of the source material, which is spread over centuries, and who at the same time can evaluate the significance of the concepts under discussion for science as a whole. I have the impression that Dr Jammer, through his work, has demonstrated that in his case these conditions are in great measure satisfied.

In the main he has limited himself – wisely, it seems to me – to the historical investigation of the concept of *space*. If two different authors use the words 'red,' 'hard,' or 'disappointed,' no one doubts that they mean approximately the same thing, because these words are connected with elementary experiences in a manner which is difficult to misinterpret. But in the case of words such as 'place' or 'space,' whose relation with psychological experience is less direct, there exists a far-reaching uncertainty of interpretation. The historian attempts to overcome such uncertainty by comparison of the texts, and by taking into account the picture, constructed from literature, of the cultural stock of the epoch in question. The scientist of the present, however, is not primarily trained or oriented as a historian; he is not capable of forming nor willing to form his views on the origin of the fundamental concepts in this manner. He is more inclined to allow his views on the manner in which the relevant concepts might have been formed, to arise intuitively from his rudimentary knowledge of the achievements of science in the different epochs of history. He will, however, be grateful to the historian if the latter can convincingly correct such views of purely intuitive origin.

Now as to the concept of space, it seems that this was preceded by the psychologically simpler concept of place. Place is first of all a (small) portion of the earth's surface identified by a name. The thing whose 'place' is being specified is a 'material object' or body. Simple analysis shows 'place' also to be a group of material objects. Does the word 'place' have a meaning independent of this one, or can one assign such a meaning to it? If one has to give a negative answer to this question, then one is led to the view that space (or place) is a sort of order of material objects and nothing else. If the concept of space is formed and limited in this fashion, then to speak of empty space has no meaning. And because the formation of concepts has always been ruled by instinctive striving for economy, one is led quite naturally to reject the concept of empty space.

It is also possible, however, to think in a different way. Into a certain box we can place a definite number of grains of rice or of cherries, etc. It is here a question of a property of the material object 'box,' which property must be considered 'real' in the same sense as the box itself. One can call this property the 'space' of the box. There may be other boxes which in this sense have an equally large 'space'. This concept 'space' thus achieves a meaning which is freed from any connection with a particular material object. In this way by a natural extension of 'box space' one can arrive at the concept of an independent (absolute) space, unlimited in extent, in which all material objects are contained. Then a material object not situated in space is simply inconceivable; on the other hand, in the framework of this concept formation it is quite conceivable that an empty space may exist.

These two concepts of space may be contrasted as follows: (a) space as positional quality of the world of material objects; (b) space as container of all material objects. In case (a), space without a material object is inconceivable. In case (b), a material object can only be conceived as existing in space; space then appears as a reality which in a certain sense is superior to the material world. Both space concepts are free creations of the human imagination, means devised for easier comprehension of our sense experience.

These schematic considerations concern the nature of space from the geometric and from the kinematic point of view, respectively. They are in a sense reconciled with each other by Descartes' introduction of the coordinate system, although this already presupposes the logically more daring space concept (b).

The concept of space was enriched and complicated by Galileo and Newton, in that space must be introduced as the independent cause of the inertial behavior of bodies if one wishes to give the classical principle of inertia (and therewith the classical law of motion) an exact meaning. To have realized this fully and clearly is in my opinion one of Newton's greatest achievements. In contrast with Leibniz and Huygens, it was clear to Newton that the space concept (a) was not sufficient to serve as the foundation for the inertia principle and the law of motion. He came to this decision even though he actively shared the uneasiness which was the cause of the opposition of the other two: space is not only introduced as an independent thing apart from material objects, but also is assigned an absolute role in the whole causal structure of the theory. This role is absolute in the sense that space (as an inertial system) acts on all material objects, while these do not in turn exert any reaction on space.

The fruitfulness of Newton's system silenced these scruples for several centuries. Space of type (b) was generally accepted by scientists in the precise form of the inertial system, encompassing time as well. Today one would say about that memorable discussion: Newton's decision was, in the contemporary state of science, the only possible one, and particularly the only fruitful one. But the subsequent development of the problems, proceeding in a roundabout way which no one then could possibly foresee, has shown that the resistance of Leibniz and Huygens, intuitively well founded but supported by inadequate arguments, was actually justified.

It required a severe struggle to arrive at the concept of independent and absolute space, indispensable for the development of theory. It has required no less strenuous exertions subsequently to overcome this concept – a process which is probably by no means as yet completed.

Dr Jammer's book is greatly concerned with the investigation of the status of the concept of space in ancient times and in the Middle Ages. On the basis of his studies, he is inclined toward the view that the modern concept of space of type (b), that is, space as container of all material objects, was not developed until after the Renaissance. It seems to me that the atomic theory of the ancients, with its atoms existing separately from each other, necessarily presupposed a space of type (b), while the more influential Aristotelian school tried to get along without the concept of independent (absolute) space. Dr Jammer's views concerning theological influences on the development of the concept of space, which lie outside the range of my judgment, will certainly arouse the interest of those who are concerned with the problem of space primarily from the historical point of view.

The victory over the concept of absolute space or over that of the inertial system became possible only because the concept of the material object was gradually replaced as the fundamental concept of physics by that of the field. Under the influence of the ideas of Faraday and Maxwell the notion developed that the whole of physical reality could perhaps be represented as a field whose components depend on four space-time parameters. If the laws of this field are in general covariant, that is, are not dependent on a particular choice of coordinate system, then the introduction of an independent (absolute) space is no longer necessary. That which constitutes the spatial character of reality is then simply the four-dimensionality of the field. There is then no 'empty' space, that is, there is no space without a field. Dr Jammer's presentation also deals with the memorable roundabout way in which the difficulties of this problem were overcome, at least to a great extent. Up to the present time no one has found any method of avoiding the inertial system other than by way of the field theory.

II SCIENCE IN A TECHNOLOGICAL SOCIETY

The four chapters in this section are all concerned with the place of science in our society. What is the status of science? What are the terms of reference for a scientific explanation? What considerations shape the direction and objectives of scientific research? In Snow's now classical argument, society is divided into two cultures, scientific and non-scientific, using distinct languages, each of which is almost meaningless to members of the other culture. Snow develops his argument in a simple and elegant way. You might feel that he slightly overstates the case. Is this a particularly British problem, the product of our education system? For a good example of how little science has made inroads into the British intellectual establishment even today, try looking at *The Times* crossword. See how long it takes you to find a word such as *Mach*, *Oestrogen* or *Bohr* among the answers!

Collins and Shapin urge that students should gain a 'feel for' the true nature of science, not as a body of immutable fact but as something that is constantly open to question and reinterpretation. Collins and Shapin discuss the phenomenon of the 'failed run', when an experiment fails to turn out the way anticipated. Psychology provides a beautiful example of this. After concluding an experiment, students will commonly make a remark of the kind 'Look, this is what our rat did. What should it have done?'. 'Platonic' ideals of what life should be like abound in the non-scientists' view of science. Collins and Shapin urge a teaching approach that counters this.

Roszak presents a critique of *objectivity* as a kind of super-goal of all our endeavours. Concerning the divide noted by Snow, Roszak has no doubts as to who is the imperialist. He thinks science is slowly taking over every aspect of our existence. Scientific models and metaphors creep in everywhere, in literature, in descriptions of eroticism and in films. Roszak urges that we put the 'whole person' back into our view of the world. There is still a place for the subjective, the emotional, the irrational. The reader who happens to be a 'hard', no-nonsense scientist might at first find this approach vague and difficult to follow. Persistence will pay off, and some very useful arguments can be derived from this reading. Such writing is salutary for the professional scientist, who is ever in danger of losing modesty in the face of nature. However, perhaps Roszak pays too little attention to the notion of *parallel* levels of discourse. For some purposes a description of a human in physico-chemical terms (e.g. nerve cells, neurochemicals) might prove useful. At other times, such a description would be irrelevant. There need not be any competition between such parallel accounts; they serve different ends. This leads us to the chapter by Rose, who himself sees little distinction between brain and mind. After putting an holistic alternative to naive reductionism, Rose looks at some of the factors that serve to give direction to scientific research, for example, economic and political considerations. He also discusses the intellectual context in which research will flourish or die.

7 The two cultures

● C. P. Snow

In his famous Rede lecture in 1959, Snow observed that scientists do not read literature and that literary people do not understand the basic ideas of science. But is it a characteristic or merely a caricature that he describes? He was looking for generalizations that applied to his colleagues in Oxford and Cambridge. Would such assertions as 'non-scientists tend to think of scientists as brash and boastful' and 'scientists are shallowly optimistic' stand up in any wider context? The cliché, 'the two cultures', is now used for much wider groups than those with which Snow claimed close acquaintance. There are some assertions that have enough wider validity to be usefully debatable. For instance, Snow states 'literature changes more slowly than science because it does not have the same automatic corrective' and 'there is a moral component right in the grain of science itself' and '(the British have a) fanatical belief in educational specialization (which) appears to get stronger the more we iron out economic inequalities'.

It is about three years since I made a sketch in print of a problem which had been on my mind for some time.[1] It was a problem I could not avoid just because of the circumstances of my life. The only credentials I had to ruminate on the subject at all came through those circumstances, through nothing more than a set of chances. Anyone with similar experience would have seen much the same things and I think made very much the same comments about them. It just happened to be an unusual experience. By training I was a scientist: by vocation I was a writer. That was all. It was a piece of luck, if you like, that arose through coming from a poor home.

But my personal history isn't the point now. All that I need say is that I came to Cambridge and did a bit of research here at a time of major scientific activity. I was privileged to have a ringside view of one of the most wonderful creative periods in all physics. And it happened through the flukes of war – including meeting W. L. Bragg in the buffet on Kettering station on a very cold morning in 1939, which had a determining influence on my practical life – that I was able, and indeed morally forced, to keep that ringside view ever since. So for thirty years

I have had to be in touch with scientists not only out of curiosity, but as part of a working existence. During the same thirty years I was trying to shape the books I wanted to write, which in due course took me among writers.

There have been plenty of days when I have spent the working hours with scientists and then gone off at night with some literary colleagues. I mean that literally. I have had, of course, intimate friends among both scientists and writers. It was through living among these groups and much more, I think, through moving regularly from one to the other and back again that I got occupied with the problem of what, long before I put it on paper, I christened to myself as the 'two cultures'. For constantly I felt I was moving among two groups – comparable in intelligence, identical in race, not grossly different in social origin, earning about the same incomes, who had almost ceased to communicate at all, who in intellectual, moral and psychological climate had so little in common that instead of going from Burlington House or South Kensington to Chelsea, one might have crossed an ocean.

In fact, one had travelled much further than across an ocean – because after a few thousand Atlantic miles, one found Greenwich Village talking precisely the same language as Chelsea, and both having about as much communication with M.I.T. as though the scientists spoke nothing but Tibetan. For this is not just our problem; owing to some of our educational and social idiosyncrasies, it is slightly exaggerated here, owing to another English social peculiarity it is slightly minimised; by and large this is a problem of the entire West.

By this I intend something serious. I am not thinking of the pleasant story of how one of the more convivial Oxford great dons – I have heard the story attributed to A. L. Smith – came over to Cambridge to dine. The date is perhaps the 1890s. I think it must have been at St John's, or possibly Trinity. Anyway, Smith was sitting at the right hand of the President – or Vice-Master – and he was a man who liked to include all round him in the conversation, although he was not immediately encouraged by the expressions of his neighbours. He addressed some cheerful Oxonian chit-chat at the one opposite to him, and got a grunt. He then tried the man on his own right hand and got another grunt. Then, rather to his surprise, one looked at the other and said, 'Do you know what he's talking about?' 'I haven't the least idea.' At this, even Smith was getting out of his depth. But the President, acting as a social emollient, put him at his ease by saying, 'Oh, those are mathematicians! We never talk to *them*.'

No, I intend something serious. I believe the intellectual life of the whole of western society is increasingly being split into two polar groups. When I say the intellectual life, I mean to include also a large part of our practical life, because I should be the last person to suggest the two can at the deepest level be distinguished. I shall come back to the practical life a little later. Two polar groups: at one pole we have the literary intellectuals, who incidentally while no one was looking took to referring to themselves as 'intellectuals' as though there were no others. I remember G. H. Hardy once remarking to me in mild puzzlement, some time in the 1930s: 'Have you noticed how the word "intellectual" is used nowadays? There seems to be a new definition which certainly doesn't include Rutherford or Eddington or Dirac or Adrian or me. It does seem rather odd, don't y'know.'[2]

Literary intellectuals at one pole – at the other scientists, and as the most representative, the physical scientists. Between the two a gulf of mutual incomprehension – sometimes (particularly among the young) hostility and dislike, but most of all lack of understanding. They have a curious distorted image of each other. Their attitudes are so different that, even on the level of emotion, they can't find much common ground. Non-scientists tend to think of scientists as brash and boastful. They hear Mr T. S. Eliot, who just for these illustrations we can take as an archetypal figure, saying about his attempts to revive verse-drama that we can hope for very little, but that he would feel content if he and his co-workers could prepare the ground for a new Kyd or a new Greene. That is the tone, restricted and constrained, with which literary intellectuals are at home: it is the subdued voice of their culture. Then they hear a much louder voice, that of another archetypal figure, Rutherford, trumpeting: 'This is the heroic age of science! This is the Elizabethan age!' Many of us heard that, and a good many other statements beside which that was mild; and we weren't left in any doubt whom Rutherford was casting for the role of Shakespeare. What is hard for the literary intellectuals to understand, imaginatively or intellectually, is that he was absolutely right.

And compare 'this is the way the world ends, not with a bang but a whimper' – incidentally, one of the least likely scientific prophecies ever made – compare that with Rutherford's famous repartee, 'Lucky fellow, Rutherford, always on the crest of the wave.' 'Well, I made the wave, didn't I!'

The non-scientists have a rooted impression that the scientists are shallowly optimistic, unaware of man's condition. On the other hand, the scientists believe that the literary intellectuals are totally lacking in foresight, peculiarly unconcerned with their brother men, in a deep sense anti-intellectual, anxious to restrict both art and thought to the existential moment. And so on. Anyone with a mild talent for invective could produce plenty of this kind of subterranean back-chat. On each side there is some of it which is not entirely baseless. It is all destructive. Much of it rests on misinterpretations which are dangerous. I should like to deal with two of the most profound of these now, one on each side.

First, about the scientists' optimism. This is an accusation which has been made so often that it has become a platitude. It has been made by some of the acutest non-scientific minds of the day. But it depends upon a confusion between the individual experience and the social experience, between the individual condition of man and his social condition. Most of the scientists I have known well have felt – just as deeply as the non-scientists I have known well – that the individual condition of each of us is tragic. Each of us is alone: sometimes we escape from solitariness, through love or affection or perhaps creative moments, but those triumphs of life are pools of light we make for ourselves while the edge of the road is black: each of us dies alone. Some scientists I have known have had faith in revealed religion. Perhaps with them the sense of the tragic condition is not so strong. I don't know. With most people of deep feeling, however high-spirited and happy they are, sometimes most with those who are happiest and most high-spirited, it seems to be right in the fibres, part of the weight of life. That is as true of the scientists I have known best as of anyone at all.

But nearly all of them – and this is where the colour of hope genuinely comes in – would see no reason why, just because the individual condition is tragic, so must the social condition be. Each of us is solitary: each of us dies alone: all right, that's a fate against which we can't struggle – but there is plenty in our condition which is not fate, and against which we are less than human unless we do struggle.

Most of our fellow human beings, for instance, are underfed and die before their time. In the crudest terms, *that* is the social condition. There is a moral trap which comes through the insight into man's loneliness: it tempts one to sit back, complacent in one's unique tragedy, and let the others go without a meal.

As a group, the scientists fall into that trap less than others. They are inclined to be impatient to see if something can be done: and inclined to think that it can be done, until it's proved otherwise. That is their real optimism, and it's an optimism that the rest of us badly need.

In reverse, the same spirit, tough and good and determined to fight it out at the side of their brother men, has made scientists regard the other culture's social attitudes as contemptible. That is too facile: some of them are, but they are a temporary phase and not to be taken as representative.

I remember being cross-examined by a scientist of distinction. 'Why do most writers take on social opinions which would have been thought distinctly uncivilised and démodé at the time of the Plantagenets? Wasn't that true of most of the famous twentieth-century writers? Yeats, Pound, Wyndham Lewis, nine out of ten of those who have dominated literary sensibility in our time – weren't they not only politically silly, but politically wicked? Didn't the influence of all they represent bring Auschwitz that much nearer?'

I thought at the time, and I still think, that the correct answer was not to defend the indefensible. It was no use saying that Yeats, according to friends whose judgment I trust, was a man of singular magnanimity of character, as well as a great poet. It was no use denying the facts, which were broadly true. The honest answer was that there is, in fact, a connection, which literary persons were culpably slow to see, between some kinds of early twentieth-century art and the most imbecile expressions of anti-social feeling.[3] That was one reason, among many, why some of us turned our backs on the art and tried to hack out a new or different way for ourselves.[4]

But though many of those writers dominated literary sensibility for a generation, that is no longer so, or at least to nothing like the same extent. Literature changes more slowly than science. It hasn't the same automatic corrective, and so its misguided periods are longer. But it is ill-considered of scientists to judge writers on the evidence of the period 1914–50.

Those are two of the misunderstandings between the two cultures. I should say, since I began to talk about them – the two cultures, that is – I have had some criticism. Most of my scientific acquaintances think that there is something in it, and so do most of the practising artists I know. But I have been argued with by non-scientists of strong down-to-earth interests. Their view is that it is an over-simplification, and that if one is going to talk in these terms there ought to be at least three cultures. They argue that, though they are not scientists themselves, they would share a good deal of the scientific feeling. They would have as little use – perhaps, since they knew more about it, even less use – for the recent literary culture as the scientists themselves. J. H. Plumb, Alan Bullock and some of my American sociological friends have said that they vigorously refuse to be corralled in a cultural box with people they wouldn't be seen dead with, or to be regarded as helping to produce a climate which would not permit of social hope.

I respect those arguments. The number 2 is a very dangerous number: that is why the dialectic is a dangerous process. Attempts to divide anything into two ought to be regarded with much suspicion. I have thought a long time about going in for further refinements: but in the end I have decided against. I was searching for something a little more than a dashing metaphor, a good deal less than a cultural map: and for those purposes the two cultures is about right, and subtilising any more would bring more disadvantages than it's worth.

At one pole, the scientific culture really is a culture, not only in an intellectual but also in an anthropological sense. That is, its members need not, and of course often do not, always completely understand each other; biologists more often than not will have a pretty hazy idea of contemporary physics; but there are common attitudes, common standards and patterns of behaviour, common approaches and assumptions. This goes surprisingly wide and deep. It cuts across other mental patterns, such as those of religion or politics or class.

Statistically, I suppose slightly more scientists are in religious terms unbelievers, compared with the rest of the intellectual world – though there are plenty who are religious, and that seems to be increasingly so among the young. Statistically also, slightly more scientists are on the Left in open politics – though again, plenty always have called themselves conservatives, and that also seems to be more common among the young. Compared with the rest of the intellectual world, considerably more scientists in this country and probably in the U.S. come from poor families.[5] Yet over a whole range of thought and behaviour, none of that matters very much. In their working, and in much of their emotional life, their attitudes are closer to other scientists than to non-scientists who in religion or politics or class have the same labels as themselves. If I were to risk a piece of shorthand, I should say that naturally they had the future in their bones.

They may or may not like it, but they have it. That was as true of the conservatives J. J. Thomson and Lindemann as of the radicals Einstein or Blackett: as true of the Christian A. H. Compton as of the materialist Bernal: of the aristocrats de Broglie or Russell as of the proletarian Faraday: of those born rich, like Thomas Merton or Victor Rothschild, as of Rutherford, who was the son of an odd-job handyman. Without thinking about it, they respond alike. That is what a culture means.

At the other pole, the spread of attitudes is wider. It is obvious that between the two, as one moves through intellectual society from the physicists to the literary intellectuals, there are all kinds of tones of feeling on the way. But I believe the pole of total incomprehension of science radiates its influence on all the rest. That total incomprehension gives, much more pervasively than we realise, living in it, an unscientific flavour to the whole 'traditional' culture, and that unscientific flavour is often, much more than we admit, on the point of turning anti-scientific. The feelings of one pole become the anti-feelings of the other. If the scientists have the future in their bones, then the traditional culture responds by wishing the future did not exist.[6] It is the traditional culture, to an extent remarkably little diminished by the emergence of the scientific one, which manages the western world.

This polarisation is sheer loss to us all. To us as people, and to our society. It is at the same time practical and intellectual and creative loss, and I repeat that it is false to imagine that those three considerations are clearly separable. But for a moment I want to concentrate on the intellectual loss.

The degree of incomprehension on both sides is the kind of joke which has gone sour. There are about fifty thousand working scientists in the country and about eighty thousand professional engineers or applied scientists. During the war and in the years since, my colleagues and I have had to interview somewhere between thirty to forty thousand of these – that is, about 25 per cent. The number is large enough to give us a fair sample, though of the men we talked to most would still be under forty. We were able to find out a certain amount of what they read and thought about. I confess that even I, who am fond of them and respect them, was a bit shaken. We hadn't quite expected that the links with the traditional culture should be so tenuous, nothing more than a formal touch of the cap.

As one would expect, some of the very best scientists had and have plenty of energy and interest to spare, and we came across several who had read everything that literary people talk about. But that's very rare. Most of the rest, when one tried to probe for what books they had read, would modestly confess, 'Well, I've *tried* a bit of Dickens', rather as though Dickens were an extraordinarily esoteric, tangled and dubiously rewarding writer, something like Rainer Maria Rilke. In fact that is exactly how they do regard him: we thought that discovery, that Dickens had been transformed into the type-specimen of literary incomprehensibility, was one of the oddest results of the whole exercise.

But of course, in reading him, in reading almost any writer whom we should value, they are just touching their caps to the traditional culture. They have their own culture, intensive, rigorous, and constantly in action. This culture contains a great deal of argument, usually much more rigorous, and almost always at a higher conceptual level, than literary persons' arguments – even though the scientists do cheerfully use words in senses which literary persons don't recognise, the senses are exact ones, and when they talk about 'subjective', 'objective', 'philosophy' or 'progressive',[7] they know what they mean, even though it isn't what one is accustomed to expect.

Remember, these are very intelligent men. Their culture is in many ways an exacting and admirable one. It doesn't contain much art, with the exception, an important exception, of music. Verbal exchange, insistent argument. Long-playing records. Colour-photography. The ear, to some extent the eye. Books very little, though perhaps not many would go so far as one hero, who perhaps I should admit was further down the scientific ladder than the people I've been talking about – who, when asked what books he read, replied firmly and confidently: 'Books? I prefer to use my books as tools.' It was very hard not to let the mind wander – what sort of tool would a book make? Perhaps a hammer? A primitive digging instrument?

Of books, though, very little. And of the books which to most literary persons are bread and butter, novels, history, poetry, plays, almost nothing at all. It isn't that they're not interested in the psychological or moral or social life. In the social life, they certainly are, more than most of us. In the moral, they are by and large the soundest group of intellectuals we have; there is a moral component right in the grain of science itself, and almost all scientists form their own judgments of the moral life. In the psychological they have as much interest as most of us, though occasionally I fancy they come to it rather late. It isn't that they lack the interests. It is much more that the whole literature of the traditional culture doesn't seem to them relevant to those interests. They are, of course, dead wrong. As a result, their imaginative understanding is less than it could be. They are self-impoverished.

But what about the other side? They are impoverished too – perhaps more seriously, because they are vainer about it. They still like to pretend that the traditional culture is the whole of 'culture', as though the natural order didn't exist. As though the exploration of the natural order was of no interest either in its own value or its consequences. As though the scientific edifice of the physical world was not, in its intellectual depth, complexity and articulation, the most beautiful and wonderful collective work of the mind of man. Yet most non-scientists have no conception of that edifice at all. Even if they want to have it, they can't. It is rather as though, over an immense range of intellectual experience, a whole group was tone-deaf. Except that this tone-deafness doesn't come by nature, but by training, or rather the absence of training.

As with the tone-deaf, they don't know what they miss. They give a pitying chuckle at the news of scientists who have never read a major work of English literature. They dismiss them as ignorant specialists. Yet their own ignorance and their own specialisation is just as startling. A good many times I have been present at gatherings of people who, by the standards of the traditional culture, are thought highly educated and who have with considerable gusto been expressing their incredulity at the illiteracy of scientists. Once or twice I have been provoked and have asked the company how many of them could describe the Second Law of Thermodynamics. The response was cold: it was also negative. Yet I was asking something which is about the scientific equivalent of: *Have you read a work of Shakespeare's?*

I now believe that if I had asked an even simpler question – such as, What do you mean by mass, or acceleration, which is the scientific equivalent of saying, *Can you read?* – not more than one in ten of the highly educated would have felt that I was speaking the same language. So the great edifice of modern physics goes up, and the majority of the cleverest people in the western world have about as much insight into it as their neolithic ancestors would have had.

Just one more of those questions, that my non-scientific friends regard as being in the worst of taste. Cambridge is a university where scientists and non-scientists meet every night at dinner.[8] About two years ago, one of the most astonishing discoveries in the whole history of science was brought off. I don't mean the sputnik – that was admirable for quite different reasons, as a feat of organisation and a triumphant use of existing knowledge. No, I mean the discovery at Columbia by Yang and Lee. It is a piece of work of the greatest beauty and originality, but the result is so startling that one forgets how beautiful the thinking is. It makes us think again about some of the fundamentals of the physical world. Intuition, common sense – they are neatly stood on their heads. The result is usually known as the non-conservation of parity. If there were any serious communication between the two cultures, this experiment would have been talked about at every High Table in Cambridge. Was it? I wasn't here: but I should like to ask the question.

There seems then to be no place where the cultures meet. I am not going to waste time saying that this is a pity. It is much worse than that. Soon I shall come to some practical consequences. But at the heart of thought and creation we are letting some of our best chances go by default. The clashing point of two subjects, two disciplines, two cultures – of two galaxies, so far as that goes – ought to produce creative chances. In the history of mental activity that has been where some of the break-throughs came. The chances are there now. But they are there, as it were, in a vacuum, because those in the two cultures can't talk to each other. It is bizarre how very little of twentieth-century science has been assimilated into twentieth-century art. Now and then one used to find poets conscientiously using scientific expressions, and getting them wrong – there was a time when 'refraction' kept cropping up in verse in a mystifying fashion, and when 'polarised light' was used as though writers were under the illusion that it was a specially admirable kind of light.

Of course, that isn't the way that science could be any good to art. It has got to be assimilated along with, and as part and parcel of, the whole of our mental experience, and used as naturally as the rest.

I said earlier that this cultural divide is not just an English phenomenon: it exists all over the western world. But it probably seems at its sharpest in England, for two reasons. One is our fanatical belief in educational specialisation, which is much more deeply ingrained in us than in any country in the world, west or east. The other is our tendency to let our social forms crystallise. This tendency appears to get stronger, not weaker, the more we iron out economic inequalities: and this is specially true in education. It means that once anything like a cultural divide gets established, all the social forces operate to make it not less rigid, but more so.

The two cultures were already dangerously separate sixty years ago; but a prime minister like Lord Salisbury could have his own laboratory at Hatfield, and Arthur Balfour had a somewhat more than amateur interest in natural science. John Anderson did some research in inorganic chemistry in Leipzig before passing first into the Civil Service, and incidentally took a spread of subjects which is now impossible.[9] None of that degree of interchange at the top of the Establishment is likely, or indeed thinkable, now.[10]

In fact, the separation between the scientists and non-scientists is much less bridgeable among the young than it was even thirty years ago. Thirty years ago the cultures had long ceased to speak to each other: but at least they managed a kind of frozen smile across the gulf. Now the politeness has gone, and they just make faces. It is not only that the young scientists now feel that they are part of a culture on the rise while the other is in retreat. It is also, to be brutal, that the young scientists know that with an indifferent degree they'll get a comfortable job, while their contemporaries and counterparts in English or History will be lucky to earn 60 per cent as much. No young scientist of any talent would feel that he isn't wanted or that his work is ridiculous, as did the hero of *Lucky Jim*, and in fact, some of the disgruntlement of Amis and his associates is the disgruntlement of the under-employed arts graduate.

There is only one way out of all this: it is, of course, by rethinking our education. In this country, for the two reasons I have given, that is more difficult than in any other. Nearly everyone will agree that our school education is too specialised. But nearly everyone feels that it is outside the will of man to alter it. Other countries are as dissatisfied with their education as we are, but are not so resigned.

The U.S. teach out of proportion more children up to eighteen than we do: they teach them far more widely, but nothing like so rigorously. They know that: they are hoping to take the problem in hand within ten years, though they may not have all that time to spare. The U.S.S.R. also teach out of proportion more children than we do: they also teach far more widely than we do (it is an absurd western myth that their school education is specialised) but much too rigorously.[11] They know that – and they are beating about to get it right. The Scandinavians, in particular the Swedes, who would make a more sensible job of it than any of us, are handicapped by their practical need to devote an inordinate amount of time to foreign languages. But they too are seized of the problem.

Are we? Have we crystallised so far that we are no longer flexible at all?

Talk to schoolmasters, and they say that our intense specialisation, like nothing else on earth, is dictated by the Oxford and Cambridge scholarship examinations. If that is so, one would have thought it not utterly impracticable to change the Oxford and Cambridge scholarship examinations. Yet one would underestimate the national capacity for the intricate defensive to believe that that was easy. All the lessons of our educational history suggest we are only capable of increasing specialisation, not decreasing it.

Somehow we have set ourselves the task of producing a tiny *élite* – far smaller proportionately than in any comparable country – educated in one academic skill. For a hundred and fifty years in Cambridge it was mathematics: then it was mathematics or classics: then natural science was allowed in. But still the choice had to be a single one.

It may well be that this process has gone too far to be reversible. I have given reasons why I think it is a disastrous process, for the purpose of a living culture. I am going on to give reasons why I think it is fatal, if we're to perform our practical tasks in the world. But I can think of only one example, in the whole of English educational history, where our pursuit of specialised mental exercises was resisted with success.

It was done here in Cambridge, fifty years ago, when the old order-of-merit in the Mathematical Tripos was abolished. For over a hundred years, the nature of the Tripos had been crystallising. The competition for the top places had got fiercer, and careers hung on them. In most colleges, certainly in my own, if one managed to come out as Senior or Second Wrangler, one was elected a Fellow out of hand. A whole apparatus of coaching had grown up. Men of the quality of Hardy, Littlewood, Russell, Eddington, Jeans, Keynes, went in for two or three years' training for an examination which was intensely competitive and intensely difficult. Most people in Cambridge were very proud of it, with a similar pride to that which almost anyone in England always has for our existing educational institutions, whatever they happen to be. If you study the flysheets of the time, you will find the passionate arguments for keeping the examination precisely as it was to all eternity: it was the only way to keep up standards, it was the only fair test of merit, indeed, the only seriously objective test in the world. The arguments, in fact, were almost exactly those which are used today with precisely the same passionate sincerity if anyone suggests that the scholarship examinations might conceivably not be immune from change.

In every respect but one, in fact, the old Mathematical Tripos seemed perfect. The one exception, however, appeared to some to be rather important. It was simply – so the young creative mathematicians, such as Hardy and Littlewood, kept saying – that the rating had no intellectual merit at all. They went a little further, and said that the Tripos had killed serious mathematics in England stone dead for a hundred years. Well, even in academic controversy, that took some skirting round, and they got their way. But I have an impression that Cambridge was a good deal more flexible between 1850 and 1914 than it has been in our time. If we had had the old Mathematical Tripos firmly planted among us, should we have ever managed to abolish it?

NOTES

1. 'The Two Cultures', *New Statesman*, 6 October 1956.
2. This lecture was delivered to a Cambridge audience, and so I used some points of reference which I did not need to explain. G. H. Hardy, 1877–1947, was one of the most distinguished pure mathematicians of his time, and a picturesque figure in Cambridge both as a young don and on his return in 1931 to the Sadleirian Chair of Mathematics.
3. I said a little more about this connection in *The Times Literary Supplement*, 'Challenge to the Intellect', 15 August 1958. I hope some day to carry the analysis further.
4. It would be more accurate to say that, for literary reasons, we felt the prevailing literary modes were useless to us. We were, however, reinforced in that feeling when it occurred to us that those prevailing modes went hand in hand with social attitudes either wicked, or absurd, or both.
5. An analysis of the schools from which Fellows of the Royal Society come tells its own story. The distribution is markedly different from that of, for example, members of the Foreign Service or Queen's Counsel.
6. Compare George Orwell's *1984*, which is the strongest possible wish that the future should not exist, with J. D. Bernal's *World Without War*.
7. *Subjective*, in contemporary technological jargon, means 'divided according to subjects'. *Objective* means 'directed towards an object'. *Philosophy* means 'general intellectual approach or attitude' (for example, a scientist's 'philosophy of guided weapons' might lead him to propose certain kinds of 'objective research'). A 'progressive' job means one with possibilities of promotion.
8. Almost all college High Tables contain Fellows in both scientific and non-scientific subjects.
9. He took the examination in 1905.
10. It is, however, true to say that the compact nature of the managerial layers of English society – the fact that 'everyone knows everyone else' – means that scientists and non-scientists do in fact know each other as people more easily than in most countries. It is also true that a good many leading politicians and administrators keep up lively intellectual and artistic interests to a much greater extent, so far as I can judge, than is the case in the U.S. These are both among our assets.
11. I tried to compare American, Soviet and English education in 'New Minds for the New World', *New Statesman*, 6 September 1956.

8 Uncovering the nature of science

● H. Collins and S. Shapin

James Conant was a distinguished American organic chemist and, in public life, reached the position of Ambassador to Germany and, later, adviser to the Atomic Energy Commission. He keenly felt the need for a widespread acquaintance with the nature and sources of scientific knowledge, because 'Big Science' (e.g. particle physics, astronomy, biotechnology), applied science and military science are sufficiently important for no-one to ignore them. Yet public opinion can be destructive if it is not well informed. To start to improve the level of public understanding, Conant produced the Harvard Case Histories in Science. These were realistic histories of advances in science, which Kuhn drew on in Structure of Scientific Revolutions. *Conant was not trying merely to 'humanise' science to make it more interesting, but to reveal the processes and ideas that guided the discoveries and were sometimes themselves overturned by the discovery. The authors of the article assert that a wider appreciation that there is 'extraordinary' as well as 'normal' science would help to prevent disillusionment and distrust of 'scientists' (used here in a broad sense). They use the case-history approach as part of a discussion of the 'tension between discovery methods and more didactic methods of teaching' and end by saying that extensions of Conant's ideas are needed even more nowadays, to stem what they perceive as an anti-science movement of opinion.*

In the late 1940s, reflecting upon the place of science in the liberal democracy and upon public understanding of science in the aftermath of the atomic bomb, the president of Harvard University James B. Conant concluded that a radically new approach to the teaching of science was required. He argued that a proper understanding of what he called 'the tactics and strategy of science' was an essential component in the education of the future citizen. Turning programmatic statements into pedagogic practice, Conant and his colleagues soon produced the celebrated *Harvard Case Histories in Experimental Science*, modelled partly upon teaching materials employed in the Harvard Business School.

For Conant a realistic understanding of experimental practice was vitally important for the student who was not going to acquire this understanding directly, at the scientist's bench. For democracy to work in an increasingly scientific and technological society, the citizen had to be put in a position where he or she could not merely see the scientist's product but also grasp the means by which scientific knowledge was generated and evaluated.

Without such information the citizen, however 'highly educated and intelligent', 'will almost always fail to grasp the essentials in a discussion that takes place among scientists'; this will be because of 'his fundamental ignorance of what science can or cannot accomplish'. A citizen who was ignorant in this way, Conant argued, was abdicating his rights of citizenship.

Thirty-five years later, Conant's analysis is even more pertinent. The vast resources demanded for the support of Big Science, the technical sophistication required for comprehensive environmental and military issues, the increasingly common spectacle of scientific experts disagreeing in the media and the law courts and, of course, the sheer scale and speed of technological change and its influence on citizens' lives, all call upon educational institutions and teachers to respond anew to Conant's programme: the education of the citizenry in 'the tactics and strategy of science' has not met the challenge.

Happily, the conceptual resources available for addressing Conant's problem have recently become more refined and more suitable for the task. Conant concluded that the best way to give the student a sense of the actual nature of science was through a selective exposure to its *history*: a history which depicted not an idealization of science but scientific practice as it really was and as it had really developed as a human activity.

At the time Conant compiled the *Harvard Case Histories* the academic discipline of the history of science was in its infancy: hagiographic history dominated, philosophers' idealizations of 'the scientific method' strongly coloured historians' accounts and the speciality called the sociology of science, to the extent it existed, was concerned with the normative structure of the scientific community rather than with scientific knowledge and practice. Interestingly, one of the seminal texts which has helped to change all this arose from the pedagogical initiative Conant set on foot: Thomas Kuhn's *Structure of Scientific Revolutions* acknowledges the influence of Conant and draws many of its exemplars from the *Case Histories*.

In the two decades since Kuhn's *Structure*, and particularly with the development over the past 10 years of the sociology of scientific knowledge, a 'new history and sociology of science' literature has come into being. This is a literature marked by its rejection of *a priori* idealized models of science. It replaces these with painstaking detailed accounts of actual experimental practice and social processes by which scientific arguments are resolved.

The existence of the new history and sociology of science literature creates both problems and opportunities for those concerned with the teaching of science. Before its availability, there was a rough 'fit' between the idealizations of science found, on the one hand, in the typical science textbook and, on the other, in the accounts of the historian and the philosopher of science. This is no longer the case. Those concerned to educate the public about the nature of science now have not only the opportunity but also the obligation to choose how to tell the story.

What is the teacher to do with this new literature? The choice depends on whether 'radical' or more 'reformist' innovations in science education are required. Do we want to use history of science merely to 'humanize' science education, while retaining its existing goals, structures and materials?

Given the real constraints posed by the existing curriculum, the lack of time available for more ambitious changes and the conservative tenor of much scientific education, this may be the only realistic goal. However, the main, if not the entire potential for the pedagogical use of the new literature is in the radical rethinking of the aims of educating *non-scientists*.

Start by considering the putative ambitions of a science teacher entering a classroom at 9.30 on a winter morning. What might such a teacher have in mind? These four goals do not seem unreasonable: to enable children to pass examinations in science subjects, to show future citizens the nature of science, to begin to teach future scientists how to do science and to teach children about some features of the natural world.

Under the 'received model' of scientific rationality these four aims coincide easily. The crucial characteristic of the received model is the contention that unbiased methods of investigation will reveal unambiguous, unique and repeatable true facts about the natural world. Thus in learning to do science properly children uncover true features of the natural world and learn, in passing, the nature of science, i.e., that careful, unbiased experiments are repeatable and do in fact reveal the truth.

The tension between discovery methods and more didactic methods of teaching as ways of fulfilling these ambitions is only a tension between, on the one hand, stress on learning features of the natural world and passing examinations and, on the other hand, stress on learning about science and learning to do it. Given that all four aims can coincide under discovery or didactic methods, the tension does not have to involve deep questions about the nature of science.

The new history and sociology of science differs from the received model principally in rejecting the view that unbiased and competent observation and experimentation is in itself enough to reveal unambiguous repeatable facts. The new view holds that how something comes to be seen as true, unambiguous and repeatable is a social process and, therefore, that it is a matter for empirical study.

The 'same' region of the natural world may seem to precipitate different facts when observed at different times or places, even though similar scientific methods are used. That there is at any given period broad consensus within the scientific community about the make-up of the natural world is to be taken as a feature of the social organization of science rather than as a passive, mirrored reflection of the structure of natural reality.

Within this perspective it is unsurprising that scientists disagree about radically new areas of research since, by definition, no consensus has yet been formed; it is unsurprising that established consensus sometimes breaks down and even from time to time that agreements are overturned in a wholesale way – Kuhn's 'scientific revolutions'.

This means that science comprises more than one sort of activity. It comprises his work within a broad consensus – 'normal science' to use Kuhn's term – and periods when findings cannot be quickly fitted into the prevailing consensus: these we will call periods of 'extraordinary science'.

Returning to the four ambitions of our science teacher with the new model in mind, we find that coincidence between the aims is no longer straightforwardly realizable; there are now some ambiguities. If we are to teach the nature of science, what sort of science is it? What sort of science are we to teach children to do? And: what features of the natural world do we want to teach?

As for this last we probably want to convey aspects of the current consensus. But do we represent them as features of a consensus or as immutable facts? The answer to this question is not separable from the answers to the others.

Experiments conducted within normal science depend upon specifying a fairly narrow range of permissible outcomes in advance. Experiments, like every other technical accomplishment, require the exercise of fallible skills. Thus an experimental run which produces results outside the expected range is accounted, and assessed as, a *failed* run. This retrospective assessment procedure is one of the ways that consensus is maintained in normal science: anomalous results are excluded by *fiat*.

Extraordinary science, on the other hand, explores regions in which a well-defined range of experimental outcomes is not available. For example, in the early 1970s debate over the existence of cosmic gravitational radiation, the question was not 'How much gravitational radiation is there?' but rather, 'Is gravitational radiation detectable on earth?' In such a situation it is often unclear whether a scientist *has* developed the skills to make the experiment work. The scientist is not able to refer to the acceptable range of experimental outcomes in order to determine if that experiment should be accounted a success or a failure.

In extraordinary science scientists tend to disagree about what is to count as a successful experiment, eg is it one that has detected gravitational radiation or is it one that has not? Science of this sort is confused, unclear, indecisive, often characterized by bitter personal dispute and long-running controversy. Under these conditions a failure of expertise to bring about consensus over the constituents of the natural world is very evident. And in these circumstances the received model of scientific rationality is most clearly wanting.

Nearly all science is 'normal science'. In so far as the concern of the science educator is to begin the training of scientists, then it is the abilities associated with the practice of normal science that ought to be taught.

Nevertheless, several features of the understanding of science offered by the new history of sociology of science could be considered even here. For example, it has been suggested that there is often a sort of 'trauma' attending the passage from the state of being a science student to the state of being a scientific researcher. If the science student is wholly trained in circumstances where the answers are pregiven in the questions, he or she may experience disorientation when confronted by real science. In real science the range of answers may not be known in advance, and (particularly in extraordinary science) the existence of natural phenomena cannot be decided so simply as it seemed to be in the classroom or in the undergraduate teaching laboratory.

There has been concern over 'dropout' or 'wastage' at this stage of the production of scientists. Wastage might conceivably be diminished by exposing science students to the contingencies affecting real scientific experimentation, including the social processes by which scientific consensus is brought about.

More important however, the future citizen and the democratic society of which he or she is to become a member, is ill-served if education provides only the 'ideology' of science. One of the most important reasons for saying this involves the problem of 'anti-science' attitudes.

As we have indicated, disagreements among scientific experts is an increasingly visible feature of modern scientific and technological society. Experts disagree and citizens (and the institutions which are said to be answerable to the citizen) are asked to react and to decide. How will the citizen react to the spectacle of disagreeing experts if he or she is offered only the passive mirror model of scientific knowledge? The reaction will be polarized. In the mirror version, facts are either wholly true or wholly baseless.

If this is what is believed, then disagreement among experts will generate profound disillusionment about what is taken to be science as a whole. Scientists, it will be thought, are all incompetents, or liars, or intellectuals available for hire to powerful interest groups. There will be no shades of opinion, no feeling that disagreement is natural to much of science; no tendency, that is, to cope with the spectacle of disagreeing experts as an endemic feature of 'good' science.

Thus, the 'ideological' version of science, so often believed to be the best way of guaranteeing proper respect for science in a democratic society, may actually be responsible for much of the anti-science attitude that concerns scientists and science teachers. The new perspective, contrarily, may assist the future citizen in regarding scientists as 'the best possible experts', while not generating the unreasonable expectations and consequent polarizations which are responsible for anti-science opinions and the exclusions of the citizen from responsible participation in such matters.

School and university science teaching has the potential to reveal the real nature of science to the future citizen. Anomalous results, which must be immediately reinterpreted as experimental errors if the mirror model is to be properly internalized, should be displayed as typical outcomes of experiment in extraordinary science.

It is the very *disorganization* of the discovery method of teaching – its greatest liability in terms of conventional goals – which has heuristic value seen from this point of view. The student can be shown why there is disagreement and disorganization when experts are asked to comment upon matters at the limit of their expertise. Demonstrating this becomes the point of the discovery method.

Moreover, the next step, the process of forming the consensus from this chaos, can be practically revealed in the classroom. After all, the students, when they are being taught as potential scientists, are being shown how to reduce disorder to order.

This is what their practice comprises when informed by the received model of scientific rationality. Classroom experiments continue as before, but it is the social organization of consensus that is the focus of attention rather than an abstract idea of the proper outcome of the work. The achievement of consensus in the classroom is taken to be a microcosm of the achievement of consensus – over a much larger time period – in the scientific community.

Now and again, we suggest, students' attention might be drawn to the way the class, in the hour or two under the direction of the teacher, reduces an initially disordered set of quasi-findings into experimental support from the 'correct' hypothesis. The parallels between the classroom lesson and the life histories of scientific controversies, as they move towards closure, are striking.

Although these are clearly very early days for the project of incorporating the new history and sociology of science into innovatory science teaching, some provisional practical recommendations can be offered.

First, the time is ripe for new teaching resources along the lines of the *Harvard Case Histories* developed 35 years ago. Just as Conant drew upon the best historical accounts of the actual nature of science available to him, so we can now do the same, using the radically different picture of science provided in the new literature. However, the aims will be very much the same as Conant's and our target will be very much the same as that envisaged by him: the group of students somewhere between the last years of school and the early years of university education.

Second, we have suggested that the actual teaching of experiments could (at least occasionally) be turned into a topic for study and reflection. Along with teaching students the appropriate skills and aspects of the natural world, we could make experimental teaching into an object lesson in the processes by which scientific skills are transmitted and social consensus about reality is produced.

9 The myth of objective consciousness

• T. Roszak

Science is to be characterized not so much by the content of current scientific knowledge but by a particular mode *of looking at the world. Unlike previous faiths, science is often said to* de-mythologize *our set of beliefs about the world. It is argued that* objective consciousness, *often seen as the hallmark of the scientific expert, is itself a myth. Some philosophical problems associated with the notion of objectivity are discussed. In the face of the challenge from scientific reductionism, a place for the subjective and irrational dimension to human existence is emphasized. This article presents some strongly expressed views from a social and psychological perspective. These ideas encouraged a debate that requires the attention of the whole scientific community.*

Science was almost invariably seen as an undisputed social good, because it had become so intimately related in the popular mind (though not often in ways clearly understood) to the technological progress that promised security and affluence. It was not foreseen even by gifted social critics that the impersonal, large-scale social processes to which technological progress gives rise – in economics, in politics, in education, in every aspect of life – generate their own characteristic problems. When the general public finds itself enmeshed in a gargantuan industrial apparatus which it admires to the point of idolization and yet cannot comprehend, it must of necessity defer to those who are experts or to those who own the experts; only they appear to know how the great cornucopia can be kept brimming over with the good things of life.

Centralized bigness breeds the regime of expertise, whether the big system is based on privatized or socialized economies. Even within the democratic socialist tradition with its stubborn emphasis on workers' control, it is far from apparent how the democratically governed units of an industrial economy will automatically produce a general system which is not dominated by co-ordinating experts. It is both ironic and ominous to hear the French Gaullists and the Wilson Labourites in Great

Britain – governments that are heavily committed to an elitist managerialism – now talking seriously about increased workers' 'participation' in industry. It would surely be a mistake to believe that the technocracy cannot find ways to placate and integrate the shop floor without compromising the continuation of super-scale social processes. 'Participation' could easily become the god-word of our official politics within the next decade; but its reference will be to the sort of 'responsible' collaboration that keeps the technocracy growing. We do well to remember that one of the great secrets of successful concentration camp administration under the Nazis was to enlist the 'participation' of the inmates.

It is for this reason that the counter culture, which draws upon a profoundly personalist sense of community rather than upon technical and industrial values, comes closer to being a radical critique of the technocracy than any of the traditional ideologies. If one starts with a sense of the person that ventures to psychoanalytical depths, one may rapidly arrive at a viewpoint that rejects many of the hitherto undisputed values of industrialism itself. One soon begins talking about 'standards of living' that transcend high productivity, efficiency, full employment, and the work-and-consumption ethic. Quality and not quantity becomes the touchstone of social value.

The critique is pushed even further when the counter culture begins to explore the modes of non-intellective consciousness. Along this line, questions arise which strike more deeply at technocratic assumptions. For if the technocracy is dependent on public deference to the experts, it must stand or fall by the reality of expertise. But what *is* expertise? What are the criteria which certify someone as an expert?

If we are foolishly willing to agree that experts are those whose role is legitimized by the fact that the technocratic system needs them in order to avoid falling apart at the seams, then of course the technocratic status quo generates its own internal justification: the technocracy is legitimized because it enjoys the approval of experts; the experts are legitimized because there could be no technocracy without them. This is the sort of circular argument student rebels meet when they challenge the necessity of administrative supremacy in the universities. They are invariably faced with the rhetorical question: but who will allocate room space, supervise registration, validate course requirements, co-ordinate the academic departments, police the parking lots and dormitories, discipline students, etc., if not the administration? Will the multiversity not collapse in chaos if the administrators are sent packing? The students are learning the answer: yes, the multiversity will collapse; but *education* will go on. Why? Because the administrators have nothing to do with the reality of education; their expertise is related to the illusory busywork that arises from administrative complexity itself. The multiversity creates the administrators and they, in turn, expand the multiversity so that it needs to make place for more administrators. One gets out of this squirrel cage only by digging deep into the root meaning of education itself.

The same radicalizing logic unfolds if, in confronting the technocracy, we begin looking for a conception of expertise which amounts to something more than the intimidating truism that tells us experts are those in the absence of whom the technocracy would collapse.

An expert, we say, is one to whom we turn because he is in control of reliable knowledge about that which concerns us. In the case of the technocracy, the experts are those who govern us because they know (reliably) about all things relevant to our survival and happiness: human needs, social engineering, economic planning, international relations, invention, education, etc. Very well, but what is 'reliable knowledge'? How do we know it when we see it? The answer is: reliable knowledge is knowledge that is scientifically sound, since science is that to which modern man refers for the definitive explication of reality. And what in turn is it that characterizes scientific knowledge? The answer is: objectivity. Scientific knowledge is not just feeling or speculation or subjective ruminating. It is a verifiable description of reality that exists independent of any purely personal considerations. It is true . . . real . . . dependable . . . It works. And that at last is how we define an expert: he is one who *really* knows what is what, because he cultivates an objective consciousness.

Thus, if we probe the technocracy in search of the peculiar power it holds over us, we arrive at the myth of objective consciousness. There is but one way of gaining access to reality – so the myth holds – and this is to cultivate a state of consciousness cleansed of all subjective distortion, all personal involvement. What flows from this state of consciousness qualifies as knowledge, and nothing else does. This is the bedrock on which the natural sciences have built; and under their spell all fields of knowledge strive to become scientific. The study of man in his social, political, economic, psychological, historical aspects – all this, too, must become objective: rigorously, painstakingly objective. At every level of human experience, would-be scientists come forward to endorse the myth of objective consciousness, thus certifying themselves as experts. And because they know and we do not, we yield to their guidance.

* * * *

But to speak of 'mythology' in connection with science would seem at first glance to be a contradiction in terms. Science, after all, purports to be precisely that enterprise of the mind which strips life of its myths, substituting for fantasy and legend a relationship to reality based, in William James' phrase, on 'irreducible and stubborn facts.' Is not scientific knowledge, indeed, that residue which is left when all the myths have been filtered away? One might in fact argue that this is exactly what distinguishes the scientific revolution of the modern West from all previous cultural transitions. In the past, when one cultural epoch has displaced another, the change frequently involved little more than a process of mythological transformation: a *re*-mythologizing of men's thinking. So the figure of Christ stepped into the place prepared long since by the savior figures of various pagan mystery cults, and in time the Christian saints inherited their status from the deities of the Greco-Roman, Teutonic, or Celtic pantheons.

But science, we are to believe, does not re-mythologize life; it *de*-mythologizes it. This is supposedly what makes the scientific revolution a radically different, if not a final, cultural episode. For, with the advent of the scientific world view, indisputable truth takes the place of make-believe.

There is no doubting the radical novelty of science in contrast to all earlier mythological world views. What all non-scientific cultural systems have had in common is the tendency to mistake their mythologies for literal statements about history and the natural world – or at least the tendency to articulate mythological insights in what a scientific mind mistakes for propositional assertions. In this way, imaginative expressions rich in moral drama or psychic perception easily degenerate into fabulous conjectures about the exotic reaches of time and space. This is how we most often use the world 'mythology' in our time: to designate the telling of unverifiable, if not downright false, tales about remote ages and places. The story of the Garden of Eden is a 'myth' we say, because insofar as any believing Christian or Jew has ever tried to locate the story geographically and historically, skeptics have been able to call his evidence, if any, quite cogently into question.

Mythologies which are imaginative exaggerations of our ordinary perceptions or displacements of them to other times and places – let us call them in this sense temporal-physical mythologies – have always been vulnerable to critical inquiry. The doubting Thomas in the case need not even be a scientific skeptic. A devout Christian can practice an uncompromising skepticism toward the mythologies of other faiths and cultures, in the fashion of Charlemagne striking down the Saxon idols and defying their wrath, confident that no such heathen divinities existed. But a Christian's skepticism is necessarily partisan, sparing the believer any critical examination of his own dogmas. Even liberal Christian demythologizers like Rudolph Bultmann have had to stop short of extending their project to such essential teachings as the resurrection of Christ.

In contrast to such selective skepticism, the wholesale skepticism of science shows up to brilliant advantage. Science is the infidel to all gods in behalf of none. Thus there is no way around the painful dilemma in which the religious traditions of the world have found themselves trapped over the last two centuries. Every culture that has invested its convictions in a temporal-physical mythology is doomed before the onslaught of the scientific unbeliever. Any village atheist who persists in saying 'show me' is in the position to hold up to ransom an entire religious culture, with little expectation that it will be able to find the price demanded. It would be difficult to say whether this situation partakes more of farce or of tragedy. Only a few generations ago, Clarence Darrow, no more than a skillful courtroom lawyer armed with a Sunday supplement knowledge of Darwin, was able to make laughingstock of a Judeo-Christian mythology that had served to inspire the finest philosophical and artistic minds of our culture over hundreds of generations. Yet, under unrelenting skeptical pressure, what choice have those who cling to temporal-physical mythologies but to undertake strategic retreat, conceding ever more ground to secular, reductionist styles of thought. The line of retreat falls back to interpretations of myth that are primarily ethical . . . or aesthetic . . . or, in some unspecified fashion, symbolic. Within the Christian tradition, this is a resort which is bound to weaken and confuse, since Christianity has had a uniquely significant commitment to the literal truth of its teachings. Indeed, the sweeping secularization of Western society that has come in the wake of scientific advance can be seen as a product of Christianity's peculiar reliance on a precarious, dogmatic literalism. Such a religious tradition need only prick its finger in order to bleed to death. And if the hard-pressed believer does turn to 'symbolic' interpretations, even here the secular temperament tends to sweep the field by asserting reductionist psychological or sociological correlatives for the myth. The only other defense, that of standing fast in behalf of the literal truth, leads, as Kierkegaard recognized more than a century ago, to the crucifixion of the intellect.

The scientific world view is of course invulnerable to criticism at the same level as a temporal-physical mythology. It would be a ludicrous mistake to contend that the things and forces with which science fills time and space – electrons and galaxies, gravitational fields and natural selection, DNA and viruses – are the cultural equivalents of centaurs and Valhallas and angelic beings. What science deals in is not so poor in ordinary sensory verification – nor so rich in imaginative possibilities. Unlike the mythological traditions of the past, science is not in the first instance a body of supposed knowledge about entities and events. Science would still be science and very much in business if it encompassed no knowledge at all other than the ruins of proven ignorance and error. The scientific mind begins in the spirit of the Cartesian zero, with the doubting away of all inherited knowledge in favor of an entirely new *method* of knowing, which, whether it proceeds on rationalist or empiricist lines, purports to begin from scratch, free of all homage to authority.

What scientists know may therefore wax or wane, change in part or whole as time goes on and as evidence accumulates. If the Piltdown fossil proves to be a hoax, it can be discarded without calling the science of physical anthropology into question. If the telescopes of astronomers were to discover angels in outer space, science as a method of knowing would not be in any sense discredited; its theories would simply be reformulated in the light of new discoveries. In contrast to the way we use the phrase 'world view' in other contexts, science rests itself not in the *world* the scientist beholds at any particular point in time, but in his mode of *viewing* that world. A man is a scientist not because of what he sees, but because of *how* he sees it.

At least, this is what has become the conventional way of regarding scientific knowledge. Thomas Kuhn, who has looked at the matter more carefully, has recently thrown strong and significant doubt on this 'incremental' conception of the history of science. His contention comes close to suggesting that the progressive accumulation of 'truth' in the scientific community is something of an illusion, created by the fact that each generation of scientists rewrites its textbooks in such a way as to select from the past what is still considered valid and to suppress the multitude of errors and false starts that are also a part of the history of science. As for the all-important principles of validation that control this natural selection of scientific truth from era to era – the so-called 'scientific method' – Kuhn is left unconvinced that they are quite as purely 'rational' or 'empirical' as scientists like to think.[1]

Yet the incremental conception of scientific knowledge is very much part of the mythology we are concerned with here. The capacity of science to progress stands as one of the principal validations of its objectivity. Knowledge progresses only when it is understood to survive the passing of particular minds or generations. Science, understood as the expanding application of a fixed method of knowing to ever more areas of experience, makes such a claim. A scientist, asked to explain why science progresses when other fields of thought do not, would doubtlessly refer us to the 'objectivity' of his method of knowing. Objectivity, he would tell us, is what gives science its keen critical edge and its peculiarly cumulative character.

Are we using the word 'mythology' illegitimately in applying it to objectivity as a state of consciousness? I think not. For the myth at its deepest level is that collectively created thing which crystallizes the great, central values of a culture. It is, so to speak, the intercommunications system of culture. If the culture of science locates its highest values not in mystic symbol or ritual or epic tales of faraway lands and times, but in a mode of consciousness, why should we hesitate to call this a myth? The myth has, after all, been identified as a universal phenomenon of human society, a constitutive factor so critical in importance that it is difficult to imagine a culture having any coherence at all if it lacked the mythological bond. Yet, in our society, myth as it is conventionally understood has become practically a synonym for falsehood. To be sure, we commonly hear discussion of various social and political myths these days (the myth of the American frontier, the myth of the Founding Fathers, etc.); the more enlightened clergy even talk freely of 'the Christian myth.' But myths so openly recognized as myths are precisely those that have lost much of their power. It is the myth we accept without question as truth that holds real influence over us. Is it possible that, in this sense, scientific culture is uniquely a-mythical? Or is it the case that we simply fail to look in the right place – in the deep personality structure of the ideal scientist – for the great controlling myth of our culture?

Such, at least, is what I propose here, though it would be pointless to press any further the purely semantic question of whether or not objective consciousness meets all the requirements of a 'mythology'. What is essential here is the contention that objective consciousness is emphatically *not* some manner of definitive, transcultural development whose cogency derives from the fact that it is uniquely in touch with the truth. Rather, like a mythology, it is an arbitrary construct in which a given society in a given historical situation has invested its sense of meaningfulness and value. And so, like any mythology, it can be gotten round and called into question by cultural movements which find meaning and value elsewhere. In the case of the counter culture, then, we have a movement which has turned from objective consciousness as if from a place inhabited by plague – and in the moment of that turning, one can just begin to see an entire episode of our cultural history, the great age of science and technology which began with the Enlightenment, standing revealed in all its quaintly arbitrary, often absurd, and all too painfully unbalanced aspects.

Perhaps, as Michael Polanyi has argued,[2] there is no such thing as objectivity, even in the physical sciences. Certainly his critique is a formidable challenge to scientific orthodoxy. But for our purposes here, this narrowly epistemological question is a subordinate consideration. Science, under the technocracy, has become a total culture dominating the lives of millions for whom discussions of the theory of knowledge are so much foreign language. Yet objectivity, whatever its epistemological status, has become the commanding life style of our society: the one most authoritative way of regarding the self, others, and the whole of our enveloping reality. Even if it is not, indeed, possible to be objective, it *is* possible so to shape the personality that it will feel and act *as if* one were an objective observer and to treat everything that experience presents to the person in accordance with what objectivity would seem to demand.

Objectivity as a state of being fills the very air we breathe in a scientific culture; it grips us subliminally in all we say, feel, and do. The mentality of the ideal scientist becomes the very soul of the society. We seek to adapt our lives to the dictates of that mentality, or at the very least we respond to it acquiescently in the myriad images and pronouncements in which it manifests itself about us during every waking hour. The Barbarella and James Bond who keep their clinical cool while dealing out prodigious sex or sadistic violence . . . the physiologist who persuades several score of couples to undertake coitus while wired to a powerhouse of electronic apparatus so that he can achieve a statistical measure of sexual normalcy . . . the characters of *Last Year at Marienbad* who face one another as impassively as empty mirrors . . . the Secretary of Defense who tells the public without blinking an eye that our country possesses the 'overkill' capacity to destroy any given enemy ten times . . . the high-rise glass and aluminum slab that deprives of visual involvement by offering us only functional linearity and massive reflecting surfaces . . . the celebrated surgeon who assures us that his heart transplant was a 'success' though of course the patient died . . . the computer technician who blithely suggests that we have to wage an 'all-out war on sleep' in order to take advantage of the latest breakthrough in rapid communications . . . the modish expert who seeks (with phenomenal success) to convince us that the essence of communication lies not in the truth or falsehood, wisdom or folly of the message that person transfers to person, but rather in the technical characteristics of the intervening medium . . . the political scientist who settles for being a psephological virtuoso, pretending that the statistics of meaningless elections are the veritable substance of politics . . . all these (or so I would argue) are life under the sway of objective consciousness.

In short, as science elaborates itself into the dominant cultural influence of our age, it is the psychology and not the epistemology of science that urgently requires our critical attention; for it is primarily at this level that the most consequential deficiencies and imbalances of the technocracy are revealed.

* * * *

We can, I think, identify three major characteristics of the psychic style which follows from an intensive cultivation of objective consciousness. I have called them: (1) the alienative dichotomy; (2) the invidious hierarchy; (3) the mechanistic imperative.

(1) Objective consciousness begins by dividing reality into two spheres, which would seem best described in 'In-Here' and 'Out-There.' By In-Here is meant that place within the person to which consciousness withdraws when one wants to know without becoming involved in or

committed to that which is being known. There are many kinds of operations that can be conducted by In-Here. In the natural sciences, the usual activities of In-Here would include those of observing, experimenting, measuring, classifying, and working out quantitative relationships of the most general kind. In the humanities and what we call the behavioral sciences, the operations are more various, but they include numerous activities that seek to imitate the natural sciences by way of tabulating, pigeonholing, applying information theory or game strategies to human affairs, etc. In-Here may be involved, however, in something as simple as the detached scrutiny of a document, a book, an *objet d'art* – meaning the study of this thing as if one's feelings were not aroused by it, or as if such feelings as might arise could be discounted or screened out.

Whatever the scientific method may or may not be, people think they are behaving scientifically whenever they create an In-Here within themselves which undertakes to know without an investment of the person in the act of knowing. The necessary effect of distancing, of estranging In-Here from Out-There may be achieved in any number of ways: by the intervention of various mechanical gadgets between observer and observed; by the elaboration of chilly jargons and technical terms that replace sensuous speech; by the invention of strange methodologies which reach out to the subject matter like a pair of mechanical hands; by the subordination of the particular and immediate experience to a statistical generalization; by appeal to a professional standard which excuses the observer from responsibility to anything other than a lofty abstraction – such as 'the pursuit of truth,' 'pure research,' etc. All these protective strategies are especially compatible with natures that are beset by timidity and fearfulness; but also with those that are characterized by plain insensitivity and whose habitual mode of contact with the world is a cool curiosity untouched by love, tenderness, or passionate wonder. Behind both such timidity and insensitivity there can easily lurk the spitefulness of a personality which feels distressingly remote from the rewards of warm engagement with life. It is revealing that whenever a scientific method of study is brought into play, we are supposed to regard it as irrelevant, if not downright unfair, to probe the many very different motivations that may underlie a man's desire to be purely objective. It is little wonder, then, that the ideal of objectivity can easily be invoked to cover a curiosity of callousness or hostility, as well as a curiosity of affectionate concern. In any event, when I convince myself that I can create a place within me that has been cleansed of all those murky passions, hostilities, joys, fears, and lusts which define my person, a place that is 'Not-I,' and when I believe that it is *only* from the vantage point of this Not-I that reality can be accurately perceived, then I have begun to honor the myth of objective consciousness.[. . .]

[. . .] The spectating In-Here has been called by many names: ego, intelligence, self, subject, reason. . . . I avoid such designations here because they suggest some fixed faculty or psychic entity. What I prefer to emphasize is the *act* of contraction that takes place within the person, the sense of taking a step back, away from, and out of. Not only back and away from the natural world, but from the inarticulate feelings, physical urges, and wayward images that surge up from within the person. To these 'irrationalities' Freud gave the revealing name, 'the *it*': a something which is Not-I, but alien, incomprehensible, and only to be known reliably when it, too, is forced Out-There to become an object for analysis.

The ideal of the objective consciousness is that there should be as little as possible In-Here and, conversely, as much as possible Out-There. For only what is Out-There can be studied and known. Objectivity leads to such a great emptying-out operation: the progressive alienation of more and more of In-Here's personal contents in the effort to achieve the densest possible unit of observational concentration surrounded by the largest possible area of study. The very word 'concentration' yields the interesting image of an identity contracted into a small, hard ball; hence a dense, diminished identity, something which is less than one otherwise might be. Yet the predilection of In-Here is to remain 'concentrated' as long and as often as possible. Curiously, this great good called knowledge, the very guarantee of our survival, is taken to be something that is forthcoming only to this lesser, shriveled-up identity.

The scientific observer who comes to feel that Out-There has begun to implicate him personally – say, in the manner of a lover spellbinding one's sympathies so that one cannot tell clearly where one's self leaves off and the other begins – has begun to lose his objectivity. Therefore, he must fight back this irrational involvement of his personal feeling. Like Odysseus in the presence of the sirens' song, In-Here must be lashed to the mast, or its mission may never be completed. But if body, feelings, emotions, moral sentiment, sensuous enchantment are all to be located Out-There, then who is this In-Here that is so stalwartly struggling against the siren song? It is a weird identity indeed, this In-Here. More and more it looks like Kafka's castle: a stronghold well defended, but manned by . . . parties unknown.

It would be an interesting line of questioning to put to our experts, would it not? Who are 'you' when you are being purely objective? How did you manage to bring this purely objective 'you' into existence – and how can you be so sure you really pulled it off? Moreover, does this purely objective 'you' prove to be an enjoyable identity? Or is that beside the point?

(2) The act of psychic contraction that creates In-Here simultaneously creates Out-There, which is whatever gets left behind in the wake of the contraction. The line which divides In-Here from Out-There now be-

comes a line between a place where it is desirable and secure to be (In-Here) and a place that is untrustworthy, perhaps downright dangerous (Out-There). In-Here is the center of reliable knowledge; it knows what it is doing; it learns, plans, controls, watches out cunningly for threats and opportunities. The alternative to being in a place of reliable knowledge is, obviously, to be in a place of drift, unpredictability, stupidity. Such is what Out-There becomes.

Now, in fact, anyone, even the most objective scientist, would fall into a state of total paralysis if he *really* believed that Out-There (beginning with his own organism and unconscious processes) was totally stupid. Nevertheless, In-Here is committed to studying Out-There *as if* it were completely stupid, meaning without intention or wisdom or purposeful pattern. In-Here cannot, if it is to be strictly objective, strive to empathize in any way with Out-There. It must not attribute to Out-There what cannot be observed, measured, and – ideally – formulated into articulate, demonstrable propositions for experimental verification. In-Here must maintain its alienative dichotomy at all times. And like the racist who cannot under Jim Crow conditions come to see the segregated black man as anything but a doltish and primitive nigger, so In-Here, as the unmoved spectator, cannot feel that Out-There has any ingenuity or dignity. Under this kind of scrutiny, even the other human beings who inhabit Out-There can be made stupid, for they were not made to function within laboratory conditions or according to the exacting needs of questionnaires and surveys. Under the eyes of an alien observer they also begin to lose their human purposefulness.

As soon as two human beings relate in detachment as observer to observed, as soon as the observer claims to be aware of nothing more than the behavioral surface of the observed, an invidious hierarchy is established which reduces the observed to a lower status. Of necessity he falls into the same category with all the stupid things of the world that fill Out-There. For consider the gross impertinence of this act of detached observation. Psychologist confronting his laboratory subject, anthropologist confronting tribal group, political scientist confronting voting public . . . in all such cases what the observer may very well be saying to the observed is the same: 'I can perceive no more than your behavioral facade. I can grant you no more reality or psychic coherence than this perception allows. I shall observe this behavior of yours and record it. I shall not enter into your life, your task, your condition of existence. Do not turn to me or appeal to me or ask me to become involved with you. I am here only as a temporary observer whose role is to stand back and record and later to make my own sense of what you seem to be doing or intending. I assume that I can adequately understand what you are doing or intending without entering wholly into your life. I am not particularly interested in what *you* uniquely are; I am interested only in the general pattern to which you conform. I assume I have the right to use you to perform this process of classification. I assume I have the right to reduce all that you are to an integer in my science.'

At the extreme, this alienated relationship is that of the Nazi physician experimenting upon his human victims, learning interesting new things about pain, suffering, privation. One cringes from the reference and protests, '*That* was an abnormal case. Normally, research involving human subjects stops short of inhumanity. And, in any event, whatever laboratory work is involved takes place in limited episodes; it is not a total way of life for experimenter or subject.' Unhappily, however, the ethos of objectivity has gotten well beyond limited research episodes. Already legions of scientists and military men throughout the world, the products of careful training and selection, give themselves to whole lives of ultimate objectivity. They systematically detach themselves from any concern for those lives their intentions and weapons may someday do to death. They do their job as they are ordered to do it . . . objectively. For them the world at large has become a laboratory – in the same sense that when they enter upon their professional capacity, they leave their personal feelings behind. Perhaps they even take pride in their capacity to do so, for indeed it requires an act of iron will to ignore the claims that person makes upon person.

When In-Here observes Out-There, it is with the intention of giving order to what it perceives. The order can be understood to be that of 'law,' or statistical generalization, or classification. This orderliness is what sometimes leads scientists to speak of the 'beauty of nature' – a notion to which we will return in the next chapter. But what is important about all these kinds of order is that they may concede no credit to Out-There for being autonomously clever or marvellous. The scientist's nature becomes 'beautiful' when it has been tidied up and pigeonholed. The achievement lies in the scientist's 'discovery' of this order; the credit belongs to the observing mind. It is a situation which reminds one of the quaint use of the term 'discovery' in relationship to the European voyages of discovery. The phrase suggests that the Americas, Africa, and Asia, with all their indigenous peoples had been waiting eagerly to be found by the white man. We now recognize the comic ethnocentrism of that view; the cerebral anthropocentrism of scientific discovery is less obvious. But Abraham Maslow offers us one lovely example of the subliminal presumption. He mentions the scientist who praised a book on 'the difficult problem of woman's sexuality' because it at last took up a subject 'about which so little is known'! He goes on to comment on the psychology of the scientist's nomothetic project:

> Organizing experience into meaningful patterns implies that experience itself has no meaningfulness, that the organizer creates or imposes or donates the meaning . . . that it is a gift from the knower to the known. In

> other words, 'meaningfulness' of this kind is of the realm of classification and abstraction rather than of experience. . . . Frequently I sense also the implication that it is 'human-created', i.e., that much of it would vanish if human beings disappeared.[3]

The relationship Maslow describes is obviously an hierarchical one. In-Here is the superior of Out-There. Out-There has no way to lay claim upon In-Here, to appeal for kindness, appreciation, adoration, etc., because it is In-Here that monopolizes meaning. Out-There is left without voice to speak in behalf of its sanctity or in its defense. Moreover, In-Here knows how Out-There works and therefore has power over Out-There. Since In-Here is the sole dispenser of meaning, who then can gainsay In-Here when it grants itself the unabridged right to use that power? The dead and the stupid are objects of contempt – or at best of condescension; they must submit to the scrutiny, experimentation, and exploitation of In-Here. The fact that Out-There seems not to recognize this hierarchical order only proves how dead or stupid it really is. Instead of making life secure for In-Here, Out-There blunders about producing disease, famine, death, riot, protest, and the many misfortunes of existence. Out-There is obviously unreliable. And the unreliability begins very close to home. It begins with those outbursts of fluid, imprecise, distractive imaginings that well up from the 'irrational'; as well as with this troublesome body, which seems to do almost nothing properly.

If In-Here did not constantly intervene in the behavior of Out-There, what an impossible chaos would ensue! But fortunately In-Here, being vigilant and clever, is able to keep Out-There in line: to conquer it, to manipulate it, to improve upon it – beginning with the witless body, which is forever proving to be incompetent. In-Here must therefore devise forms of surgical and chemical intervention that will make sure the body sleeps, wakes, digests, excretes, grows, relaxes, feels gay, feels blue, has sex, etc., correctly, at the right time and place. In-Here may even devise ways to keep the body functioning indefinitely, so that it does not commit the ultimate incompetence of dying. Similarly, the natural environment must be conquered and subjected to forceful improvement. Climate and landscape must be redesigned. Waste space must be made livable, meaning covered over with an urban expansion into which nothing that is not man-made or man-arranged will intrude itself. Similarly, the social environment – the body politic – must be brought as completely under centralized, deliberative control as the physical body has been brought under the domination of the cerebrum. Unless the order of things is readily apparent to a command and control center – in the individual, it will be the forebrain; in the society, it will be the technocracy – and available for manipulation, it cannot be respected as order at all.

So, at last, Out-There emerges as a pitiful disappointment: an underdeveloped country awaiting the competent management of In-Here. As Joseph Wood Krutch comments, this reverses the age-old relationship of man to nature and rapidly leads to the unbridled assertion of human hubris: 'Is there anything *we* can't do better?'

> No age before ours would have made such an assumption. Man has always before thought of himself as puny by comparison with natural forces, and he was humble before them. But we have been so impressed by the achievement of technology that we are likely to think we can do more than nature herself. We dug the Panama Canal, didn't we? Why not the Grand Canyon?[4]

An objective, meaning an alienated, attitude toward the natural environment comes easily these days to a population largely born and raised in the almost totally man-made world of the metropolis. It would be difficult for anyone so raised, including a scientist, *not* to be objective toward a 'nature' which he has only known in the form of tidy, if boring, artificialities arranged by the parks and gardens authorities. The flora, fauna, landscape, and increasingly the climate of the earth lie practically helpless at the feet of technological man, tragically vulnerable to his arrogance. Without question, we have triumphed over them . . . at least until the massive ecological consequences catch up with us.

(3) But there are other areas of nature which pose a more serious problem for the objective consciousness. They appear within the person.

No matter how strenuously In-Here strives to thrust out the 'irrational,' it continues to intrude itself with its claims in behalf of sensuous contact, fantasy, spontaneity, and concern for the person. From somewhere nearby, In-Here continues to feel the pressure of a strange need to moralize, to joke, to hate, to love, to lust, to fear. . . . Obviously the citadel of objectivity is a precarious place. This mysterious organism which In-Here pilots about is not a trustworthy machine. Therefore, In-Here, in search of impregnable objectivity, takes the final step. It sets about inventing a superior command and control center that will take over whenever In-Here's capacity to achieve perfect impersonality breaks down: an electronic nervous system! Such a device will never lose control of itself, never weaken, never turn unpredictably personal, for it will never have been a person in the first place.

Man's infatuation with the machine is frequently misunderstood as being a love affair with mere power. 'Here I sell what all men crave: power!' So said Matthew Boulton, referring to the first steam-engine factory. But the great virtue of the machine lies not only in its power: many mechanisms – like timers or electric eyes or most cybernated systems – are not particularly powerful and yet are highly valued. Is it not the machine's capacity to be severely routinized that we admire quite as much as its sheer strength? Unlike the human organism, the machine can achieve perfect concentration, perfect self-control. It performs the one task to which it is assigned, with no possibility of being distracted. It acts without involvement in what it does. Indeed, the burden which industrialization lifted from men's backs was not physical labor so much as it was deadly routine, with its demand for unrelenting and exhaustive concentration. Thus, the archetypal machine in our society is not the gargantuan steam engine, but the lilliputian clock. For even the steam engine had no industrial significance until it became part of a regulated system of production, a system which ran like 'clock-work.' As Lewis Mumford reminds us, 'the clock . . . is the paragon of automatons. . . . The automation of time, in the clock, is the pattern of all larger systems of automation.'

So then: if muscle power can be replaced by a mechanism, how much more desirable still to replace the mind behind the muscle with a mechanism! If In-Here cannot be entirely relied upon to remain objective, then why not design a machine whose In-Here is a totally controlled program which specifies unambiguous objectives and procedures? 'Artificial intelligence' is the logical goal toward which objective consciousness moves. Again, it is the clock which anticipates the computer. True time (what Bergson called 'duration') is properly the living experience of life itself and therefore radically intuitive. But for most of us, this true time has been hopelessly displaced by the rigid rhythm of clock time. What is fundamentally the vital flow of experience then becomes an arbitrarily segmented, external measuring rod imposed upon our existence – and to experience time in any other way becomes 'mystical,' or 'mad.'

If the experience of time can be thus objectified, then why not everything else? Why should we not invent machines that objectify thought, creativity, decision making, moral judgment . . .? Let us have machines that play games, make poems, compose music, teach philosophy. To be sure, it was once thought that such things were to be done for the joy of the playing, the making, the composing, the teaching. But scientific culture makes no allowance for 'joy,' since that is an experience of intensive personal involvement. Joy is something that is known only to the person: it does not submit to objectification.

To a mournfully great extent, the progress of expertise, especially as it seeks to mechanize culture, is a waging of open warfare upon joy. It is a bewilderingly perverse effort to demonstrate that nothing, *absolutely nothing* is particularly special, unique, or marvelous, but can be lowered to the status of mechanized routine. More and more the spirit of 'nothing but' hovers over advanced scientific research: the effort to degrade, disenchant, level down. Is it that the creative and the joyous embarrass the scientific mind to such an extent that it must try with might and main to degrade them? Consider the strange compulsion our biologists have to synthesize life in a test tube – and the seriousness with which this project is taken. Every dumb beast of the earth knows without thinking once about it how to create life: it does so by seeking delight where it shines most brightly. But, the biologist argues, once we have done it in a laboratory, *then* we shall really know what it is all about. Then we shall be able to *improve* upon it!

What a measure of our alienation it is that we do not regard that man as a fool who grimly devotes his life to devising routine laboratory procedures for that which is given to him like a magnificent gift in the immediacy of his own most natural desire. It is as if the organism could not be trusted with a single one of its natural functions, but this brain of ours must be brought forward to control and supervise and make sure everything is running along as efficiently as a well-programmed machine.

> Neurology [Michael Polanyi reminds us] is based on the assumption that the nervous system – functioning automatically according to the known laws of physics and chemistry – determines all the workings which we normally attribute to the mind of the individual. The study of psychology shows a parallel tendency toward reducing its subject matter to explicit relationships between measurable variables; relationships which could always be represented by the performances of a mechanical artifact.

Once conceive of human consciousness in this way, and the inevitable next step is to replace it with a machine just as good . . . or better. So we come to the ultimate irony: the machine which is a creature of the human being becomes – most fully in the form of the computerized process – its maker's ideal. The machine achieves the perfect state of objective consciousness and, hence, becomes the standard by which all things are to be gauged. It embodies the myth of objective consciousness as Jesus incarnated the Christian conception of divinity. Under its spell, a grand reductive process begins in which culture is redesigned to meet the needs of mechanization. If we discover that a computer cannot compose emotionally absorbing music, we insist that music *does* have an 'objective' side, and we turn that into our definition of music. If we discover that computers cannot translate normal language, then we invent a special, more rudimentary language which they can translate. If we discover that computers cannot teach as teaching at its most ideal is done, then we redesign education so that the machine can qualify as a teacher. If we discover that computers cannot solve the basic problems of city planning – all of which are questions of social philosophy and aesthetics – then we redefine the meaning of 'city,' call it an 'urban area,' and assume that all the problems of this entity are quantitative. In this way man is replaced in all areas by the machine, not because the machine can do things 'better,' but rather because all things have been reduced to what the machine is capable of doing.

It is unlikely that any single scientist, behavioral scientist, or technician would plead guilty to so sweeping a charge. None of them, as individuals, are involved in so global a project. But Jacques Ellul observes the key point:

> . . . one important fact has escaped the notice of the technicians, the phenomenon of technical convergence. Our interest here is the convergence on man of a plurality, not of techniques, but of systems or complexes of techniques. . . . A plurality of them converge toward the human being, and each individual technician can assert in good faith that his technique leaves intact the integrity of its object. But the technician's opinion is of no importance, for the problem concerns not *his* technique, but the convergence of all techniques.[5]

There could be no better definition of the technocracy than to identify it as the center where, subtly, steadily, ingeniously, this convergence is brought into existence. Ellul, in his somber analysis, overlooks only one dismal possibility. The final convergence he predicts may not have to postpone its completion until the technocracy has acquired mechanisms and techniques that will replace the human being in all areas of our culture. Instead, we may only have to wait until our fellow humans have converted themselves into purely impersonal automatons capable of total objectivity in all their tasks. At that point, when the mechanistic imperative has been successfully internalized as the prevailing life style of our society, we shall find ourselves moving through a world of perfected bureaucrats, managers, operations analysts, and social engineers who will be indistinguishable from the cybernated systems they assist. Already we find these images of internally deadened human beings appearing in our contemporary novels and films. Dispassionate lovers, dispassionate killers fill the movies of Godard, Truffaut, Antonioni, Fellini with their blank gaze and automatized reactions. So too in the absurdist plays of Harold Pinter and Samuel Beckett we find the logical – or rather psychological – conclusion of life dominated by ruthless depersonalization. Here we have the world of completely objectified human relations: people hopelessly locked off from one another, maneuvering their isolated In-Heres around and about each other, communicating only by their externalized behavior. Words become mere sounds, concealing more than they convey; gestures become mere physiological twitches; bodies touch without warmth. Each In-Here confronts the others Out-There with indifference, callousness, exploitive intention. Everyone has become a specimen under the other's microscope; no one can any longer be sure that anyone else is not perhaps a robot.

* * * *

We have C. P. Snow to thank for the notion of the 'two cultures.' But Snow, the scientific propagandist, scarcely grasps the terrible pathos that divides these two cultures; nor for that matter do most of our social scientists and scientistic humanists. While the art and literature of our time tell us with ever more desperation that the disease from which our age is dying is that of alienation, the sciences, in their relentless pursuit of objectivity, raise alienation to its apotheosis as our *only* means of achieving a valid relationship to reality. Objective consciousness *is* alienated life promoted to its most honorific status as the scientific method. Under its auspices we subordinate nature to our command only by estranging ourselves from more and more of what we experience, until the reality about which objectivity tells us so much finally becomes a universe of congealed alienation. It is totally within our intellectual and technical power . . . and it is a worthless possession. For 'what does it profit a man that he should gain the whole world, but lose his soul?'

When, therefore, those of us who challenge the objective mode of consciousness are faced with the question 'but is there any *other* way in which we can know the world?', I believe it is a mistake to seek an answer on a narrowly epistemological basis. Too often we will then find ourselves struggling to discover some alternative method to produce the same sort of knowledge we now derive from science. There is little else the word 'knowledge' any longer means besides an accumulation of verifiable propositions. The only way we shall ever recapture the sort of knowledge Lao-tzu referred to in his dictum 'those who know do not speak,' is by subordinating the question 'how shall we know?' to the more existentially vital question 'how shall we live?'

To ask this question is to insist that the primary purpose of human existence is not to devise ways of piling up ever greater heaps of knowledge, but to discover ways to live from day to day that integrate the whole of our nature by way of yielding nobility of conduct, honest fellowship, and joy. And to achieve those ends, a man need perhaps 'know' very little in the conventional, intellectual sense of the word. But what he does know and may only be able to express by eloquent silence, by the grace of his most commonplace daily gestures, will approach more closely to whatever reality is than the most dogged and disciplined intellectual endeavor. For if that elusive concept 'reality' has any meaning, it must be that toward which the entire human being reaches out for satisfaction, and not simply some fact-and-theory-mongering fraction of the personality. What is important, therefore, is that our lives should be as *big* as possible, capable of embracing the vastness of those experiences which, though yielding no articulate, demonstrable propositions, nevertheless awake in us a sense of the world's majesty.

The existence of such experiences can hardly be denied without casting out of our lives the witness of those who have been in touch with such things as only music, drama, dance, the plastic arts, and rhapsodic utterance can express. How dare we set aside as a 'nothing but,' or a 'merely,' or a 'just' the work of one artist, one poet, one visionary seer, without diminishing our nature? For these, as much as any scientist or technician, are our fellow human beings. And they cry out to us in song and story, in the demanding beauty of line, color, shape, and movement. We have their lives before us as testimony that men and women have lived – and lived magnificently – in communion with such things as the intellective consciousness can do no justice to. If their work could, after some fashion, be explained, or explained away, if it could be computerized – and there are those who see this as a sensible project – it would overlook the elemental fact that in the making of these glorious things, these images, these utterances, these gestures, there was a supreme joy, and that the achievement of that joy was the purpose of their work. In the making, the makers breathed an ecstatic air. The technical mind that bypasses the making in favor of the made has already missed the entire meaning of this thing we call 'creativity.'

When we challenge the finality of objective consciousness as a basis for culture, what is at issue is the size of man's life. We must insist that a culture which negates or subordinates or degrades visionary experience commits the sin of diminishing our existence. Which is precisely what happens when we insist that reality is limited to what objective consciousness can turn into the stuff of science and of technical manipulation. The fact and the dire cost of this diminishing is nothing that can be adequately proved by what I write here, for it is an experience which every man must find in his own life. He finds it as soon as he refuses to block, to screen out, to set aside, to discount the needs his own personality thrusts upon him in its fullness, often in its terrifying fullness. Then he sees that the task of life is to take this raw material of his total experience – its need for knowledge, for passion, for imaginative exuberance, for moral purity, for fellowship – and to shape it *all*, as laboriously and as cunningly as a sculptor shapes his stone, into a comprehensive style of life. It is not of supreme importance that a human being should be a good scientist, a good scholar, a good administrator, a good expert; it is not of supreme important that he should be right, rational, knowledgeable, or even creatively productive of brilliantly finished objects as often as possible. Life is not what we are in our various professional capacities or in the practice of some special skill. What is of supreme importance is that each of us should become a person, a whole and integrated person in whom there is manifested a sense of the human variety genuinely experienced, a sense of having come to terms with a reality that is awesomely vast.

It is my own conviction that those who open themselves in this way and who allow what is Out-There to enter them and to shake them to their very foundations are not apt to finish by placing a particularly high value on scientific or technical progress. I believe they will finish by subordinating such pursuits to a distinctly marginal place in their lives, because they will realize that the objective mode of consciousness, useful as it is on occasion, cuts them off from too much that is valuable. They will therefore come to see the myth of objective consciousness as a poor mythology, one which diminishes life rather than expands it; and they will want to spend little of their time with it. That is only my hunch; I could be wrong.

But of this there can be no doubt: that in dealing with the reality our non-intellective powers grasp, *there are no experts*. The expansion of the personality is nothing that is achieved by special training, but by a naive openness to experience. Where and when the lightning will strike that unaccountably sets one's life on fire with imaginative aspirations is beyond prediction. Jakob Boehme found his moment when a stray beam of sunlight set a metal dinner dish flashing. Supposedly the Zen master Kensu achieved illumination upon biting into a shrimp he had just caught. Tolstoy was convinced that the moment came in the experience of self-sacrifice to one's fellows, no matter how inconsequential and obscure the act. The homely magic of such turning points waits for all of us and will find us if we let it. What befalls us then is an experience of the personality suddenly swelling beyond all that we had once thought to be 'real,' swelling to become a greater and nobler identity than we had previously believed possible. It is precisely this sense of the person we should look for in all those who purport to have something to teach us. We should ask: 'Show us this person you have made of yourself. Let us see its full size. For how can we judge what you know, what you say, what you do, what you make, unless in the context of the whole person?' It is a matter of saying, perhaps, that truth ought not to be seen as the property of a proposition, but of the person.

This would mean that our appraisal of any course of personal or social action would not be determined simply by the degree to which the proposal before us squares with objectively demonstrable knowledge, but by the degree to which it enlarges our capacity to experience: to know ourselves and others more deeply, to feel more fully the awesomeness of our environment. This, in turn, means that we must be prepared to trust that the expanded personality becomes more beautiful, more creative, more humane than the search for objective correctness can make it. To take this attitude is, I think, far from eccentric. Is it not the attitude we feel spontaneously compelled to assume whenever we find ourselves in the presence of an authentically great soul? I, who do not share any of Tolstoy's religion or that of the prophets of Israel, and who do not believe that a single jot of Dante's or Blake's world view is 'true' in any scientific sense, nevertheless realize that any carping I might do about the correctness of their convictions would be preposterously petty. Their words are the conduit of a power that one longs to share. One reads their words only with humility and remorse for having lived on a lesser scale than they, for having at any point foregone the opportunity to achieve the dimensions of their vision.

When a man has *seen* and has *spoken* as such men did, the criticisms of the objective consciousness fade into insignificance. What men of this kind invite us to do is to grow as great with experience as they have, and in so doing to find the nobility they have known. Compared with the visionary powers that moved in these souls, what is the value of all the minor exactitudes of all the experts on earth?

Were we prepared to accept the beauty of the fully illuminated personality as our standard of truth – or (if the word 'truth' is too sacrosanctly the property of science) of ultimate meaningfulness -- then we should have done with this idiocy of making fractional evaluations of men and of ourselves. We should stop hiding behind our various small-minded specializations and pretending that we have done all that is expected of us when we have flourished a tiny banner of expertise. We should be able to ask every man who desires to lead us that he step forward and show us what his talents have made of him as a whole person. And we should reject the small souls who know only how to be correct, and cleave to the great who know how to be wise.

1. Kuhn T., (1962) *The Structure of Scientific Revolutions* (Chicago: The University of Chicago Press).
2. Polanyi, M., (1959) *Personal Knowledge: Towards a Post-Critical Philosophy* (Chicago: The University of Chicago Press).
3. Maslow, A., (1966) *The Psychology of Science* (New York: Harper and Row).
4. Krutch, J. W., (1958) *Grand Canyon* (New York: William Slone Associates, 1958 p. 25).
5. Ellul, J., *The Technological Society* (1964) trans. John W. Wilkinson (New York: A. A. Knopf).

10 The limits to science

S. P. R. Rose

To fully describe and understand the world about us would be an endless task, but two factors will intervene to limit the advance of science. First, resources. The cost of science doubled every decade or two for more than two hundred years, but is now inevitably levelling off. It cannot become much bigger as a fraction of the GNP, and GNPs are themselves near maximum. 'Big Science' feels the pinch first, both because of the high cost and because those areas are already so far advanced that it is questionable whether further advance is useful. Particle physics is a clear-cut example, molecular biology a more complicated one.

Since not all problems can be studied, how are areas selected for funding? Among the chosen, which are given 'Big Science' status? First, one chooses problems that can at least be presented in a clear way: that is an academic choice. Next, those problems on a critical path to a useful advance in understanding are selected – and the word useful *already introduces a social judgement. Thirdly, there is a limit to which reductionist approaches can solve questions of human concern, and Rose dwells on a number of examples. Finally, he discusses the extent to which ethical concerns should close off some areas of research, particularly on animals.*

For the great ideological 'spokesmen' of science, from Francis Bacon to James Watson, science has always been without limits; about 'the effecting of all things possible'. Human curiosity, after all, is boundless. There seems to be an infinity of questions one can ask about nature. At the end of his long scientific career Isaac Newton felt, he said, as if he had merely stood at the edge of a vast sea, playing with the pebbles on the beach. What is more, because science is not merely about passive knowledge concerning nature but about the development of ways of changing nature, of transforming the world through technology, these same apologists offer us a breathtaking vision of the prospect of a world, a nature – including human nature – made over in humanity's image to serve human needs. It is only when one looks a little more closely at these visions that one sees that a science which claims to speak for the universality of the human condition, and to seek disinterestedly to make over the world for human need, is in fact speaking for a very precise group. Its universalism turns out to be a projection of the needs, curiosity and ways of appreciating the world not of some classless, raceless, genderless humanity, but of a particular class, race and gender who have been the makers of science and the framers of its questions indeed from Francis Bacon onwards.

The ideology is powerful, and in the second half of this century has been of endless fascination to politicians as well as scientists. Towards the end of the Second World War, in the USA, Vannevar Bush, whose life had been spent with '*Pieces of the action*' of science, offered Presidents Roosevelt and Truman '*Science, the Endless Frontier*' as a vision of how the greatness and power of the USA could be indefinitely extended. In Britain the visonary Marxist tradition of J. D. Bernal inspired Harold Wilson in 1964 to speak of the 'building of socialism in the white heat of the scientific and technological revolution' and Soviet scientists and politicians to speak of the 'scientific and technical revolution' which has, rather than politics of the class struggle, become the motor of the growth of Soviet society.

Against Watson's claims for the limitless nature of human curiosity and the techno-enthusiasms of the politicians, the anti-science movement of recent decades has cried a series of halts. Halts to the 'tempering with nature' of the nuclear industry and militarism; halts to the possibility of knowledge by the endless dissection of animals into molecules, and molecules into elementary particles; halts to the restless experimentation implied by the very scientific method itself as a way of knowing the universe, as opposed to the contemplative knowledge offered by alternative philosophical systems.

I am not an anti-scientist in this, or indeed in any sense that I would accept. I want to argue, however, that we cannot understand science or speak of its limits or boundlessness in the abstract. To speak of 'science for science's sake' – as if, to paraphrase Samuel Butler on art, science had a 'sake' – is to mystify what science is and what scientists do. This mystification, still often on the lips of the ideologues of science, serves to justify specific interests and privileges. Instead, we have to consider *this* science in *this* society. I shall argue that it is indeed limited, and that its limits are provided by a combination of two major, though only partially separable, factors. The first is material, the second ideological. I will consider each in turn.

The material factor is of course that of resource. Science costs money, and in the advanced industrial countries of Europe, East and West and the USA, consumes anything from 2 to 3 per cent of GNP. From 1945 to the late 1960s, science was expanding at an enormous rate, an exponential growth with a doubling period of 10–15 years or so. A historian of science, Derek de Solla Price, pointed out that the doubling rate had been constant from about the seventeenth century on. However, like population growth, scientific growth could not continue unchecked. It became fashionable in the 1960s to calculate that by the twenty-first century every man, woman, child and dog in the world would be a scientist and the mass of published research papers would exceed that of the earth.

Something had to stop, and indeed it did; from the late 1960s on, in most countries, the growth of science as a proportion of GNP slowed, halted or was even, in Britain, reversed. Sheer resource limitations were limiting the growth of science. You can see this in the development of the physicists' accelerators. First, each country had its own. Then there was the West European CERN project at Geneva, and matching machines in the USA and USSR. Now, even if Britain were to stay in CERN, which is at present doubtful, the costs of the new generation of machines make the 'world accelerator' the logical next step. And beyond this? Just how much resource is going to be devoted to whirling particles around at speeds closer and closer to that of light? Boundless human curiosity is going to be bounded.

Of course the particle accelerator episode is revealing in another way. Ask high-energy physicists why anyone should spend hundreds or thousands of millions of pounds on them, and you are likely to get the answer that it is high culture, and surely society can afford it, like subsidizing Covent Garden. But they will be fooling themselves – or you; because it is not the story they have been telling the politicians, who have gone on shelling out vast sums of money for physics since Hiroshima and Nagasaki in the not unreasonable belief that they would get bigger and better bombs, or new sources of power, out of the investment.

This brings us to the more important point about the material limits on science; for funding is not merely limited: it is *directed*. Of the 2–3 per cent of GNP Britain has spent on science since the 1950s, getting on for 50 per cent, year in, year out, has gone on military research. The figure is now about 53 per cent – the highest for many years, and much more, incidentally, than is spent by any other Western country except the USA – compare France's 35 per cent, Germany's 12 per cent and Japan's less than 5 per cent. If you want to know why so much scientific endeavour is directed to military ends, you must ask political questions about how the decisions are made. There can be no doubt, however, that this concentration on directing research towards military needs, and towards the industrial priorities of production and profit, as Hilary Rose and I have described it, profoundly shapes the direction in which science goes.

Apologists for the purity of science (though it is the purest of high-energy physics that gave us the bomb) may argue that this is all technology – real science is unaffected by such directive processes. They are on shaky ground, making this science/technology distinction, of course.

The distinguished American organic chemist, Louis Fieser, invented that nastiest of conventional weapons, napalm, experimenting on it in the playing fields of Harvard during the 1939–45 war. He wrote about his discovery afterwards in a fascinating book called simply *The Scientific Method*. The argument that pure science is divorced from direction cannot be sustained for a moment.

Take the triumphant progress of molecular biology these past decades. There have always been two broadly contrasting traditions in biology: a reductionist, or analytic and atomizing one; and a holistic or more synthetic one. This latter tradition – and I will have more to say about both in a moment – was strongly represented in the 1930s by such developmental and theoretical biologists as Needham, Woodger and Waddington. There was a proposal to set up a major institute of theoretical biology in Cambridge which would have brought the field together; but the funding agency was to be Rockefeller, and Rockefeller, under the guidance of Warren Weaver, decided that the future was to be chemical. They backed biochemistry and molecular biology instead. The double helix and all that followed from it from 1953 on was a direct result of that funding decision. Many people would argue it was a correct one, and I might well agree. The fact is that it changed the direction of biology by a deliberate act of policy. Rockefeller's decision is thus comparable to those being made routinely by government and charitable funding agencies as they decide which are high-priority areas to back, and which should not be supported. MRC, SERC and the rest have their priorities. They are, as it happens, still mainly molecular, even though most of the problems which MRC ostensibly exists to help solve are clearly not going to be resolved by more molecular biology. One of the things that is clear from the combined efforts of Richard Nixon and Jim Watson in the 1970s to 'cure' cancer by the end of the decade is that the most exquisite molecular biology has brought us no nearer controlling a disease many of whose precipitating causes are located in the chemical environment of our industrial society. The vast funds Nixon allocated *have* given us more and more molecular biology, though.

Let me move from the material to the ideological limits to science. The point I want to make here is not just that we get the science we pay for, but that at a deeper level, what science we do, what questions scientists consider important and worth asking at any time – indeed, the very way they frame the questions – are profoundly shaped by the historical and social context in which we frame our hypotheses and realize our experiments. Let me spell this out at three levels:

First, we can only ask questions we can begin to frame; the question of the role of chromosomes in cell replication and genetic transmission was unaskable until there were microscopes powerful enough to see the chromosomes, as well as a genetic theory to be tested. The technology and the theory came together at the beginning of the present century.

Second, not all scientific facts are of equal value. There is an infinity – in the strict sense of the term – of questions one can ask about the material world. Which ones are relevant at all, is strictly historically contingent. To give an example, in 1956 Sanger published the complete amino acid sequence of a protein, the first time anyone had done it. It took him about 10 years. The protein was insulin, and he got the Nobel Prize for sequencing it. That it was insulin, rather than any of the other 100,000-odd human proteins, or the thousands of millions of other naturally occurring proteins, was fortuitous. It happened to be a relatively small molecule and available pure and in bulk. Within a few years several other proteins were sequenced, each time to a great, but diminishing scientific fanfare. Today anyone can do it within a few weeks with an automated machine. But is anyone going to *want* to determine the structure of *all* naturally occurring proteins – or even all human ones? There is a law of diminishing returns, to all except stamp collectors, and sometimes PhD students. So a new fact – the sequence of another protein – is nothing like as interesting as the first protein facts were. There is a limit to how many such facts are wanted, and most protein sequencing projects are scarcely worth a research grant these days.

Third, and at a much deeper level than either of the two previous points, there is, it seems to me, a fundamental limit to the capacity of science, framed within the dominant paradigm in which most of us work to give meaningful – let alone satisfying – answers to the great questions of human concern today. The issue of reductionism and its alternatives runs like a thread through many of the discussions on this topic, so I will do no more than sketch the issues here. I have written more fully on the subject of reductionism elsewhere (e.g. *Not in our Genes,* and *More than the Parts*). The point is that the mode of thinking which has characterized the period of the rise of science from the seventeenth century is a reductionist one. That is, it believes not merely that to understand the world requires disassembling it into its component parts, but that these parts are in some way more fundamental than the wholes they compose. To understand societies you study individuals, to understand individuals you study their organs; for the organs their cells; for the cells their molecules; for the molecules their atoms . . . right down to the most 'fundamental' physical particles. Reductionism is committed to the claim that this is *the* scientific method, that ultimately the knowledge of the laws of motion of particles will enable us to understand the rise of capitalism, the nature of love or even the winner of the next Derby. It also claims that the parts are ontologically prior to the wholes they compose.

The fallacies of such reductionism should be apparent. We cannot understand the music a tape recorder generates simply by analysing the chemical and magnetic properties of the tape or the nature of the recording and playing heads – though these are *part* of any such explanation. Yet reductionism runs deep. For Richard Dawkins the well-springs of human motivation are to be interpreted by analysis of human DNA; for Jim Watson 'What else is there but atoms?' Well, the answer is – the organizing relations *between* the atoms, which are strictly not deducible from the properties of the atoms themselves. After all, quantum physics cannot even deal with the interactions of more than two particles simultaneously, or predict the properties of a molecule as simple as water from the properties of its constituents. Think of a Martian coming to earth and being confronted with the parts of an internal combustion engine. What are they for? The parts do not make sense by themselves; not even when they are reassembled into a car, unless you know as well that the car is part of a transportation system.

Yet why do scientists of experimental ingenuity and reputation consistently claim that you can understand the transportation system from the parts of the car engine? The roots of that belief go back, I think, to the Newtonian and Cartesian project for science as it has developed from the seventeenth century, and, in ways I have not space to elaborate here, are profoundly interconnected with the process by which north-western Europe gave birth in the mid-seventeenth century not to a single child, science, but to the twins of science and capitalism, whose growth has subsequently been inextricably intertwined. Reductionism was a scientific philosophy customized for capital's needs, and has remained so since. The trouble is that just as capitalism was once a progressive force but has now become profoundly oppressive of human liberation, so too with reductionism. Beginning as a way of acquiring new and real knowledge about the world – from the structure of molecules to the motions of the planets – it has become an obstacle to scientific progress.

So long as science – in the questions it asks, and the answers it accepts – is couched in reductionist and determinist terms, understanding of complex phenomena is frustrated. A reductionist science, I believe, cannot advance knowledge of brain functions, or solve the riddle to the relationship between levels of description of phenomena such as the 'mind-brain problem', which Western science is almost incapable of conceiving except in Cartesian dualist or mechanical materialist terms. Reductionism cannot cope with the open, richly interconnected systems of ecology, or with integrating its scientific understanding of the present frozen moment in time with the dynamic recognition that the present is part of a historical flux, be it of development of the individual or of evolution of the species.

Failing to approach the complexity of such systems, reductionism resorts to more or less vulgar simplifications which, in the prevailing social climate, become refracted into defences of the *status quo* in the form of biological determinism, which claims that the present social order, with all its inequalities in status, wealth and power, between individuals, classes, genders and races, is 'given' inevitably by our genes. This limit to the scientific vision is compounded by the closed recruitment process into science as an institution which effectively ensures its preservation as the privilege of the Western white male. However, referring to *that* limit to science extends my agenda here further than space allows. I want to conclude by referring to the one limit to science I have not yet mentioned, and that is the *ethical* one.

Ethical issues in science have been repeatedly discussed in recent years. They take several forms. On the one hand, some claims have been made that certain types of knowledge are too dangerous for humanity in its present state, and therefore some types of experiment should not be made. For instance, nuclear power, or gene cloning, are considered to present hazards which make it inappropriate to pursue them experimentally. Or research on the so-called 'genetic basis of intelligence' might reveal biological 'facts' which would be unpalatable. On the other hand, it has been argued that the conduct of certain types of experiment – for instance, those which cause pain to animals, or for that matter to humans – contravene absolute moral principles and should not be performed. All of these considerations may be regarded as limiting science.

From what I have already said it should be apparent that I have a complicated response to that rather abstract approach to ethics. For me, the resource and ideological questions are paramount, and most ethical questions eventually break down to ones about priority and ideology. For instance, there has been a lot of attention given to the ethics of *in vitro* fertilization – should we or shouldn't we? To me, the question seems wrongly posed; instead, one should ask the prior question, which the *in vitro* fertilization techniques are presumably designed to help answer: how can we increase the number of wanted, healthy babies? If I ask that question, I also begin to ask what prevents wanted, healthy babies surviving; and I note that in Britain the perinatal mortality rate – that is, the number of babies dying at or just after birth – is much higher in certain geographical areas – for instance, Liverpool – than others – such as, for instance, Hampstead. I note that there is a severalfold greater chance of a baby not surviving if it is born to a mother in poverty, or in the manual working class, than if it is born to a wealthy or upper-middle class mother. So if we want to save babies, I conclude, we can do so best by applying known social, economic and health care improvements to deprived geographical areas and classes in Britain. *In vitro* fertilization is a method which is of relevance to a small number of relatively privileged mothers. The language of priorities says that we should not get excited about that new set of techniques until we have addressed the question of how we save babies we *know* statistically will die from lack of application of quite simple preventative and health care measures.

That is an ethical question, certainly, but it is also one about politics and economics. Personally, I would not do research funded by, or with obvious applications to, the military. I will try to persuade as many of my fellow scientists as possible to take a similar ethical and political decision. But in the last analysis in a militarist society *anything* one does can be, and potentially will be, co-optable for military purposes. If we do not want war-oriented research, individual ethical decisions are not enough. We need the *political* decision not to finance war research.

Similarly, I accept the case made by the animal liberationists that it is undesirable to use procedures likely to cause pain or distress to animals – though in the last analysis I owe my prior loyalty to my own species, and to argue otherwise seems perverse. I care more about saving people than saving whales. But a vast proportion of the animal experimentation done in Britain is either for relatively trivial commercial purposes – for instance, developing new drugs when it is at least arguable that there are enough or even too many drugs available already. What is needed is not new magic drugs but a health-producing society. Indeed many drugs which are developed and tested are not new in a real sense, but part of the endless process of molecular roulette played by the drug companies in their efforts to circumvent patent laws or maximize profits. It is also true that a fair number of the animal experiments done in 'basic science' labs are, on close analysis, carried out in the pursuit of trivial or 'me-too'-type research aims. Remember that the average scientific paper is probably read by only one or two other people apart from the editor of the journal in which it appeared and the referees. So part of my answer to the question of ethics and animal experiments is to rephrase the question in terms of whether the research is worth doing anyhow, animals or no.

So too with the question of 'things we are not meant to know'. These are often just things it is not worth trying to know – like the sequence of every possible naturally occurring protein that I referred to earlier. Sometimes, however, they are things which *cannot* be known because the questions are simply wrongly or meaninglessly phrased. As someone who has been involved in what has become known as the 'race-IQ' debates, I have often been asked whether I am opposed to work on 'the genetics of average race differences in IQ' on ethical grounds. My response is that I am opposed to it on the same grounds that I am opposed to research on whether the backside of the moon is made of gorgonzola or of stilton. That is, it is a silly question, incapable of scientific answer and actually, *sensu strictu*, meaningless. The question makes grammatical, but not scientific, sense, because 'IQ' is not a phenotype susceptible to genetic measurements and heritability estimates cannot be applied to average differences in phenotypes between groups.

All this is not to duck the questions of ethics. There are issues of real choice and dilemma in medicine, in the use of animals, and indeed in some aspects of biotechnology, which cannot simply be reduced to issues of economics and ideology. They are few, but important, and they set limits to our science. How should they be resolved? In the last analysis, it seems to me, not by scientists playing god-in-white-coat and refusing to allow anyone else in on the decision. And not by committees of professional ethicists and philosophers. The only way of dealing with such issues is by democratic participation in the decision-making about what science is done. My own aim would be for a way of controlling and directing research which opened all laboratories up to community involvement in their direction, and planned work by a combination of the tripartite structure of decision-making by scientists and technicians in the lab itself, by the community in which the lab was embedded and by discussion of overall priorities and resources at a national level. I believe that if we did organize our science in this way, not merely would new priorities set different limits to our work, but we might also begin to see the makings of a new, less reductionist and more holistic, human-centred science.

III SCIENCE IN EDUCATION

Ziman, in his contribution to this section, argues that 'science education serves a variety of purposes that are seldom clearly defined'. The historical shifts and present tensions in the content and manner of science teaching is richly documented in this and later sections, but here the contributors indicate clear preferences on the purposes of science in education.

Layton argues that a participatory democracy requires a recoupling of science education and values education — but one that allows for the form of participation to remain open. For Selley the focus for participation should be on the involvement of learners in the process of developing better scientific theory. Often, he argues, attempts to invite pupils into debates over theory involve the use of models that are too difficult. Rather, teachers should introduce accessible models that are readily understood and allow an unguided choice among learners. Ziman argues that the demands upon science education can be stratified with learners entering various more or less scientific careers at different stages. Too often the demands of the next stage determine teaching rather than relevance to that level. Ziman suggests that, while science education of necessity needs to meet several demands from different groups of learners, what is required is greater attention to 'valid' science at each stage. Soloman, returning to some of the ideas in Layton's contribution, urges a science education that emphasizes its 'living use' in a modern society. She argues that 'science technology and society' (STS) courses broke new ground in establishing a greater utility for science in schools.

11 Science education and values education — an essential tension

D. Layton

Layton examines the assumptions of the contemporary movement in education to connect science and values, particularly the teaching goals associated with Science, Technology and Society curricula. He regards these goals as revealing not only views of society but also as promoting contestable concepts, for example, the premium on individualism and public participation. Layton argues that, whereas early in the nineteenth century scientific problems were closely related in science education, in the second half of the century it was increasingly accepted that the pursuit of free scientific inquiry should not be restricted by considerations of social purpose. The teaching of science reflected this separation and sought primarily the development of intellectual skills and preparation for scientific careers. Layton raises issues about whether the attempt to re-couple science and values in the school curriculum is realistic. For example, do teachers have the power to shift goals? Can all students participate knowledgeably in science-related decisions?

1 INTRODUCTION

1.1 It is now widely advocated that secondary school science education should include an emphasis on values and the social aspects of science and technology.

In the USA, Project Synthesis (1981)[1] has defined new goals for science teaching which include an understanding of value, ethical and moral considerations of science-related problems and issues. In so doing, it reinforced views expressed by the National Science Teachers Association and by others such as the participants at the Exeter Conference (1980).[2] To assist an understanding of the complexity of science-technology-society (STS) issues, new curriculum materials have been developed, e.g. the BSCS module 'Quality of Life and the Future'.[3]

In the UK, the recently published Policy Statement (1981) of the Association for Science Education[4] emphasised that science should be studied from the viewpoint of its interactions with 'the worlds of work, citizenship, leisure and survival'; amongst its aims for science education were 'the attainment of a basic understanding of . . . the interactions between science and society' and 'the realization that scientific knowledge and experience is of some value in the process of establishing a sense of personal and social identity.' Two projects, *Science in Society* and *Siscon in Schools*, have developed teaching materials in relation to these aims and Examination Boards offer syllabuses and examinations at sixth form level.

Movement to include consideration of social problems and social policy issues in science education is now widespread. In *Physics in Society* (1981)[5], a new textbook for an optional subject in the university entrance examination in the Netherlands, the authors tell the reader that 'we show how a knowledge of physics can be used to help you form your own point of view' on social problem areas in which science and technology play a part. Similar examples could be drawn from countries as far apart as Australia, Canada, Israel, Mexico, the Philippines and Zimbabwe.[6] The international character of the movement is well illustrated in the report of the Malvern Seminar (1980), organised by the Committee on Science Teaching of the International Council of Scientific Unions, in collaboration with UNESCO.[7]

1.2 It is not my purpose in this chapter to consider reasons for this emphasis on STS issues in science education today; satisfactory accounts of the rationale exist elsewhere.[8] Rather, I wish to take a critical look at certain assumptions and manifestations of the movement to connect science and values education. The perspective is that of someone working in the history, sociology and politics of science education. In particular, I draw attention to one aspect of current developments which does not seem to have been considered adequately by advocates of STS courses and to some implications of increased attention to STS issues in secondary school science education.

Comment is limited to situations in which the cultural context of science education places a high premium on individualism and 'participatory democracy', such as is said to be the case in the USA and the UK. In cultural contexts where the balance between individualism and collectivism is otherwise, conclusions of a different kind might emerge.[9] This is not to say that the connection between science education and values education has not been, and is not being, made elsewhere; but – to take an example – the 'Islamicising' of science education, involving the attempt to imbue science education with Muslim values expressed in the Shariah, in a context where 'democracy is not allowed to go unchecked;

it is always subject to the law of the Qur'an', is somewhat outside my experience.[10] On the face of it, however, such developments would seem to be merely particular instances of a general trend.

1.3 That the political and social contexts of education influence the learning objectives which can be associated with STS curricula is well illustrated by the following formulation.[11]

> (i) Students' interests in science and technology issues should increase. Increased interest should result in increased consumption of relevant public affairs information about topics related to STS and increased knowledge about them.
> (ii) Students should come to understand and appreciate that scientific and technological developments produce major effects in their lives and the lives of others. These effects are both good and bad, and social policies are required in order to optimise the uses and minimize the abuses of the power inherent in scientific and technological developments.
> (iii) Students should come to understand and appreciate that citizen participation in policy-making is required if policies are to incorporate a common, public interest and are not to be over-influenced by various special interests as policy conflicts are resolved.
> (iv) Students should come to understand how citizens are dependent upon the knowledge of experts, scientists and engineers among others, in making valid and workable policies. But they should come to recognize that policies also involve moral and value judgements about the optimal way to control the human effects of science and technology. They should come to see that humane value judgements cannot be properly delegated solely to the experts but must be based on as wide a sampling of citizen judgements as possible.
> (v) Students should be encouraged to clarify their own values with respect to social issues raised by scientific and technological breakthroughs. They should be encouraged to learn and to use methods of clarifying their values anew as recent scientific and technological developments precipitate fresh social issues for public debate, discussion and resolution.
> (vi) Students should learn effective ways of translating their clarified and informed values into participatory action, including: presenting their views on issues effectively to others; listening to and dealing with people who hold different and opposed views; distinguishing between factual information and interpretations placed upon this information; using the resources of experts without surrendering responsibility for choice to them; and influencing decision-makers and opinion leaders.

There are many comments which could be made on this interesting formulation of learning objectives for STS courses. For present purposes, however, the important point is that, implicit in the formulation, is a view about the nature of society and, in particular, a concept of 'public participation', which, elsewhere than the USA and UK, and even there, might be regarded as contestable. There is by no means general agreement in the western world about which one of several recent theories of democracy either adequately describes the existing situation or should in fact prevail.[12] Equally, as a recent OECD report on '*Public Participation in Decision-making Related to Science and Technology*' stated, 'The concept of public participation is an elusive one. It means many different things to many different people'.[13] Indeed, scepticism about the effectiveness of 'public participation' in technological decisions, in many cases the 'inquiries' being structured discussions over pre-determined policy, with few real options,[14] has led some 'to question the validity of the premise that democratic public policy considerations dictate that the general public be informed about science and technology'.[15]

2 SCIENCE EDUCATION BEFORE THE PROFESSIONALIZATION OF SCIENCE

To the historian of science education, some at least of the justificatory rhetoric associated with STS courses has a tired look and one is tempted to say, 'We have been here before'. Certainly, what we know about science education, and the learning of science, in the first half of the nineteenth century would support an assertion that educational organisations of scientific knowledge were then primarily in terms of relevance to societal problems.

In the USA, as George H. Daniels has shown in the period before the Civil War, science was 'sold' to the public by virtue of its contribution to important American values – utilitarian, egalitarian and religious. Science education, it was agreed, was necessary because 'it would powerfully conduce to benefit the morals'.[16]

In the UK similarly, science education in that period had a number of well-defined and diverse social functions.[17] For some its purpose was conservative, confirming religious beliefs; 'reconcilers', who could harmonize the testimony of nature with that of the Bible, flourished. For others, science was an instrument of radicalism, knowledge which conveyed power to its possessors in the battle against the forces of authority, persecution and dogma.[18] Yet again, it was diffused and learnt because of its utility. The agricultural and colonial interests which supported the educational work at the Royal Institution in its early years have been well documented by Morris Berman.[19] At a more homely level, the work of scientists such as Priestley, Lavoisier, Dalton and Graham had made possible a science of ventilation; poor ventilation, with lack of sanitation and defective diet, being the most urgent social problems of the 'condensed populations' arising from industrialisation and urbanisation in the early century. By the 1830s, the *Edinburgh Review* could report that 'The sacred thirst for science is epidemic', a judgement scarcely supportable by present day evidence on students' dispositions.[20]

The important point, however, is that the bonding of science to society was strong in this early period. A high practicality underlay the whole of the scientific enterprise, and, in Daniels' words, 'its justification depended, in some sense or other, upon the manner in which it served the public'.[21]

3 THE 'SOCIAL CONTRACT' BETWEEN PROFESSIONAL SCIENCE AND SOCIETY

The professionalization of science in the second half of the nineteenth century had, as a central requirement, the acquisition of autonomy in relation to the direction of scientific research and the winning of freedom from external controls associated with utilitarian judgements on its activities.[22] A tacit 'social contract' was negotiated whereby direct utilitarian evaluations of science were to be abandoned, the sovereign goal of science becoming free enquiry into nature untrammelled by any considerations of social purpose. In the words of Lyon Playfair, science had become 'too lofty for measurement by the yardstick of utility'. In return for resources for research from society, these to be allocated by scientists themselves according to their perceptions of the internal dictates of their disciplines, the prospect was held out to society of unspecified future material benefits.

This disconnection of science from societal values, and the burnishing of the ideal of pure science, were fundamental to the development of modern science. As Thomas Kuhn has noted, 'The insulation of the scientific community from society permits the individual scientist to concentrate upon problems that he has good reason to believe he will be able to solve. Unlike the engineer, and many doctors, and most theologians, the scientist need not choose problems because they urgently need solution and without regard for tools available to solve them.'[23]

Of course some breaching of the 'contract' was inevitable. As Daniels has argued, democratic politics demands that *no* expenditure of public funds be separated from political control.[24] But the stance of professional science has always been to limit control to the minimum necessary to secure resources. Nowhere is this seen better than in the periods immediately following the wartime yoking of science to utilitarian and military ends. In the USA, the NSF was established in 1950, after five years of controversy about its precise role, to support '*basic* research' and science education. A similar spirit informed the warning to the Royal Society in 1943, delivered by Professor P. M. S. Blackett and Sir Ralph Fowler, of a danger that developments in fundamental physics might be neglected in comparison with applied physics, as a consequence of the successful application of physics to the purposes of war.[25] The extraordinary 'purity' of courses such as PSSC in the late 1950s, and the Nuffield 'O' level projects in the early 1960s, are reflective of this determination to uncouple science and society in the postwar years.

4 THE SCHOOLING OF SCIENCE – A PRODUCT FOR ALL PURPOSES

The incorporation of science into the late nineteenth-century school curriculum was not achieved without some notable exercises of accommodation. Few, if any, of the socially oriented versions of scientific knowledge from the early nineteenth century became institutionalized. Instead, first chemistry, then physics, were re-fashioned to serve the ends of liberal education as then defined in terms of mental training.[26]

Such versions of school science, with an emphasis on analysis in chemistry and on measurement in physics, consorted happily with the requirements of professional science. Considerations of utility did not intrude into the school curriculum; instead, the prime education objective was the development of intellectual skills. Furthermore, in the words of an influential report, 'In order that the study of physical science may effect this mental education, it is necessary that . . . the learners be put in the attitude of discoverers'.[27] It seemed that chemistry and physics had been fashioned into effective instruments for both intellectual education *and* the production of embryonic scientists. A common means had been devised to the twin ends of a liberal education and the advancement of science.

Though different formulations of the desired outcomes of education were to appear throughout the twentieth century, and different versions of school science were to emerge in response, for the most part the characteristics of purity and social disconnection remained constant and the needs of professional science were served equally with those of general education. Indeed, for its critics, this characteristic of school science, its strength from the standpoint of professional science, was its fundamental weakness, in comparison with arts subjects, as a branch of education. It might yield power over material forces of the universe, but it left untouched 'the greater forces of the human heart'. Whereas literature cultivated 'that part of our nature by which we are brought into contact with men and with moral agents', science could never rise 'to touch the sense of personality or responsibility'.[28] In short it lacked any connection with human values.

5 THE ATTEMPT TO RE-COUPLE SCIENCE AND VALUES IN EDUCATION

The development of STS courses, with their association of scientific knowledge with value, ethical and moral considerations, might then be regarded as a matter of satisfaction. It could be said that science education has at last come of age and its educational potential fulfilled, at a stroke.

Such enthusiasm needs to be tempered, however, by recognition of the extent of the departure involved from the traditional 'value-disconnected' science education deemed necessary for pre-professional training. Indeed, borrowing from Thomas Kuhn, there would seem to be 'an essential tension' between science education for personal development and science education for professional initiation. Historically the tension has been resolved by the incorporation in school curricula of 'pure', socially disconnected and uncontexted scientific knowledge. STS represents a radical departure from this.

Expressed in terms of the 'Goal Clusters' of Project Synthesis the question is about the educational compatibility of Goal Clusters I and II ('Personal Needs' and 'Social Issues') with, in particular, Goal Cluster III ('Academic Preparation').[29] Norris Harms states that in USA textbooks, goals related to personal use of science in everyday life, and to scientific literacy for societal decision-making are largely ignored[30] and diagnoses the challenge of STS as: 'Can we shift our goals, programs and practices from the current overwhelming emphasis on academic preparation for scientific courses for a few students to an emphasis on preparing all students to grapple successfully with science and technology in their own, everyday lives, as well as to participate knowledgeably in the important science-related decisions our country will have to make in the future?'[31]

This is a deeply political statement in at least two senses. First, an alternative formulation, in terms of the analysis in this paper, might be, 'Have we (ie teachers and science educators) the *power* to shift our goals etc.?' The record of history does not suggest we should be optimistic in responding to this question. In particular, the power of professional science to protect its own interests in school education should not be underestimated. In the UK a recent event of significance is that, simultaneously with the setting up of a joint Schools Council/Association for Science Education project on the secondary school science curriculum, the Royal Society has 'established a small group of Fellows to undertake a study of science education for the 11 to 18 age group', and, as the announcement of this development reminded readers, 'the main aim and concern of the Society is the protection and encouragement of scientific activity at the highest level'.[32]

Second the statement is political in the sense that it embodies a particular, and debatable, view of society in its reference to *all* students being prepared for participation in science-related decisions. Additionally, the point might be made that, from what we know of students' ability to master scientific concepts, as well as from what we know of students' moral development,[33] the reference to *all* students, participating *knowledgeably* is either an expression of an unreal hope or a rhetorical indulgence. Arguably, it does the cause of STS no good to set unrealistic goals.

6 PROSPECTS AND PROBLEMS

What then might realistically be achieved under the STS heading in secondary schools? In terms of a spectrum of learning objectives such as that outlined in section 1.3 above, there would seem to be severe limits on how far we can progress. To hope to achieve value clarification on conceptually complex STS issues (Piaget, Stage 3) by application of self-selected ethical principles (Kohlberg, Stage 6) is asking a great deal within the years of compulsory schooling. The STS in Secondary Schools Focus Group's emphasis on continuing education, ie lifelong science education, seems well-placed for this reason.[34] Additionally, STS issues are continually changing and no 'school package' can prepare adequately for what might eventually confront the adult. But what is entailed by this emphasis, ie institutional provision at adult level for the learning of socially relevant science, is notably lacking, at least in the UK. We have had nothing comparable to the Swedish Study Circles on Nuclear Energy, for example.

A particular difficulty confronts the science teacher trying his hand at STS courses, because he will not normally have had to handle controversial value issues in his previous teaching; the problems of bias and indoctrination will be new to him in relation to the preparation and use of course materials. The ASE *Science in Society* course has been severely criticised in the UK because of its 'establishment' stance, its failure to introduce for consideration radical alternatives and new frameworks for decision-making on STS issues, as well as for its exclusively masculine orientation. Whilst the treatment of controversial issues has been seized upon by many as a central problem confronting science teachers who introduce STS courses, the danger has perhaps been overplayed. Our history and English teacher colleagues have lived with the same problem for decades without undue catastrophe.

At least as important, if not more so, is the question of access to data and information necessary for decision making. We do not have in the UK legislation comparable to the *Freedom of Information Act* and the *National Environmental Policy Act* in the USA. A requirement for effective participation is the unrestricted availability of relevant information. In an age of 'multinational/corporation' science, to say nothing of 'government/military' science, this requirement is frequently difficult to satisfy. Participatory groups, often uncoordinated, and working with limited resources and partial information, have too often proved to be self-cancelling in their attempts to exert influence on decision-making on STS issues. Without the necessary freedom of access to information, and knowledge of the politics of decision-making in the adult world, a focus on STS issues at school level could be nothing more than a recipe for frustration, holding out the prospect of influence without providing the necessary equipment and conditions. At the same time, to overbid and fail to deliver, could leave the field open to reactionary forces and a return to the classical, socially-disconnected model of school science.

REFERENCES

1. N. C. Harms and R. E. Yager (eds) (1981): *What research says to the science teacher*, National Science Teachers Association.
2. *The Exeter Conference on Secondary School Science Education* (1980): Phillips Exeter Academy, Exeter, New Hampshire.
3. Mary C. McConnell (1980): *Teaching about science and society*. Unpublished paper for the UNESCO/ICSU Seminar, Science and Society, Malvern.
4. The Association for Science Education (1981): *Education through science. Policy statement*, Hatfield.
5. Harrie M. C. Eijkelhof, E. Boeker, J. H. Raat, N. J. Wijnbeck (1981): *Physics in Society* (English translation).
6. P. J. Fensham (1981): 'Heads, Hearts and Hands – future alternatives for science education': *Australian Science Teachers Journal*, *27*(1), 53–60.

   Glen S. Aikenhead (1980): *Science in Social Issues. Implications for Teaching*. Science Council of Canada.
7. International Council of Scientific Unions (July 1980): *Newsletter from the Committee on the Teaching of Science*, No. 5.
8. Paul De Hart Hurd (1975): 'Science, Technology and Society. New Goals for Interdisciplinary Science teaching', *The Science Teacher*, 42, 27–30.

   David Layton (1973): 'The Secondary School Curriculum and Science Education', *Physics Education* 8, 19–23.

   E. Mendelsohn, P. Weingart (1978): 'The social assessment of science; issues and perspectives'. In: E. Mendelsohn, D. Nelkin, P. Weingart (eds) *The Social Assessment of Science*: Conference Proceedings, University of Bielefeld.

   Dorothy Nelkin (1978): *Science, Technology and the Public*: Unpublished paper, prepared for Division of Science and Technology Policy, UNESCO for MINESPON II, February 1978.

9. Bryan Wilson (1981): *Cultural Contexts of Science and Mathematics Education. A bibliographical guide*. Centre for Studies in Science Education, University of Leeds.
10. A. O. Nasseef (1980): 'Planning for an Islamic science curriculum', *Times Educational Supplement*, 5 September 1980.

    Ziauddin Sardar (1977): *Science, Technology and development in The Muslim World*, London, Crown Helm in association with the Muslim Institute, p. 53.
11. Taken from: Mary McConnell (1980) op cit. ref.3 above.
12. See for example Carole Pateman (1970): *Participation and Democratic Theory*, Cambridge University Press.
13. *Technology on Trial. Public Participation in Decision-Making related to Science and Technology*: Organisation for Economic Co-operation and Development, Paris, 1979, p. 15.
14. Dorothy Nelkin and Michael Pollak (1979): 'Public Participation in Technological Decisions. Reality or Grand Illusion?', *Technology Review*, Aug/Sept. 1979, pp. 55–64.
15. Leon A. Trachtman (1981): 'The Public Understanding of Science Effort: a Critique', *Science, Technology and Human Values*, No. 36, Summer 1981, pp. 10–15.
16. George H. Daniels (1967): 'The Pure-Science Ideal and Democratic Culture', *Science*: 156, No. 3783, p. 1699.
17. David Layton (1977): 'Founding fathers of science education. The Benjamin of studies', *New Scientist*, 11 Aug. 1977, pp. 363–365.
18. See for example Richard Carlile (1822): *An Address to Men of Science*, London.
19. Morris Berman (1978): *Social change and scientific organisation. The Royal Institution 1799–1844*, London, Heinemann.
20. See for example J. Dudley Herron (1977): 'Declining enrolments: here are the facts. Where are the answers?', *The Science Teacher*, Jan. 1977, pp. 26–29.
21. George H. Daniels op cit. (ref. 16 above), p. 1700.
22. George H. Daniels (1967): 'The emergence of science as a profession in nineteenth century Europe', in: K. Hill (ed). *The management of scientists*, Beacon Press.
23. T. Kuhn (1970): *The Structure of Scientific Revolutions*, 2nd edition, Chicago. University of Chicago Press, p. 164.
24. G. H. Daniels (1967): op.cit. (ref. 16 above), p. 1704.
25. *Proceedings of the Royal Society of London* (1975): A. Mathematical and Physical Sciences. Vol. 342, No. 1631, pp. 525–6.
26. For an account of these and related issues see:
    David Layton (1981): 'The schooling of science in England, 1854–1939', in Roy MacLeod and Peter Collins (eds): *The Parliament of Science. The British Association for the Advancement of Science*. London, Science Reviews Ltd. pp. 188–210.

27. British Association for the Advancement of Science, *Report for 1889*, London, 1890, p. 299.

28. The passages come from Frederick Temple's evidence to the Public School Commissioners in 1862. *Report of Her Majesty's Commissioners appointed to Inquire into the Revenues and Management of Certain Colleges and Schools, and the Studies pursued and Instruction given therein.* Vol. 4. Evidence, Part 2, pp. 270–1. London, 1864.

29. N. C. Harms and R. E. Yager (1981): op.cit. (ref. 1 above), p. 7.

30. Ibid. p. 115.

31. Ibid. p. 119.

32. Sir Harry Pitt, Science in Secondary Education, *Royal Society News*, Issue 9, May 1981, pp. 1–2.

33. For an interesting attempt to relate Kohlberg's theory of moral development to the teaching of science and societal issues see

C. R. Barman, J. J. Rusch, T. M. Cooney (1979), *Science and Societal Issues. A Guide for Science Teachers*, Price Laboratory School, University of Northern Iowa, Cedar Falls, Iowa 50613.

34. N. C. Harms and R. E. Yager (eds). (op.cit.), p. 103.

12 The place of alternative models in school science

● N. J. Selley

Selley discusses the uses of models and theories in school science. He argues that 'good theory' should make sense, have explanatory power and stimulate further inquiry. He suggests that it is not enough for pupils to know something, knowledge must also be available to them to be used in further investigations. He criticizes the uses of oversimplified and incomplete models and rejects explanatory schemes that, in later stages of students' learning, are discarded as erroneous. He prefers simple but comprehensible models which allow pupils to discuss the limitations of models and encourage pupils to revise and improve them.

One of the main ideas behind the science curriculum revisions of about ten years ago was the recognition that one distinctive feature of science as an activity is the forming and testing of hypotheses. This led to the belief that school science courses should present the theories of science as tentative proposals which stood or fell by their success in standing up to experimental test. This sounds very well, in general terms, but it does seem to have generated some very impracticable and unworkable schemes in those cases where the major, basic models have been used as material for 'discovery' learning.[1] Insuperable problems arise from the clash between the conflicting aims of:

1. Teaching a complex scientific theory (as yet unfamiliar to the pupils) as accurately and 'correctly' as possible, and
2. Ensuring that this emerges as a hypothesis arising from the pupils' own investigations.

(An example from elementary chemistry is the well-known investigation into the change in weight which occurs when certain substances are heated in air: the pupils' results are often inaccurate and inconsistent, yet the discussion of them is supposed to lead to hypotheses concerning chemical combination and decomposition.)

This chapter proposes an alternative approach, which may gradually convey the nature of scientific theory, without requiring the absurd assumption that major truths can be tested and confirmed by schoolchildren in one double period.

SCIENTIFIC 'TRUTH'

Science teachers cannot avoid philosophy, since their teaching methods necessarily reflect their own view of the philosophy of science, even though this may be an implicit, unformulated view. The rapid developments in this field which are now being brought to their notice[2] may have given rise to a sense of not knowing what they are now expected to do in the way of teaching, or conveying, the 'meaning of science'. This is especially so in the case of the meaning of 'truth' in science, for the traditional view, that scientists discover (through observation, experiment and inductive inference) true knowledge about the world, is now distrusted. We are told that 'there is no absolute truth', yet the whole science curriculum (at least post-primary) seems based on the assumption that there is: that is, that there is a well-defined, unique system of facts, theories and concepts which pupils must eventually learn to understand and use.

MODELS AND THEORIES

A commonly held interpretation of 'theory' is that it is a guess at some aspect of nature which cannot be observed directly, but which can be inferred from indirect evidence. This interpretation is located within the 'Naive Realist' view of truth: viz. that there exists 'out there' a real world which it is the task of scientists to discover. On this principle, the truth about nature can be discovered, and it is possible that many of our current theories of science (e.g. elements and compounds, the electron-flow theory of electricity, and Mendel's laws) are true, and will never be disproved.

An alternative interpretation, less well-known but more satisfactory (e.g. more consistent with the historical development of science) is that theories are attempts at representing the regularities in natural phenomena, through suggested pictures of what the natural world *might be like* in order that it should give rise to the observable effects. The subtle difference in this 'Critical Realism' is that although a real world exists 'out there' (i.e. independently of human thought), there is no possibility of our ever knowing just what it is like.[3] We can only hypothesize, examine our hypotheses for self-consistency, and devise experimental tests. In recognition of this change in meaning, the word 'theory' is often replaced by 'model'.[4]

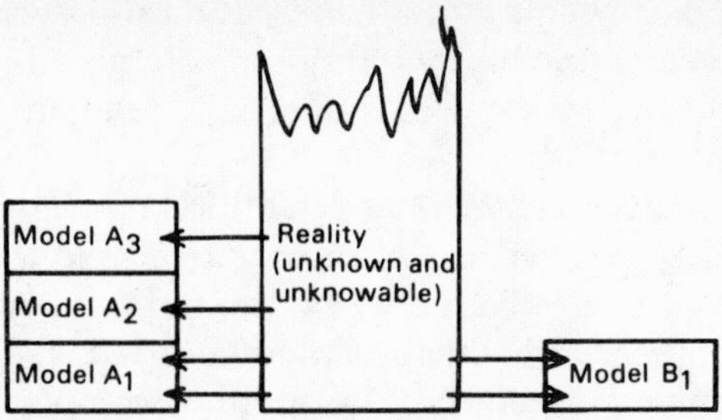

A diagram showing a Critical Realist interpretation of scientific knowledge. The arrows represent observable facts which are the data base for each model. Models A_1 and B_1 (and perhaps also C_1, . . .) explain the same observable phenomena, while Models A_2 and A_3 are elaborations of A_1, able to explain a wider range of phenomena. (The observable phenomena, or 'facts', are not necessarily theory-free sense data, but may be interpretations based on some taken-for-granted theory.)

The figure is a Critical Realist interpretation of scientific knowledge, showing two different models for some limited aspect of the world; of these, Model A is shown as having greater explanatory scope than Model B, though the latter may have some merits, such as greater simplicity or familiarity, which make it worth retaining.

It goes almost without saying that we must carefully distinguish the meaning of model as used in the present discussion from the more colloquial use of the word, denoting a tangible piece of apparatus, the purchased or homemade gadget designed as a teaching aid, and which we are now being asked to call an 'analogue'.

IMPLICATIONS FOR SCIENCE EDUCATION

The view that scientific theories/models are not absolutely true, but only *relatively* fruitful as schemes for systematizing observations, gives the teacher a new freedom to deal with more than one model in a given area of science. It also places importance on our reasons for preferring one model to another, since it can no longer be maintained simply that one is true and the others false.

This pluralistic approach could bring science education more into line with other areas of the curriculum, such as English, religious education and the humanities, in which the pupils' personal opinions are given some respect, and in which the discussion, clarification and criticism of such opinions is enocuraged. It should be possible to avoid the authoritarian mode of presentation of science as entirely a pre-existing, nonnegotiable body of concepts and theories; and this in turn might free the pupil from the feeling that his own thoughts on the subject are bound to be inadequate in comparison with the 'correct' (and often incomprehensible) orthodox version.

After all, it is now accepted that scientific knowledge changes with time, that theories are overthrown or modified, and that the 'truth' of any proposition can be judged only by the number and strength of its logical compatibilities with other accepted knowledge. This need not, as critics of Kuhn have pointed out,[5] go so far as complete relativism (the claim that there is *no* way of judging the relative merits of completely different theories); but it does establish that it is irrational to ask anyone to abandon one theory and give allegiance to another without demonstrating any empirical advantages of the latter.

If the position of an individual learning science is analogous to that of a group of scientists considering a radical revision of their theories, it follows that he, too, must be given good reasons (internal to his scientific development) for leaving a comfortable explanatory scheme and braving the rigours of a new and unfamiliar one. For the individual, what is true is what he has the best reason to believe.

The teacher who sees things this way need have no unease of conscience when he allows pupils to use, in understanding phenomena, models which he himself would reject. The old adage 'Never teach anything you will later have to unteach' should not be followed too faithfully. If the teacher can establish the attitude that he does not necessarily *endorse* everything that is discussed in his classroom, then he creates for himself the freedom to exploit the possibilities of some model which his pupils find meaningful and, for the moment at least, useful.

Furthermore, there could be an additional benefit from this on a future occasion. The pupils may learn something very important about the nature of science precisely *through* the experience of finding it necessary to revise (modify or even abandon) their earlier beliefs. The teacher should, at this later moment, assure the pupils that their earlier notions were true to an extent, and should point to the revision as an improvement rather than a correction.

'INCOMPLETE MODELS' AND 'MISCONCEPTIONS'

I wish to distinguish two categories of ultimately inadequate model, which may be encountered in school science. The first is the incomplete, oversimplified model, suitable for teaching to beginners. An example might be the fluid model for heat, which can account for many of the observable facts encountered in the first year of study of physics, especially conduction and heat capacity, but which will eventually be replaced by the completely different kinetic model.

The second category is the misconception, which we may define as an explanatory conceptual scheme which is erroneous in that it is in conflict with facts which are, or will shortly be made, known to the student. Misconceptions may be based on (i) once respectable but now discredited theories which survive in popular books or 'folk wisdom'; or they may be (ii) original creations (hypotheses), constructed by the student by analogy with or extension of other scientific knowledge. An example of variant (i) might be some Aristotelean notion such as the cause of falling stones being their wish to rejoin the earth, or the flow of rivers being due to their attraction to the ocean; in contrast, misconceptions of variant (ii) are generally idiosyncratic and unique, and remarkable for their ingenuity, as for example the 14-year-old's explanation of the perpetuation of Brownian motion as due to the energy released by the occasional 'explosion' of particles of smoke (an optical effect which can be seen in the Whitley Bay smoke cell, as particles which move vertically go out of focus and create diffraction rings).

It might be thought that, in practice, the distinction between an incomplete model and a misconception is that the teacher may well teach his class one of the former, knowing that before they finish the course the model will have to be revised and expanded, whereas the misconception will only make its appearance through some pupil's contribution to the discussion, and can, after token consideration, be dispatched to oblivion. I wish to show that the situation is not that simple, and that greater tolerance of misconceptions is necessary, if pupils are to learn to *use* theoretical models.

FUNCTIONAL KNOWLEDGE

One line of reasoning which points to the value of at least delaying the attempt to 'correct' a pupil's own conceptions is based on the learning theories of Polanyi, Ausubel and others.[6] Briefly, it is not enough to *know that* something is so, for to be of any value to the knower, the knowledge must be available for use in examining further matters. The act of thinking about some new question involves the deployment of previous knowledge: we attend *to* the new material by simultaneously attending *from* existing knowledge, which has already been accepted as true and meaningful. Such knowledge I will refer to as 'functional knowledge'.

It will be recognized that this analysis provides a terminology by which we can define the 'inert knowledge' which Halliwell[7] and other Nuffield course authors warned us against: inert knowledge is knowledge which the possessor cannot attend from. One wonders why it is that, despite the good intentions implicit in the 'Nuffield philosophy', so much of the scientific knowledge held by, say, fifth-formers is so obviously 'inert'.

This theory of functional knowledge does more, however, than simply reiterate the uselessness of rote learning: it provides a means of selecting and evaluating alternative learning modes. About every concept, which it is proposed to try to teach, one should ask the following questions:

1 Is it intelligible, i.e. logically linked with the learner's existing knowledge?

2 Is it likely to be functional, in the short term? (If so, give *specific* examples of matters which the new knowledge will help to explain or elucidate.)

One cannot, of course, be sure of the answer to **1** *a priori*, and one way of finding out is simply to try it and see. The new concept, theory or whatever is taught, and subsequent testing (written or oral) is employed to diagnose success or failure. Another way, which is more time-consuming but arguably more valid, is to explore the area with the pupils through discussion (usually verbally, with the whole class), to get some feel of how the knowledge is likely to be received. If it *is* intelligible, then suitable prompting should elicit appropriate suggestions. (This is, of course, one of the central techniques of the 'guided discovery method'.)

Similarly with **2** it will soon be found whether the knowledge *is* going to be functional, by the extent to which the pupils begin to use it with confidence in the discussion of its various applications.

The teacher faces a problem, however, if these techniques reveal that a substantial number of the pupils are not yet ready to accept the new knowledge. What if it is found that they are more comfortable with some alternative (simpler, less abstract, or just more familiar) conceptual scheme? Should the use of such a scheme (or possibly, several such schemes) be encouraged? Should the teacher proceed to develop scientific thinking through the clarification, formulation and criticism of these alternative explanations? Does he not run the risk of legitimizing them, and giving the impression, for example, that they will be acceptable to the examiners?

There is something approaching a moral dilemma here. The pupils seem to understand, and be able to use intelligently, a theoretical scheme which is 'untrue', being perhaps out-dated and discredited, or perhaps an oversimplification or distortion of the orthodox version. Yet it is not in conflict with their existing knowledge, nor with the data under consideration, and could only be shown to be inadequate through reference to data which the teacher judges to be too complex or remote (e.g. from a field of science which he does not wish to teach yet) for him to bring in.

I think that this situation needs to be illustrated by an example or two, although I recognize the danger that attention will be deflected from the general point to the merits of the particular examples. Consider a lesson on convection, to 12-year-olds. The familiar glass-fronted box has two chimneys, with a lighted candle under one of them. A smouldering paper is placed above the other chimney, and the smoke is 'sucked in'. The pupils interpret this demonstration as showing that (i) hot air rises, and (ii) the hot air leaves the box through the chimney, thereby creating a 'vacuum' inside, which sucks in fresh air. Note that the lesson is on convection and thermal currents, not on atmospheric pressure, which has not yet been taught. Should the teacher tolerate these two venerable misconceptions, (i) and (ii)?

Some teachers may think that the use by pupils of imperfect explanations is less of a problem in the early stages, when the basic concepts are still being acquired, than in the upper forms; so my second example will be set in the third or fourth form. Suppose that pupils there, knowing that (a) pure water does not conduct electricity appreciably, and (b) when sulphuric acid is added, a current passes and oxygen is produced at the (inert) anode, conclude that the oxygen is produced by a mechanism involving the discharge of the sulphate ion, followed immediately by reaction of the 'sulphate molecule' with water, thus:

$$SO_4^{2-} \quad SO_4 + 2e^-; \quad \text{then } SO_4 + H_2O \quad H_2SO_4 + \tfrac{1}{2}O_2$$

The teacher knows that this explanation is no longer approved of, but he cannot (without resorting to advanced arguments, or to authority) offer an alternative which satisfies both observations (a) and (b). Should he permit his pupils to continue to discuss electrolysis in terms of this old 'primary and secondary products' model?

TEACHING THE NATURE OF MODELS

It looks as though the current provision for teaching the nature and function of scientific models is so inadequate (depending as it does on the casual comments the teachers may choose to make in passing), that major curriculum development in this area is called for: and some work in this direction is being undertaken.[8] It has often been wrongly assumed that to teach science process must involve the abstract, philosophical discussion of process – an activity which teachers rightly judge their pupils to be incapable of, and uninterested in. Rather, the teaching of process should be through the active involvement of pupils in that process, through examples appropriate to their level of development. Hence, teaching for understanding of models should include the involvement of pupils in the discussion of the relative merits of alternative models, in specific cases.

An early attempt at such an approach was the strategy of inviting pupils to debate the merits of two major alternative theories, for example the particulate and the continuous models for matter (Nuffield Chemistry, Nuffield Combined Science, Nuffield Secondary Science), or the kinetic and the static molecular models for the Boyle's Law behaviour of gases (Nuffield Physics).[9] While the intention behind these proposals is praiseworthy, I feel that they are unlikely to succeed if both the models are unfamiliar to the pupils (especially since both make considerable demands upon the imagination). The pupils at this stage are unskilled in the art of model-testing, and need to start with far easier examples. Furthermore, the whole enterprise is likely to be vitiated by the teacher's anxiety that the 'right' model shall emerge triumphant from the contest. These typically Nuffield proposals suffer from the same fatal misjudgement of the situation as did the attempts to use the discovery method to teach major scientific theories, as mentioned at the start of this article. Pupils cannot be expected to recognize, immediately and spontaneously, the truth and usefulness of a model/theory which they are encountering for the first time.

For a discussion of the strengths and weaknesses of two alternative models to be of any value, both models must be fully understood by the pupils. I suggest that any science teacher can, with forethought, achieve this. He should look ahead at his syllabus for the course, and select a few topics for which two different (and defensible) explanations exist. If, as is usually the case, the 'better' one is also the more complex, he might plan to teach the simpler one first, and then re-visit the topic a year or so later, this time showing reasons why the earlier model might need to be revised. This would give the pupils direct experience of having to reconsider and perhaps give up a scientific model which they were committed to, and which they had some incentive to defend.

Examples of topics which lend themselves to such treatment are quite easy to find, if one can suppress one's reflex reaction to reject as 'wrong' any theory which one personally finds inadequate. Yet, since teachers will differ in their judgements, the selection must be left to the individual. A cautious approach would be to select, for the initial stage, an explanatory model which has had historical respectability (e.g. the model for a liquid as consisting of spaced, independently mobile molecules), and to raise objections to it later (e.g. the 4°C density maximum of water, pointing to a model with clustered molecules). This is no doubt a common teaching practice already, but perhaps the philosophical issues need pointing out more clearly.

A bolder move would be to allow the pupils to develop and criticize a model selected because, though initially plausible, it soon leads to difficulties which even they will recognize. If, for a lesson or two, the objective is to teach the *process* of scientific understanding, then the using of a model in the discussion of observations, and the exploring of the scope and limitations of that model, must temporarily take precedence over the acquisition of accurate information. So the teacher must concentrate on stimulating discussion and maintaining a high standard of scientific debate – not on directing the arguments towards a pre-determined 'orthodox' conclusion. His most difficult task, I imagine, will await him at the end, when he must resist the temptation to step in and say 'Well, you have had a good discussion; now I will tell you the *real* explanation'.

SUMMARY

In this chapter I have set out briefly what I take to be the current position in the philosophy of science, namely that the essential thing about a good scientific theory is not that it should be 'true' in some absolute way, but that it should make sense, have extensive explanatory scope, and stimulate further enquiry. It would appear that school science courses commonly make too little provision for the learning of this important philosophical viewpoint. I then argued, using a theory of 'functional knowledge', that pupils would benefit from greater opportunity to use in discussion simple models which they find comprehensible, rather than the 'better' but more remote models known to the teacher. They could then also experience and discuss the process of model revision, on a subsequent occasion when evidence is presented which shows up weaknesses or limitations of their earlier model. Finally I suggested that a speculative discussion would be of greater educational effectiveness, in conveying the nature of science, if the teacher could refrain from exercising his intellectual authority and 'having the last word'.

If it should prove that I have been preaching to the converted, and that strategies of this kind are already in regular use, I shall be delighted: and I would be very glad to hear about any results.

REFERENCES

1. Coulson, E. H. (ed.), *Nuffield Chemistry: Handbook for Teachers* (Longmans/Penguin, 1967), p. 63: 'Given sound preparation and skilful guidance the class will discover or invent the main postulates of Dalton's atomic theory and indeed go beyond them . . .'
2. See initially, for example: Richardson, M. and Boyle, C., *What is Science?* ASE Study Series No. 15 (ASE, 1979). Also Donelly, J., 'The work of Popper and Kuhn on the nature of science' *S.S.R.*, 1979, 212, **60**, 489–500.
3. See Barbour, I. G., *Issues in Science and Religion* (SCM Press, 1966), p. 172; Caws, P., *The Philosophy of Science* (Van Nostrand, 1965), p. 291.

4. Forge, J. C., 'A role for the philosophy of science in the teaching of science', *J. Philos. Educ.* 1979, **13**, 109–18.
5. See, for example, Toulmin, S., *Human Understanding* (Oxford University Press, 1972), pp. 98 ff.
6. See Allen, R. T., 'The philosophy of Michael Polanyi and its significance for education', *J. Philos. Educ.*, 1978, **12**, 167–77. Ausubel, D. P., et al, *Educational Psychology—a Cognitive View* (Holt, Reinhart & Winston, 1978).
7. Halliwell, H. F. (ed.), *Nuffield Chemistry: Introduction and Guide* (Longmans/Penguin, 1966).
8. See Selley, N. J., 'Teaching scientific thinking', *Educ. in Science*, Jan 1981, **91**, 24.
9. See Neville, P., *S.S.R.*, 1968, 169, **49**, 859–67; and Mee, A. J. et al. *Science for the Seventies* (Heinemann, 1971), Unit 1. These authors suggest the technique of using optical illusions to convince pupils that there is uncertainty in all interpretation of sensory experience, and hence in all scientific theories. I feel that this philosophical argument is unlikely to impress beginners unless supported by some much more direct experience of the construction of scientific theories.
10. Nuffield Chemistry: Sample Scheme Stages I and II (1966), p. 222; Nuffield Combined Science: *Teachers' Guide II* (1970), p. 80; Nuffield Secondary Science: Theme 7 *Using Materials* (1971), p. 16; Nuffield Physics: *Teachers' Guide I* (1966), pp. 228 ff.

13 Science education – for whom

● J. Ziman

Ziman suggests that our technological civilization would collapse but for the work of teachers. He argues that it is easy to forget the difficulties of teaching and learning the natural sciences. He emphasizes that the science that different people need to know in life is very diverse indeed. He discusses and contrasts the demands in the professional formation of researchers and technologists, and the preparation for technical employment. Ziman argues that the intellectual demands of science are severe, that principles of science have to be taught and that intellectual imperatives of 'valid' science must be respected.

THE VOCATIONAL IMPERATIVE

Science is taught to many different people, at many different levels. The exact reasons why particular items of scientific knowledge are taught in particular ways to particular groups of students cannot always be determined, except by reference to traditional practice. For teachers and for pupils, science education serves a variety of purposes that are seldom clearly defined.

But one of the main reasons for including the natural sciences in secondary and tertiary education is that they are a necessary preparation for certain aspects of modern life. Many people need to know certain elements of science to practise their professions; many jobs cannot be satisfactorily performed without some degree of scientific knowledge. Not all science education is strictly *vocational*. Many school pupils and university students take courses in scientific subjects because they happen to be interested in them, or very good at them – that is for the same reason as they take 'useless' subjects such as history or classics. But the provision of the means for acquiring and transmitting scientific knowledge – schools, technical colleges, universities, teachers, lecturers, laboratories, research institutes and so on – would not be supported to the tune of so many thousands of millions of pounds if this were not an essential feature of contemporary civilization. The science that is needed by an advanced industrial society cannot be learnt by watching mother, sitting next to Nelly, watching 'Tomorrow's World' or 'Horizon' on the TV, reading the newspapers, poring over 'teach yourself' books in the evenings, or even by apprenticeship to a practical craft. Our technological civilization (for what it is worth – but that is not in question here) would slowly collapse if tens or hundreds of thousands of people were not spending some of the most formative years of their lives learning science systematically from professional teachers.

Of course, many young people have no clear idea for what career they should be diligently preparing themselves. Of course, there can be much argument over which bits of science are really essential to a particular job. Of course knowledge of some supposedly irrelevant aspect of science may prove unexpectedly valuable in later life. Of course, the 'scientific attitude' and scientific ways of thinking can be applied to advantage to all manner of practical affairs. Of course, the scientific view of the Universe and of Mankind is one of the integrating ideologies of our times. Of course, this knowledge is one of the finest and noblest achievements of our civilization. Of course, everybody needs to understand the powers and limitations of science in order to live more safely and happily with it. Of course, there is as much to learn about the precise use of language, and as much wisdom to acquire, from the study of a science as from any of the traditional humanities. And of course – this is a truism in every branch of education – if science were only taught better it would be a rewarding human experience for every pupil and for every teacher.

All these justifications and qualifications of science education are valid in themselves. It is good to be able to find so many excellent reasons for doing something so laborious as learning science – especially when it needs to be done anyway. The fundamental vocational goal of science education does not completely determine its content and style. The same end may be reached by various means, which may not be equivalent in other respects. It is important not to lose sight of these subsidiary goals in devising new educational techniques to meet new vocational challenges. In fact, this is just what this book is about.

But the vocational goal of science teaching and learning must not be played down. With the best of motives – intellectual, moral, professional, political – people with little experience of the teaching of science fasten their attention on those worthy secondary aspects. Even some teachers and lecturers, in their enthusiasm for and delight in the beauties of their subject and the insight they have gained by its study, forget how difficult it is to teach what has to be taught, and to learn what has to be learnt on the way to an actual career.

Any proposal for change in science education must be compatible with these realities. That is not to say that the way science is taught at present satisfactorily achieves its vocational purposes. On the contrary, it will be argued that many school children and college students would turn out better educated for the lives they will actually have to live if they were to be taught a little less science as such, and a little more *about* science. The practical, and entirely proper aim of preparing people for a variety of jobs where scientific knowledge is needed at various levels has been too narrowly intepreted as nothing more than the teaching of the theories, techniques, and practical capabilities of science, without reference to the context of thought and action where this knowledge is to be used.

Our starting point, therefore, is the people who need to know some science in their actual lives – mainly at work, but sometimes also at play. These needs are very diverse, not only in the various subjects required, but also in the extent to which any particular topic must be understood. The teaching of science, from the early years of the secondary school to postgraduate courses in the university, is equally diverse. Before looking for those general features to which general principles of reform might apply, let us distinguish the major groups of people for whom the modern system of science education mainly caters.

THE RESEARCH PROFESSION

The most exacting demand is for the training of research scientists. There are not very many of these – perhaps no more than one or two per thousand of the population. Only a few thousand of them need to be trained each year. Their work, as academics, as government research scientists, and in industry, is often very remote from immediate use. They are expensive to train, and sometimes apparently reckless in the extravagance of their research facilities. But their contribution to society, in the long run, is quite beyond reckoning.

Despite their small numbers, the production of research scientists is the dominant factor in the system of science education in every advanced industrial country. Many people regard it as a regrettable and outmoded tradition that the needs of this élite profession should dominate the education of the much larger mass of technologists, technicians and other useful people. But there is a rationale to this tradition that is more compelling than sentimental deference to high science and its mind-boggling discoveries.

The research scientist makes heavy demands on science education in several different dimensions. Scientific knowledge is cumulative. A scientist making an original investigation must have a firm base in what is already known. There is no profit in laboriously rediscovering past results. Somehow the research worker must be got to the existing frontiers of knowledge if he is to explore beyond them. His education must be *deep* – not just for 'training the mind', but to learn what needs to be known in a particular field to undertake research on a particular problem.

But the totality of scientific knowledge, even in what we call a 'discipline', is far beyond the grasp of any student or any teacher. Of course, not everything a research scientist needs can be acquired by formal education. The search for relevant ideas or information in the published archives of science is itself a significant part of any scientific investigation. But even an outline of the key ideas in a mature science such as physics cannot be taught or learnt in many years of full-time study at school or college. Education for the research profession must become highly *specialized* if it is to reach the necessary depth.

The frontiers of knowledge are far flung. If they are to be pushed back further in every direction, appropriately specialized research workers must be produced by the system. Science education must diversify into many special disciplines and departments, each staffed by the relevant academic experts. Science may be unified in principle by a metaphysical notion of 'validity', but without such a highly differentiated division of labour the advance of knowledge would soon falter.

Education for the research profession must, in its final stages, be deep, specialized, and diversified. Just how deep, in what manner specialized, and by what categories diversified can be a matter for endless debate in high academic circles. These debates need not concern us here – except that they are often resolved by a compromise that transfers the pressure to the earlier stages of education. If the science student who only knows one corner of physics is thought to be inadequately prepared for research in biophysics, then the necessary cellular biology must somehow be incorporated in his education at school. If it is thought to be absolutely necessary to spend at least four years studying quantum theory at successively more abstract levels in order to do research on elementary particles, then the required depth can be got by starting the subject in the Sixth Form. This is the machinery by which the educational needs of research scientists drive the whole system.

In addition to a body of knowledge, the research scientist needs training in the techniques of active research. By convention, this comes during preparation for the Ph.D. – essentially a professional apprenticeship which lies somewhat beyond the scope of this book. An important issue in science education is the extent to which the psychological experience of research can be simulated and anticipated at earlier stages of education, by 'discovery' methods of teaching, by the introduction of 'projects' to replace formal instruction, and so on. But this issue, also, would take us too far away from our main theme.

THE TECHNOLOGICAL PROFESSIONS

For simplicity, let us distinguish between the *scientist*, who is concerned with the *acquisition* of knowledge, and the *technologist*, whose work is the *application* of knowledge. The educational needs of the technologist for professional *practice* are not the same as the needs of the scientist for *research*. In reality, this distinction is not at all sharp. A professor of clinical medicine carries out research on a very practical subject and applies his knowledge for the benefit of his patients; an engineer designing a new bridge is simultaneously making an original contribution to human knowledge.

Modern technology, however, is pre-eminently scientific. The knowledge to be applied in practice derives as much from organized research as from the systematic codification of past professional experience. In many cases it derives from fundamental research, directed simply towards the understanding of natural phenomena, without any conscious practical orientation. Advanced technology is not only scientific in spirit, relying for progress on deliberate investigations of present techniques and future developments: it is also *science-based*, drawing its theoretical rationale from the basic disciplines of the natural sciences. Thus, the aeronautical engineer designs the wing of an aircraft using the mathematical theory of aerodynamics, the plant breeder applies the principles of Mendelian genetics, and the oil prospector plans explorations on hunches derived from plate tectonics and the theory of continental drift.

The technological professions cannot do without science. All courses of technological higher education – medicine, dentistry, engineering, metallurgy, electronics, geophysics, glass technology, polymer science, fuel technology, mining, etc., etc. – include major components of basic science, either in the undergraduate curriculum or as a prerequisite to entry. Would-be doctors and dentists must study physiology and biochemistry (and also, apparently for traditional reasons, more remote sciences such as physics), mechanical engineers must know a good deal of classical physics and mathematics, fuel technologists need a thorough grasp of chemical thermodynamics and so on. These are genuine vocational needs. However little anatomy your family doctor may admit to having remembered or ever used, that is the intellectual framework which makes sense of her practical skills. Most of the day-to-day work of an engineer is covered by empirical design formulae and codes of standard practice – until faced with a problem that takes him or her back to the first principles of mechanics or mathematics.

But training for a technological career does not demand a very deep knowledge of a particular field of science. Technologists must try to understand the basic scientific principles of the techniques they apply, but their education needs to be thorough and specialized only in the practice of those techniques. The 'preclinical' sciences of anatomy, physiology and pathology are preparations for training in clinical skills, which are the real goal of medical education. The basic mathematics and physics of the engineering curriculum is subordinate to training in design. The research scientist is concerned with knowledge as such; the technologist is concerned with knowledge only as a basis for action. He or she must not tarry too long in the ivory towers of academia. A sound grasp of basic principles, some acquaintance with the current body of knowledge, and a brief introduction to recent advanced theories are all that he or she can afford to pick up on the way through to the real world.

Many more people are employed in technology than in scientific research – hundreds of thousands, rather than a few tens of thousands in a country such as Britain. This includes not only the medical and engineering professions, but a whole range of jobs in industry and government for which a science-based higher education is a necessary qualification. Indeed, the majority of graduates from the traditional scientific disciplines take up technological careers and receive their practical training on the job – managing computer systems, analysing chemical products, advising farmers, running breweries, publishing technical books, and an infinity of other professions.

Education for technological practice is much wider in scope, much more diverse in its institutional setting, than education for research. From a narrowly academic point of view, it makes more demand for quantity, but less for quality, from science education as a whole. In university faculties of science, these demands are often regarded as subsidiary to those of training for research; in technological faculties and institutions, the teaching of science is often defective for lack of contact with the research community. But the differentiation of institutions, faculties, departments and disciplines is less important than the different vocational goals, the different types of careers, for which students are consciously or unconsciously being prepared.

TECHNICAL EMPLOYMENT

The vocational function of school science is much less definite. For many children, of course, scientific subjects are taken at school as stepping stones on the way into scientific or technological higher education. For many others they are merely elements in a general education that will ultimately be focussed on a career where such subjects are irrelevant. For any particular child, quite uncertain about his or her natural talents, inclination, or future profession, there may be no real distinction between vocational and general education: chemistry, or biology, or physics is chosen because it is 'interesting', or 'likely to be useful', or 'what I am good at'. Indeed, the most compelling reasons may be negative: 'It's not interesting', or 'I'm no good at it' may rule out alternatives, leaving one or more sciences to be studied by default.

But an elementary understanding of certain basic scientific principles seems almost essential for a very wide range of skilled work. The electrician and the radio repairman must know a bit about the physics of electromagnetism; the nurse and the physiotherapist must know some human anatomy; the engineering draughtsman and the computer programmer must be reasonably competent in mathematics; and the horticulturalist and the forester should not be quite ignorant of biology.

The amount of basic science that is used explicitly in such work must not be exaggerated. The excellence of a craftsman or technician lies in the skill with which he or she carries out a relatively familiar but not quite routine job, rather than in a capacity to analyse the task theoretically or to imagine an entirely novel way of doing it. This skill derives from sensitivity of hand and eye, guided by long experience, rather than from formal education or book learning. The traditional preparation for technical employment was by apprenticeship, where all that was needed of 'theory' could supposedly be learnt on the job, with very little reference to the sort of science taught in school.

For a variety of social and economic reasons this form of preparation for highly skilled technical trades has largely given way to more systematic training courses, where there may be heavier emphasis on theoretical knowledge, and hence more demand for prior qualifications in school science subjects. The traditional dividing line between a technical trade and a technological profession is now as indistinct as the boundary between research science and technological practice. Superficially, only a few additional years of academic education, leading to a higher qualification, separate the doctor from the nurse, or the production engineer from the workshop foreman. As more and more skilled trades become professionalized, and as the independent technological practitioner comes more and more under bureaucratic control in the government service or in corporate industry, these ancient class distinctions become less and less meaningful.

In any case, whether or not the demand for formal educational qualifications in science is vocationally justified, there is no doubt that a great many children take science subjects up to 'A' level on their way into employment where knowledge of these subjects is relevant to their work.

This also applies to many management and office jobs in industry, commerce and government, where it is essential to understand something of the technical and/or scientific background.

The very diversity of such employment makes it impossible to prescribe science curricula that would meet all these vocational needs in detail. What branch of physics should be emphasized at 'O' level or 'A' level: electricity and electronics for work in telecommunications; properties of matter for the civil engineer or dental mechanic; heat, light and sound for the plumber or television cameraman? Is some understanding of the electron theory of valency an essential ingredient in the training of a chemical laboratory technician? How much biochemistry and physiology should be included in a practical course of animal husbandry for farmers? Even if such questions could be given precise answers, these could not be reconciled with one another in the very rough justice of school timetables and examination syllabuses.

Nevertheless, although science subjects are usually taught in schools and technical colleges without specific applications in mind, the fact must not be ignored that many of those who study them will be putting them to vocational use in due course. What they learn *about* science from their teachers may be just as significant for their careers as the knowledge *of* science that they acquire at this impressionable stage of their lives.

SCIENCE AS GENERAL KNOWLEDGE

Even in our technological civilization, everyday life depends very little on general knowledge. Indeed, it is quite astonishing how ignorant people can be about things in general ('What is the name of the Prime Minister?', 'In what continent is Canada?', 'When do birds lay their eggs?', etc.) without apparently impairing their capabilities in work and play. One can get along quite well, doing what the doctor tells us, without knowing the difference between viruses and bacteria, just as we can go on speaking prose without knowing the difference between nouns and verbs.

Beyond the merest mechanics of the three R's, the fundamental purpose of general education must be to fill in the background against which most people take on the daily business of life. It is obvious that science is a major component of that setting. Our civilization is as much based on the physics of energy and electricity, on the chemistry of steel and polythene, on the biology of antibiotics and contraceptives, as it is on the politics of capital and labour, the history of William the Conqueror and Oliver Cromwell, or the language of Shakespeare and Churchill. Science education in the early years of the secondary school is the main source of such basic knowledge for most people.

The sort of scientific knowledge that is 'useful' in this very broad sense would include general structural concepts, such as biological evolution, chemical bonding and physical dynamics. It should convey simple representations of the astronomical universe, the earth, solid matter, living cells and the human body. It should at the same time be linked to familiar everyday reality – weather, food, materials, machines, reproduction and illness. There can be no place in such a curriculum for technologically or academically specialized topics, except to exemplify the capabilities and limitations of particular scientific concepts or techniques.

The secondary school science curriculum not only conveys a specifically scientific image of the world and its inhabitants: it also transmits an attitude towards science and scientific expertise. The place of science in the popular culture of our times and the role of the scientist in our contemporary society are largely determined by the way in which scientific knowledge is presented in the classroom. Although most people learn very little science, and make very little direct use of what they learn, they are the silent majority whose views eventually carry much more weight than the tiny minority of research workers and advanced technologists. They too must learn something *about* science as part of their education about things in general.

SCIENCE EDUCATION AND SCIENCE TEACHING

Within the educational system as a whole, science education appears as a relatively uniform and continuing process, through which each student is drawn, year by year, to successively higher levels of knowledge, conceptual grasp, technical skill, etc. This steady increase in the 'validity' of scientific education with student age is represented schematically in Fig. 1. But not all forms of employment demand the same degree of scientific competence. School children and students in higher education move out of science education at various ages, as they enter various more or less 'scientific' careers. In a natural progression according to age, we observe the majority of people leaving general science education along with all other formal schooling, at 16+. A substantial number, however, continue with school science subjects in the Sixth Form, in preparation for skilled technical employment. A smaller number, again, enter tertiary education and take scientific or technological degree courses to qualify for the higher science-based professions such as engineering and medicine. And at the most advanced and specialized levels of science education, we find a very small proportion of each generation being trained for research in the sciences they have studied.

This description of the vocational function of science education would be incomplete without reference to the training of the *teachers* of science. At every level, the intellectual demands of science are severe. No amount of pedagogical technique can hide an inadequate grasp of the principles to be taught. In terms of 'validity' this means that the science teacher should at least have passed successfully through the level of science *above* the level at which he is employed to teach. Thus, the conventional qualification for teaching to degree level is a higher degree such as the Ph.D., whilst school science to GCE A level should be taught by science graduates, and cannot safely be entrusted to teachers whose professional training has not carried them significantly beyond the A-level standard, even though this might be quite adequate for the teaching of general science in the earlier years of the secondary school.

The general system of science education must therefore make provision for training science teachers for each level. This may call for little more than studying a particular branch of science in the usual way to a more advanced standard; the higher one goes in the system, the less emphasis is laid on instruction in the arts of pedagogy. Indeed, as indicated in Fig. 1, the general rule is that the teachers at each level had passed through the next level without any special vocational differentiation before they took up teaching as a career. Thus, for example, specialist science teachers in secondary schools have usually taken university degrees in conventional science subjects, along with would-be research workers and technologists – and, unlike university lecturers, they get a year of professional training before they take up employment as teachers. The same applies even more forcibly for the academics themselves, whose postgraduate training is entirely directed towards professional research, without any reference to the undergraduate teaching for which they will in due course be employed.

This pattern of vocational training for teachers in the natural sciences derives, quite simply, from the intellectual structure of science itself. As will be shown in the next chapter, there is no escape from the hierarchical ordering of scientific concepts, where the 'validity' of knowledge at each level depends on deeper or more detailed knowledge that can only be acquired by passing through the next educational level. Quite literally, the teacher who has not passed through that further level 'does not know what he is talking about' and is therefore incompetent for his job.

But it has, nevertheless, a very significant effect on the goals of science education. At every level, the teacher's eye is fixed on entry to the level above (where he or she was trained in science) and is not always sufficiently attentive to the needs of the many students with different vocational intentions. The school science curriculum at 'A' level, for example, comes to be thought of mainly as a qualification for admission to college, where degree courses and examinations are dominated in their turn by the goal of research. Intellectual snobbery – that is, greater esteem for abstract theory and 'validity' than for practical technique and 'relevance' – is reinforced by this characteristic feature of science teaching as a profession.

Of course, it is a grave misrepresentation of human reality to describe what happens in schools and colleges as the workings of a 'system'. There are idiosyncratic historical, political and social features of these activities that defy rational analysis in terms of purpose and function. Every country has its own peculiar pedagogic traditions, and goes about its educational business in its own very peculiar way.

But our science-based civilization is much the same all over the world. It provides – or demands – much the same range of skilled jobs in much the same proportions. Much the same scientific and technological knowledge is needed everywhere to carry out these jobs satisfactorily. The fundamental vocational purpose of science education thus imposes upon it a certain degree of uniformity that seems to match the universality of science itself. Fig. 1 is labelled to represent the English pattern of

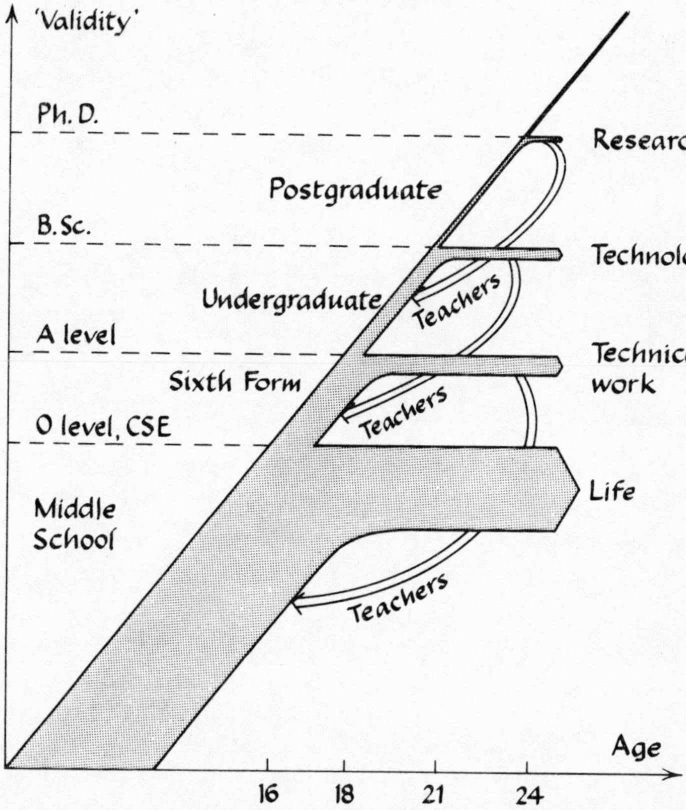

Fig. 1. Science education and vocation

science education: change the names of the formal qualifications, distort the age scales a little, and it might be made to refer to almost any advanced country in the world.

Science education has a well-defined social function, which imposes severe constraints on its pedagogic style and institutional forms. Whatever else may be expected of it in the cultural or spiritual sphere, it must continue to turn out its cohorts of technically trained or scientifically informed people, for employment as electronic engineers and veterinary surgeons, nuclear physicists and computer programmers, foresters and chemistry teachers. This means that it must also respect the intellectual imperatives of 'valid' science, the hard core of reliable knowledge that is the ultimate justification for educating people to exercise these particular skills.

14 STS for schoolchildren

J. Soloman

What is taught in schools reaches all future citizens and not just the handful that go on to the universities and polytechnics. For schools, science, technology and society (STS) cannot be classed as a minority academic discipline. It is an eminently suitable part of the education of all who live in our technological society, including those who may be put out of work by computerized factories, those who are subjected to new medical techniques, and those who, if Britain follows the example of some other European countries, may be asked to vote in referendums on nuclear power, for example.

Schoolteachers don't have to be told that they are expected to 'raise educational standards' and to teach science well. They hear plenty of vague criticism about modern methods couched in such phrases as 'we really *learned* something when I was at school'. We need not quarrel with the sentiment; but this attitude inevitably makes teachers wary of innovation for its own sake.

Major reforms have changed school science during the past 20 years, the most influential being the Nuffield science courses and the move towards 'integrated science'. On top of this schools have faced all the problems of comprehensive schooling. (Should there be streaming, setting or mixed-ability teaching?) Add to this the continuing shortage of teachers of mathematics and physics and you can excuse any head teacher if a certain weariness clouds the eyes when some enthusiast on the staff suggests yet another innovation, STS education. Yet the subject is not as new or as alien to the school curriculum as might appear.

For example, 'general studies' for sixth-formers goes back to the time before C. P. Snow's famous lecture in the 1950s on the 'two cultures'. Then the slot was devoted to 'civics', English (for those uneducated scientists!) and 'civilisation' – the latter too often delivered by a culture-conscious headmaster who liked to air his philosophical musings. Gradually the recipe for general studies changed. Technical hobbies such as photography, electronics or pottery found a place; and even a whistle-stop tour of the history of science – from the Ancient Greeks to John

Dalton – was sometimes added. There was no mention of our society and the tremendous impact of science upon it, no discussion of the risks and benefits arising from a host of new technologies from chemical insecticides to genetic manipulation.

The new generation of sixth-formers deserves a serious discussion of the new problems of society that science has produced. Nuclear power, the energy crisis, world food and resources have all proved potent enough issues to break out of the pages of *New Scientist* into television documentaries and political action groups. Our pupils are not blind to these controversies. STS is the new civics and, as such, it would be a travesty of education to omit it from the curriculum.

These topics have begun to win a place in many general studies courses, but no one can be sure of the number of schools involved. Pupils gain no great advantage from a general-studies certificate at O, O/A or A level in terms of winning a place at university or polytechnic, but the number of these syllabuses is growing. The Schools Council, for example, has produced 'Jackdaw'-style teaching packages that cover many of these STS problem areas; the Association for Science Education has designed an O/A level syllabus entirely devoted to science in society. Only the tip of the STS iceberg is visible in the material published for examination courses.

The trouble with such a piecemeal approach is that it can consider each problem only in a simplistic 'technocratic' mode. It presupposes the existence of a body of experts full of obscure but objective knowledge and assumes that all a judge, journalist or concerned citizen need do is prise out the facts by relentless questioning and then use them to put matters right. This omits any feeling for the varied needs of society. Everyone should know by now that fossil fuels are running out; the important question is how prepared are we to adapt our way of living? What plans should we and our government be making? The increase in world population is no longer news and reliable methods of contraception are taught to every schoolchild. But how do people in the Third World perceive their own population problems? These questions are every bit as human and political as they are scientific.

This is why schools must reflect on the broad philosophy of the STS movement as outlined by John Ziman (*New Scientist*, 16 October, p. 169). It is frankly offensive to our pupils to assume that a few science specialists are being trained as the decision-makers of the future on the playing fields of any educational establishment. A typical comprehensive sixth form spans a wide range of subjects and pupils, from the very bright who are coping easily with three or four A levels to the one-year hopefuls who are trying to scrape together a few O levels. But far from presenting a teaching problem this variety provides a splendid basis for that class discussion that must incorporate the other 'thread in the STS braid' – the social and political dimensions.

This is the point at which science teachers are apt to hesitate for fear of 'indoctrinating the young'. But even if some teachers do push their own political views, our opinionated teenagers should have no trouble in 'sussing out' the tendency. In any case, they are approaching the voting age so that the ability to assess propaganda might well be considered a valuable part of their education! Certainly it is neither possible nor desirable that they be wrapped in a politically sterile cocoon until their 18th birthday.

In the SISCON-in-Schools project (SISCON means 'science in a social context'), we are developing a new strategy for teaching STS to the sixth form. To give the pupils a feel for the way in which science and society interact, we begin with a brief historical study: it might be primitive astrology, the Copernican revolution, nineteenth century public health, or the development of microelectronics. This enables our pupils to see the issues in perspective and also helps them to appreciate how science itself works and grows. In the next part of the work we study the ways these topics affect us today and positively encourage our pupils to contribute their ideas of society's values and needs.

The course contains written material for nine units. These include man in his environment, the way scientific theories become accepted or rejected, conflict between science and ideology, war and the atomic bomb, science in industry, space-flight and science fiction as well as those topics I have already mentioned. Certainly the work needs thoughtful guidance but it is proving to be a most rewarding experience for pupils *and* teachers. This approach is also far better suited to our pupils than is a dry study of philosophical and sociological theory which could culminate in such tendentious questions as 'To what extent is Western philosophy of science appropriate for working in developing countries?' (This question, which actually appeared in a University of London A level general studies paper, would be taxing, I would guess, even for the editor of *New Scientist*!)

So much for special programmes in the sixth form: what is being done in the lower school? Here we find the new 'integrated science' courses which, without any explicit STS intention, have already produced a welcome change in the thrust of science teaching. In the first two or three years of the secondary school, the pupils learn science that is now much nearer to the home, where society forms its earliest image for us all. Heat energy and house insulation, acids and indigestion, the combustion of fossil fuels, food chains and nutrition – with such introductory topics children need never again regard science as that remote and different pursuit that an opening joust with Archimedes's principle or molecular weights used to imply. There are other advantages in the integrated approach. At tertiary level STS materials often induce heated debates on inter-disciplinarity; we already have it at the lower levels of school science. We can teach the biology *and* chemistry of air pollution, the physics *and* biology of muscle systems. This may not be the stuff of heated social controversy but it certainly makes our science lessons more relevant.

The most sadly barren area of school sciences is that of the 14-to 16-year olds who are firmly caught up in the grip of public examinations. The pupils and their parents are anxious to gain the proper qualifications for employment especially in the face of shrinking opportunities. The schools on their part may be driven almost to despair by the effort needed to provide adequate physics teaching. Integrated science is said to be unpopular with prospective employers and few of the more plentiful biology teachers are happy to teach the physics component of such a course. There is just one brave venture into this field which has also tried to present the social face of science; this is the SCISP (Schools Council Integrated Science Project). Here the chemistry of fertilisers is related to their use in countries with differing GNPs, there is discussion of the criteria doctors use when assigning patients to kidney machines, and even consideration of the psychology of crowd violence. This is a praiseworthy, if ambitious, [set] of STS material added to the three traditional sciences and it is generally judged to be a difficult course for pupils *and* teachers.

Though teaching about science and society in schools may still be in its infancy it is beginning to kick. We shall know it has come of age when *all* the public examination papers in science include questions related to the *living use* of science alongside those which test our pupils' ability to memorise facts and solve numerical problems.

IV SCIENCE IN THE CURRICULUM

Science has been considered to be a fundamental part of school curricula and this is a view which has been held to a greater or lesser extent for nearly a century and a half. However, the reasons *why* science is considered important, and so the aims of science teaching and the nature of the science that is taught, have changed considerably within the same time span. In this section various authors investigate the ways in which science curricula have evolved, and the principal influences on this evolution.

In his review of science teaching from the 1840s to the 1870s, Uzzell takes the view that the content of school science has been influenced by various reports, projects and policy statements which, in turn, may have been influenced by the demands of an industrial society or the reorganization of schools. Hodson and Prophet see the content of science in schools as socially constructed in that it reflects the particular choices of different interest groups at different historical times. For example, because the teaching of the 'science of common things' to elementary school children in the 1850s not only aided their mental training, but developed an understanding of their natural and technological environment denied their public school counterparts, it posed a threat to the ambient social hierarchy and so was abandoned in favour of 'pure abstract science'. This new approach rendered science inaccessible to all but those destined for future university education.

Young further explores the effects of the move towards teaching pure, abstract science in schools. The idea that science might relate to our everyday lives downgrades it academically. Resisting this shift has led to a separation between science and its applications to society and, in consequence, the alienation of many children who see school science as over-specialized and divorced from their worlds.

How can school science be re-humanized while maintaining the academic respectability required by the higher education establishments? One way suggested by Sherratt is that this can be achieved by teaching more of the history of science and technology. Biographical detail alone is meaningless, but by encouraging children to climb inside the skins of our ancestral scientists, the spirit of the original discoveries can be reincarnated. It would be interesting to debate the validity of the claim that each of us passing from childhood to maturity recapitulates the history of mankind in scientific discovery: wonder at the phenomenon; consideration of its use to society and, finally, attempts to fit the phenomenon into our picture of the world as a whole.

An alternative idea about the dominant influence on the science curriculum is put forward by Millar, who suggests that science teaching may be predicated on the notion of the 'two mentalities'; a higher intellectual mentality capable of abstract thought and active response, and a lower simplistic mentality that thinks only in concrete terms and responds passively. This notion provides food for thought given the extensive use of mixed ability teaching in Britain's comprehensive schools today.

Accepting all these reasons for teaching science provides a substantial case for maintaining its place in the curriculum. It provides good mental training, it creates an understanding of the natural world and an awareness of the technological world, it helps to supply the scientists who will underpin the country's economy, it is necessary to maintain the scientific academic establishment. Is there, though, a common core of science that should be taught to all children? Two radically opposing views are put forward by Waring and Schofield, and West.

Waring and Schofield are staunch supporters of a core approach on the grounds of both social justice (equal opportunities for all) and the need to safeguard essentials (to ensure the proper use of public monies, to supply industry with scientists and to fit children for science in society). However, West feels that it is highly unlikely that any core science based on the content of current examination board syllabuses which are geared to meet the needs of higher education could prepare children adequately for adult life — either their interaction with science in their everyday lives, or as workers in industry, where scientific awareness may prove counter-productive to efficiency.

15 The changing aims of science teaching

● P. Uzzell

Uzzell describes the influence that major reports, projects and policy statements concerning school science have had on pedagogy. He suggests, in a survey covering more than a century, that dominant theories such as 'science as mental training' or 'science as providing an understanding of the natural world' have found favour at different times. In some instances, the fashion seems best understood by referring to the demands of an industrial society for technological improvement. At other times, it may be necessary to refer in the first place to changes in school organization.

Why is science taught in the way it is? Do the present aims of science teachers owe anything to past ideals or do they just reflect the whims of fashion? A brief survey of the aims of science teaching for the 11–16 age group over about a century gives some fascinating insights, as well as providing a basis for discussion of these questions.

Science was taught in some elementary schools before the middle of the last century. Government grants for purchasing equipment began in the 1840s. The science taught in the 1840s and 1850s was not only concerned with understanding scientific principles of everyday things in the home and at work, but also with the development of logical thinking and the improved use of language. The work of Richard Dawes and Henry Moseley in this connexion was outstanding.[1] However, the climate of opinion towards science teaching in elementary schools became less favourable and the Education Department's Revised Code of 1862 virtually excluded all but grant-earning subjects – reading, writing and arithmetic – from the curriculum.

An influential essay by the Revd J. M. Wilson, science master at Rugby, appeared in 1867.[2] In the essay, Wilson, assuming that the characteristic of an educated man is his power of judging evidence and proof, argued that these were the very attributes imparted by science teaching. Wilson advocated an investigatory approach (which he used himself), beginning with the concrete experimental fact and leading to the abstract, to laws and hypotheses, from the known to the unknown. Despite tireless efforts on the part of Wilson and others, it was many years before these ideas influenced the thinking of the Government, Examination Boards, or many Headmasters.

Not much science was taught in the nineteenth-century public schools, and, with notable exceptions like Rugby, it consisted of verifying laws and illustrating properties using lecture demonstrations. Nevertheless, the Schools Inquiry Commission (1868), while deploring the lack of science teaching in public schools, perceptively stated that

> true teaching of science consists not merely of imparting facts of science, but in habituating the pupil to observe for himself, to reason for himself on what he observes, and to check the conclusion at which he arrives by further observation or experiment. (Report, Vol. II, p. 6.)

Expansion of the elementary school curriculum beyond the 3 Rs, enforced since the 1862 Code, was easier in the 1870s when the Education Department gave grants, dependent on examination results, for passes in 'specific' and 'class' subjects. Specific subjects were introduced in 1871, whereby individual students in Standards IV to VI (ages 10 to 12) could be entered for not more than two subjects chosen from a given list, one of which was natural science. Even in the 1890s only about 2 per cent of children in elementary schools studied specific subjects, and, of these, only about 2 per cent studied chemistry and 10 per cent mechanics. Preference, it seems, was given to subjects requiring little specialized equipment or accommodation.

The syllabuses for the specific science subjects, particularly chemistry, were largely academic without much emphasis on everyday applications. The nature of the teaching expected is illustrated by this quotation from the 1882 Code

> It is intended that the instruction of scholars in science subjects . . . shall be given mainly by experiment and illustration. If these subjects are taught to children by definition and verbal description, instead of making them exercise their powers of observation, they will be worthless as means of education. It cannot, therefore, be too strongly impressed on teachers that nothing like rote learning will suffice (p. 30).

Class subjects were introduced in elementary schools in 1875 for Standards II to VI, making it possible for whole classes to be examined in not more than two listed subjects, grants depending on results. It was not until 1882 that elementary science became a class subject. Lack of equipment and suitably qualified teachers curtailed the growth of class and specific science subjects. The 1882 Code was significant in that it not only introduced elementary science but also indicated its scope. The Code defined elementary science as follows:

> A progressive course of simple lessons . . . adapted to cultivate habits of exact observation, statement and reasoning

and required that

> The class subjects should be taught by means of reading books and oral lessons, illustrated, as far as possible, by maps, diagrams, specimens and simple experiments (p. 26).

Thus much of the teaching, especially in Standards I to III, would be by means of descriptive, demonstration lessons, say, on a piece of coal, most likely in an ordinary classroom, with little participation by the children except for learning or writing factual material.

The striking thing about the elementary science syllabus for Standards I to III – common objects such as familiar animals, plants, and substances employed in ordinary life – is that it completely lacked purpose and system. Given teachers without much scientific training and inadequate equipment, repetition and superficiality were likely. A more advanced knowledge was required from Standards IV and V of further limited topics in biology, chemistry and mechanics, while Standards VI and VII dealt with these same topics in greater detail. Thus the work in Standards I to III would seem to provide a very poor basis for later studies in elementary science, and even worse for specific subjects. Elementary science was made a compulsory subject in 1896. Thus, for the first time, some science instruction was obligatory for all elementary school pupils.

More active participation by pupils was encouraged in the 1890s. The committee of the British Association for the Advancement of Science, which scrutinized elementary science teaching, emphasized in the 1891 Report (p. 385) that for pupils simply to 'exercise their powers of observation' was restricting, and that they should perform experiments themselves. 'Merely to attend lessons, listening to and taking notes of what is said,' it argued, was not enough.

A class subject of revolutionary design appeared in the 1894 Code. This was 'Experimental Arithmetic, Physics and Chemistry', which bore a resemblance to H. E. Armstrong's course (discussed below), and in which the teaching was to be experimental, with work done by pupils. Armstrong's influence can also be seen in the specific subject 'Elementary Physics and Chemistry' introduced in the 1898 Code. There is a reasonable blend of the two subjects in it, with a practical approach implied. This is the first Code science syllabus in which the word discovery appears – 'discovery of the active constituents of air' (p. 58).

By 1880, ten years after the Elementary Education Act was passed, some schools were faced with the problem of children who, having reached the statutory leaving age (12) and passed through all the Standards, were still attending school. The problem was overcome by the schools organizing science classes for their upper standards which led to

Science and Art Department examinations. Alternatively, higher grade schools were established, which took children from Standard V and upwards from nearby elementary schools. These courses, which bore no relationship to the Elementary Code, earned Science and Art Department grants for examination passes. Such arrangements, which allowed work of secondary character to be done in elementary schools, were winked at by the Education Department so long as some 'elementary' education as set out in the Code was done as well.

Most schools taking Science and Art Department examinations chose to take a few, not necessarily related, subjects, that is, to have science classes rather than become 'Organized Science Schools', where a three-year course of systematic instruction in related science subjects was provided. The Science and Art Department besides offering payment by results, also gave grants for equipment and laboratory furnishings. Indeed, it was financially advantageous for schools to take their examinations in preference to those offered in the Code.

The Science and Art Department's classes and examinations, which began in the 1850s and continued until the Department ceased to function in 1899, were originally intended for working people. Thus the syllabuses were unsuitable for children, as they were never intended for school use. It was 1896 before the Department introduced day examinations as well as those normally taken at night. In general, the Department's syllabuses were too academic for school use, while its examinations, being tests of largely factual material, encouraged rote learning and cramming. In some cases school curricula became over-biased to science because of their dependence on Science and Art Department grants. Nevertheless, the Department did encourage science teaching, and set standards for equipment and laboratories.

The Royal Commission on Secondary Education (1895) made a shrewd appraisal of contemporary science teaching

> the sciences are not mere catalogues of materials that can be used in trade, or abstract principles regulative of their economical use; they are systems or symbols of great ideas that may be used to exercise reason and fill the imagination. (Report, Vol. I, p. 141.)

As the nineteenth century progressed, the argument changed from 'Why teach science?' to 'How to teach science'. H. E. Armstrong, the eminent chemist, was instrumental in bringing about the formation of the British Association committee which inquired into the methods of teaching chemistry. The committee reported in 1888. From the response to a questionnaire which the committee sent to schools and training colleges, it was clear that most of the respondents considered the purpose of chemistry teaching was to give mental training and improve intellectual discipline. It was also clear that teachers wanted advice and assistance on how to teach. To supply this need, Armstrong produced a scheme of instruction.

This 'British Association Course' which Armstrong designed was in six stages; not only did it suggest content, but it also supplied a method and implied a reason for each stage. The course began with object lessons on the child's surroundings, drawing on a range of sciences, geography, geology, natural history, so that the 'variety of things' could be learnt and facility in description be developed. Stage II involved exercises in measuring length, area, mass, volume, density, for example, assuming proficiency in the 'four rules' of arithmetic and decimals. Having learnt to measure and weigh, the child was expected to be able to express differences in properties quantitatively. The third stage was concerned with the effect (both qualitative and quantitative) of heat on various elements and compounds. As a result of such experiments, it was thought, habits of correct observation and recording would be acquired, and the insight that chemical change was not simply destruction gained. Next came the problem stage, the most original and characteristic stage, with problems like 'What happens when iron rusts?'. There are thirteen of these and they were intended to show that to solve problems 'clues' must be sought. While the majority of pupils would not pass beyond this stage, there were two more. Quantitative determination of the composition of the compounds such as water and chalk was the basis of Stage V. Stage VI extended ideas on chemical theory. The course was novel in that it illustrated scientific method by emphasizing observation, reasoning from an hypothesis, and putting the pupils in the place of discoverers when they performed experiments chosen for the purpose. Thus, the course exemplified the heuristic approach.[3]

Despite its good intentions this course gained ground slowly. It was costly in time, it did not fit the existing examination syllabuses and it was too novel for many teachers to accept its challenge. However, the course (in a modified form) was used in some London Board Schools and elsewhere, largely by teachers who had been students of Armstrong. As has been described above, Armstrong's work led to changes in the Code, in examination syllabuses and in the greater emphasis placed on individual practical work. Armstrong's course was an attempt to interest children in a wide range of sciences and in the methods of scientific enquiry. There was, however, little consideration of modern scientific developments and their everyday applications. The value of a method had been emphasized to the detriment of interest.

The Board of Education's publications for science teachers in the early years of the twentieth century described the advantages which it was considered that younger children gained from studying science as learning to observe and learning by observing. With older children teachers were expected to place more emphasis on investigations by the children and to encourage careful recording and the drawing of correct inferences from their findings. Heuristic influences are seen here. By 1915, however, a Board of Education circular laid less emphasis on children's individual experiments. While the need for regular practical work was stressed, the use of demonstration experiments was also considered useful and encouraged. Already there seems to be a reaction against the excessive practical work allegedly engendered by heurism.

The Hadow Report (1926) *Education and the Adolescent*, argued that sound teaching should be based on the pupil's interest, suggesting co-operation between science and handwork departments to achieve this. The report considered science to be a unity, not a collection of separate subjects.

In the 1920s and 1930s the *Handbook of Suggestions* published by the Board of Education offered general guidance to teachers. Two aims for science teaching were given in the 1927 edition as awakening interest in plant and animal life and natural scenery, and the investigation of common phenomena and their underlying scientific principles. By following these aims, teachers, it was said, would be able to help children to understand the rules of health, the service of science to the community, and appreciate the beauties of nature. Although practical work in small groups was encouraged, the value of the demonstration experiment was stressed, since, 'in recent years its value has been too often forgotten' (p. 35).

Science in Senior Schools (Board of Education Pamphlet No. 89, 1932), gave the results of a survey by HMIs of 384 schools in England and Wales. It is plain from this document that the majority of boys' schools taught too much physics and chemistry and that girls' schools taught too much biology. *Science in Senior Schools* also contains a list of 'values' which the writers suggested should be gained from science courses. For instance, knowledge of scientific facts and principles should lead pupils to a more rational way of life, better health and happiness and to adopt useful hobbies. Science teaching, it was said, would develop an intellectual interest in the natural universe, as well as give some training in scientific method. The 'chief danger' in science work, the authors stated, was 'too much practical work of the wrong kind'. It was of the wrong kind if it was 'too remote from the natural interests and everyday experience of the children' (p. 14). Thus, courses which were too academic or too practical were not encouraged.

A new edition of the *Handbook of Suggestions* appeared in 1937. This handbook stressed that work for older pupils should be related to their 'immediate needs and interests', leading to self-education through books and a lasting desire to continue education after leaving school. Science teaching for senior children should help them to understand the methods of science, gain the 'scientific habit of mind', see interrelationships among facts, and draw appropriate conclusions from evidence. These aims, which are more sophisticated than those in *Science in Senior Schools*, seem to some extent to lose sight of the abilities of many of the children concerned and the often inadequate facilities in these schools.

Public schools and grammar schools in the early twentieth century remained comparatively insulated from changing ideas on science education. There was some discovery teaching in the lower forms, but for the most part the curricula of both types of school were dominated by the requirements of the School Certificate examinations and later the General Certificate. No aims or objectives were suggested by Examination Boards for their examinations until the 1960s. Until this time, most of their science syllabuses were fairly academic, requiring little by way of applications. Question papers, in general, contained questions requiring factual or descriptive answers calling for little more than recall or comprehension.

In 1917 a British Association Committee chaired by Professor Gregory reported on science teaching in secondary schools. Its survey of science teaching showed that in both public schools and boys' grammar schools physics and chemistry dominated the science taught, though biology was becoming more popular. The opposite was the case in comparable girls' schools where mainly botany was taught. It is probably accurate to suppose that until the early 1940s, when general science gained in popularity, most of the pre-certificate science in these schools was taught as separate subjects.

The publication in 1916 of *Science for All*[4] by a group of public school science masters is important partly because of its content and partly because of its influence on later thinking. *Science for All* advocated a broad approach to science teaching, including work on plants, animals (not common at this time), as well as aspects of physics and chemistry. Contemporary applications were also a notable inclusion. The course was intended to capture the pupils' interest and to make science alive and personal for them. In effect, *Science for All* was advocating compulsory science, and a broad generalized science at that. Although it had little immediate impact on schools, its influence on later thinking was considerable.

The Gregory report of 1917, referred to above, encouraged the teaching of a wide selection of sciences in schools and also discouraged excessive practical work. The committee formulated the aims of science teaching at length, including among their aims training in observation and description, use of scientific method, gaining knowledge of the environment and man's relation to it, and acquaintance with current scientific words and ideas.

Yet another of the influences which encouraged general science was *Natural Science in Education*, published in 1918. This was the report of a committee set up by the Prime Minister, under the chairmanship of Sir J. J. Thomson, to advise, among other things, on what measures were needed to promote the study of natural science. (Other similar reports were commissioned on English, Modern Languages, and Classics.) The Thomson report favoured a science course for all boys and girls up to the age of 16. This course was to include, besides physics and chemistry, a study of plant and animal life, together with matters of everyday experience. The report defined the aims of science courses as giving students training in reasoning, interpreting evidence and acquainting them with scientific principles and their applications. While applauding practical work as a means of obtaining explanations of problems and giving experience of scientific method, the report was very scathing about heurism, and also considered that concentrating on those aspects of subjects which best lend themselves to practical work was unsatisfactory.

In the wake of these reports the Science Masters' Association published the pamphlet *General Science* in 1924 containing a syllabus in three sections, biology, chemistry and physics, fulfilling many of the recommendations of earlier reports. The Hadow Report (1926) on the education of the adolescent also contained a syllabus embracing biology, chemistry and physics as well as astronomy and meteorology. In 1936 the Science Masters' Association published *The Teaching of General Science Part I*. In this report general science was defined as a course of 'scientific study and investigation' based on the 'common experience of children', while not excluding 'any of the fundamental special sciences'. General science, it was said

> seeks to elucidate general principles . . . without emphasizing the traditional divisions into specialized subjects until such time as this is warranted by the increasing complexity of the field of investigation, by the developing unity of the separate parts of that field, and by the intellectual progress of the pupils (p. 30).

Thus, not only is an analytical definition given, but attention is drawn to the pupils' intellectual development. The aims of teaching general science were given as utilitarian, mind-sharpening, and cultural.

Part II of *The Teaching of General Science*, which appeared in 1938, contains a remarkable chapter on examinations. It is remarkable because it contains a list of what pupil abilities should be tested by examinations based on the proposed general science syllabus (set out in Part I and Part II). These abilities are given under four headings and can be summarized as follows: the first, acquisition of scientific information and knowledge, includes knowledge of facts and technical terms, as well as the ability to reproduce laws and principles and to explain their meaning. The next concerns development of scientific modes of thought, that is, ability to explain principles from facts and support principles with facts, to distinguish between fact and hypothesis, and to plan experiments and draw conclusions. Application of scientific knowledge to socially desirable ends is the third set. Finally, there is a section on practical powers and skills, including such things as manual skill and dexterity, together with the ability to do neat, accurate work and to apply science to solve practical problems. (Illustrative questions were also given to show how some of these abilities and skills could be tested.) Although the writers of this chapter admit their debt to other authors, this list of abilities and skills is a landmark in thinking in this sphere in Britain, for not only are quite high level intellectual abilities specified, but practical skills as well. Implicit in all this is the idea that not only should examinations test such abilities, but teaching should encourage them. However, it was not until well after World War II, when emphasis on objectives, particularly in examinations involving objective questions, stimulated by Nuffield courses and some Examination Boards, that these ideas began significantly to influence school science teaching.

The Spens Report (1938) on secondary education contains a confused mixture of earlier ideas. It describes the aims of science teaching as giving pupils knowledge of natural laws operating in the universe and their applications, 'an appeal to wonder, interest, as well as utility', understanding of the influence of science, and an insight into 'scientific methods of thought and investigation'. The report rejected specialization in science before the age of sixteen, implicitly accepting general science. Echoing earlier reports, the Spens Committee repeat the claim that much laboratory work is a waste of time. The start of World War II in 1939 soon after these reports delayed any possible action.

The Norwood Report (1944) was concerned with secondary school curricula and examinations. Like the Spens Report it favoured general science below the sixth form, defining it in much the same terms as Spens, although admitting some pupils could study separate subject science after the age of thirteen.

An important book, *The Teaching of Science in Secondary Schools*, was published in 1947 by a joint committee of the Incorporated Association of Assistant Masters and the Science Masters' Association. (The outbreak of war prevented publication in 1939.) When discussing aims, the compilers, besides expecting a broad factual knowledge, stressed the value of accurate observation, good practical technique and critical assessment of experimental results. Adequate communication of ideas was considered important as was the appreciation of the connexion between science and everyday life, culture and human development. Although general science is admitted to be 'still in the experimental stage', its teaching is recommended, though allowing single subjects instead. The cramping influence of public examinations requiring memorizing of facts is lamented.

The years after the war were difficult because of shortage of teachers, equipment and accommodation. However, during the 1950s developments occurred some of them influenced by work in the USA which produced the Physical Science Study Committee materials, the Biological Sciences Curriculum Study, CHEM Study and other schemes.

The Science Masters' Association report *The Teaching of General Science* (1950) was a revised version of earlier reports (1936 and 1938). While embracing similar aims, it places more stress on practical work as enquiry.

Education through science was the keynote of *Secondary Modern Science Teaching* (Science Masters' Association, 1953). This report attached importance to arousing and maintaining pupils' interest. Besides gaining factual knowledge, it was thought that pupils should gain an appreciation of the 'scientific method of study'. Active experimenting was encouraged and there was a hint of the use of discovery methods.

A second revised edition of *The Teaching of Science in Secondary Schools* was produced in 1958. The aims do not differ greatly from those in the 1947 version, but the emphasis placed on adequate communication of results and unbiased judgement, whether in grammar or modern schools, is new. While the earlier version reviews research evidence regarding the relative merits of individual work or demonstrations, finding it inconclusive, the 1958 edition discusses the heuristic method, noting that the principle involved is widely used.

In a section dealing with the 11–15 age range, the Ministry of Education Pamphlet No. 38, *Science in Secondary Schools* (1960), suggests study of geology and astronomy as well as biology, chemistry and physics. The selection of topics for courses, it is said, should depend on their interest and importance to pupils. The two major aims of science courses are given as acquisition of knowledge and development of objective thinking. In addition, the 'spirit of investigation', gained through first hand experimenting, is to be cultivated, as is an understanding of scientific method. Improvement of self-expression and careful reasoning is also recommended.

Policy statements of major importance appeared in 1957 and 1961 entitled *Science and Education*. (The former was compiled by a committee of the Science Masters' Association, the latter by a joint committee of the SMA and the Association of Women Science Teachers.) The 1957 statement was concerned mainly with grammar school children. By the O-level stage, the report considered that children should have a basis of scientific facts and principles 'rooted firmly in practical experience'. Practical work was seen as a means of solving problems and instilling good technique. An understanding of the methods of science was also expected. The 1961 statement is very similar, but makes specific reference to the relationship between science and technology and its implications for schools not found in the earlier version. Likewise, the desirability of children in the 13–16 age group having a 'reasonable amount of factual knowledge', (p. 9) and more quantitative and systematic work appears only in the 1961 version. In justifying the place of science in the curriculum the humanity of science is stressed in both statements.

Biology for Grammar Schools, with booklets of similar titles for chemistry and physics, were published by the SMA and AWST in 1961. These booklets which were based on the principles set out in *Science and Education*, offered up-dated syllabuses with suggestions on how to teach them. They had considerable influence on the early Nuffield science projects.

One of the highlights of the 1960s was the devising of the Nuffield biology, chemistry and physics O-level projects, having aims reflecting those in *Science and Education*. The aims of these three projects differ in detail, but two major ideas stand out. First, underlying principles are stressed; understanding principles is considered to be more important than just learning facts. Related to this is the ability to distinguish between facts, generalizations and hypotheses. Secondly, the discovery approach to practical work is prominent, with the intention that, where possible, principles should be established through practical work. In addition to acquiring manipulative skills and accuracy in observation, opportunities to plan experiments are recommended so that pupils may appreciate the limitations of experiments and the value of the data they collect. In brief, to 'encourage enquiry' and 'develop curiosity'. In all three schemes the content is up-dated and includes consideration of the relation between science and the community. Special examination papers from these Nuffield courses, based on their specified objectives, were also introduced.

Science for General Education (the Scottish Education Department's Curriculum Paper No. 7, 1969) has had considerable influence in Scotland and elsewhere. Detailed objectives are given for the first two years of secondary education (12–14 age group in Scotland) and also pupils who will not stay in school after the statutory leaving age. These objectives are derived from general aims including problem-solving, scientific thinking and the cultural value of science. Thus as well as factual knowledge, comprehension, application and synthesis are expected. The content which includes biology, chemistry and physics (integrated where appropriate), is selected to stimulate pupils' interest and enjoyment. Good communication of ideas is encouraged and discovery methods are used in practical work.

The increase in the number of comprehensive schools in England and Wales, and classes having wide ability range led to the development of a combined science course. The Nuffield *Combined Science* materials for the 11–13 age group were published in 1970. The course materials were selected from appropriate parts of the three O-level courses, giving an introductory science course involving pupils in active enquiry. Thus, *Combined Science* shared a similar approach and similar aims as the O-level schemes, but was intended for able and less-able pupils, who, it was hoped, will learn how the various sciences interrelate and gain a 'unity of outlook and consistency of method which belong to the whole of Science' (*Teachers' Guide I*, p. xi).

Another set of combined science materials was published in 1970. This was Nuffield *Secondary Science*, designed for 13–16-year-olds not taking GCE O-level. It differs from *Combined Science* in using a thematic approach. Teachers are intended to plan their courses by selecting material from the eight themes to give pupils a broad background of science, related to their interests, needs and future employment. Pupils are encouraged to plan their own experiments (some involving care of animals and plants), and to be accurate when making observations. They are also expected to gain understanding of generalizations and hypotheses as well as improving literacy and numeracy. The choice of content for the eight themes was governed by the criterion of 'significance', that is the underlying interest and relevance to pupils' experience, in and outside of school, as well as illustrating basic scientific principles. Besides dealing with applications of science, the course touches on moral and social problems.

Of all the recent science projects perhaps the most unusual in content and approach is the *Schools Council Integrated Science Project* (1973). While not using a thematic approach, it draws together biology, chemistry and physics as well as earth sciences and the social sciences. There is considerable emphasis on 'relevance', which in this context means not only the applications of science to technology but also the importance of science in society. SCISP is for the 13–16 age group of O-level ability. 'Patterns', that is generalizations, figure prominently in SCISP materials. Apart from acquiring factual knowledge and understanding patterns, pupils are expected to view evidence critically, use reasoned judgements in problem solving, design experiments, and communicate their findings. Pupils are also expected to develop attitudes such as working alone or in groups, appreciating the scope and shortcomings of science, and caring about the implications to mankind of the applications of science.

The change in emphasis in these projects towards integrated science with increasing reference to social and technological problems arises in part from attempts to combat the worsening popular image of science. A similar change of emphasis can be seen in the ASE publications of this period.

School Science and General Education, the ASE policy statement issued in 1965, does not differ greatly from the 1961 policy statement. However, the 1965 version emphasizes that it is addressed to all schools, not just grammar schools. This was followed in 1967 by *Science in the Introductory*

Phase (the 11–13 age group). Three integrated science courses are offered, based on the ideas in *School Science and General Education* (1965). These three courses, it was hoped, would provide material for the growing number of schools teaching integrated science at this level. The courses were designed to develop a scientific attitude using an investigatory approach, at the same time encouraging interest and enthusiasm.

A revised version of *Secondary Modern Science Teaching* appeared in 1967 entitled *Teaching Science at the Secondary Stage*. This book was prepared by an ASE committee for teachers of 'average' pupils. It suggests that science courses should be based on pupils' day-to-day experience. It also recommends that modern applications should be used as starting points for teaching to encourage interest. There is an emphasis on discovery practical work, whether demonstration or individual. Skill in use of apparatus and equipment is encouraged, as is a critical approach to evidence.

The third revised edition of *The Teaching of Science in Secondary Schools*, devised by a committee of the ASE, the Assistant Masters' Association and the Association of Assistant Mistresses, was published in 1970. This book is now addressed to teachers in all types of school. After dealing with several misconceptions of what science is, the importance of science as a 'major human activity' is discussed. The aims of science teaching are discussed in general terms, reference being made to acquiring factual knowledge as a means of acquiring appropriate intellectual abilities and skills, including applying knowledge to solving unfamiliar problems. Manipulative skills are also considered important. The aims of the Nuffield O-level chemistry course are quoted as being generally appropriate for science teaching.

Finally, the recent ASE policy statements must be considered. *Science and General Education* (1971) takes into account the increased complexity of school organization and the growing use of mixed-ability classes. Science teaching, the statement argues, should illustrate the effect of science on modern life and social organization. It should also show that science demands 'creative insight and imagination' to counter current misconceptions of science. Teachers choosing course materials should remember the children's needs, the relevance and social implications of topics. In a section on the future, the 'laboured insistence' of recent curriculum developments on discovering concepts and principles is noted, with the hope that besides discovering principles, opportunities will be taken of 'creatively following up the implications of principles' in applied science and technology (p. 8).

Science and General Education was followed by *Science for the Under-Thirteens* (1971). This report suggests objectives which would help pupils to 'gain experience and acquire techniques appropriate to their personal abilities', which would fit them for future courses at the 13–16 stage.

Science for the 13–16 Age Group (another ASE report published in 1973) describes the scope of science for this age group in three sections. This is an attempt 'to achieve a balance between three aspects of science education'. The first section on basic principles is called 'Science for the Inquiring Mind'. Then comes 'Science in Action', suggesting pupils should have 'a basic knowledge of themselves, their physical and biological environments and the interrelationships between them'. Thirdly, 'Science for Citizenship' concerns knowledge needed for making personal and collective decisions. The purpose of courses based on these principles is specified by means of a list of aims for teachers. Included in this list are relating science to life, developing manipulative skills and caring for things, teaching for understanding rather than recall, the methods of science, encouraging communication, imagination, and inventiveness, as well as providing training for decision-making. Science is to be seen, the report states, as a human activity 'offering both promise and threat' (p. 8).

Having surveyed the changes in the aims of science teaching, and briefly sketched in some of the influences responsible for change, a number of important points stand out. The last twenty years have seen the most rapid and radical changes in science curricula and the approach to science teaching. Views on the nature and purpose of practical work have swung back and forth over the years, though ideas on what the teaching of science involves have grown, ranging from a factual knowledge of single subjects to an understanding of aspects of several sciences, together with related moral and social issues. The intellectual demands of what is taught have increased from rote learning in the nineteenth century to the sophisticated abilities and attitudes expected in recent years. Factors influencing change are difficult to quantify, often resulting from the aspirations or constraints of the times. However, with a background of these various changes, it is possible to consider current and future developments in science education in a truer perspective.

NOTES AND REFERENCES

1. See, for example, Layton, D., *Science for the People* (George Allen and Unwin, 1973).
2. Wilson's essay appears in Farrar, F. W., *ed.*, *Essays on Liberal Education* (Macmillan, 1867).
3. There is much background material in Brock, W. H., *ed.*, *H. E. Armstrong and the Teaching of Science* (Cambridge University Press, 1973) and Armstrong, H. E., *The Teaching of Scientific Method* (Macmillan, 1903).
4. Reprinted in *School Science Review* 1926, 6, **2**, 203.

16 Why the science curriculum changes – evolution or social control?

● D. Hodson and R. B. Prophet

Hodson and Prophet seek to provide an explanation of the shifts in the aims and practice of school science detailed by Uzzell (Chapter 15). They suggest that social Darwinist explanations, emphasizing the failure of certain modes of teaching, are inadequate: it is more pertinent to examine the interests of those who control the curriculum in order to explain the abandonment of certain practices. Although they reject the idea that all knowledge is socially constructed, they use the theoretical framework of the 'new sociologists' to show that school science is so constructed in that it is the product of particular sets of choices made by particular groups of people at particular times.

Peter Uzzell[1] has traced the changing aims of science education from the early days of school science in the nineteenth century through to the Nuffield projects of the 1960s and the more recent Schools Council project in integrated science (SCISP). What is absent from this admirable article and from other works dealing with the history and development of the science curriculum (such as Jenkins[2], Layton[3] and Turner[4]) is any convincing account of *why* the curriculum changed in the particular way that it did. In a later article exploring the changing status of science in the curriculum as reflected in official reports, Uzzell concludes:

> . . . What is taught, the manner of teaching and the resources for teaching are of crucial importance, as are the needs of children and our country. *Who will decide and on what grounds?*[5] (our italics)

This chapter speculates on these questions by taking a historical perspective, in the belief that some light may be shed on the question 'Who *will* decide curriculum issues?' by attempting to ascertain who decided them in the past – for example, in the period so carefully documented by Uzzell and others.

Underpinning the curricular arguments concerning the relative importance of 'content' or 'method', the role of practical work, the issue of separate versus combined (or integrated) science, which concerned the attention of teachers throughout this period, is the perception of 'science', and of 'school science' in particular, held by curriculum writers, teachers of science and scientists. Just as the science curriculum has changed, so too has the prevailing view of what is appropriate 'school science'. Layton[3] provides a most interesting and useful account of the process leading to the establishment of one particular conception of school science, that of *pure laboratory science*. It is this view which has provided the basic framework of school science in modern times. Layton argues that this particular view of science emerged in preference to alternative approaches because the alternatives had become 'casualties in a process of natural selection as the educational environment had become progressively more sharply defined'.[6] In our opinion, social Darwinist explanations of this kind are inadequate and must be replaced by a more radical historiographic account. They are inadequate because they treat the social processes of decision making as though they are *natural* processes, and because they ignore the motives and interests of the decision makers.

In the mid-nineteenth century at least two alternative conceptions of school science were available to teachers: 'the Science of Common Things' and 'pure laboratory science'. That the latter became established as the *correct* view is not disputed in this article. However, Layton's explanation of *why* the latter view became established ('survival of the fittest') *is* challenged, and two important questions concerning the science curriculum are raised:

1 How does the selection of what is to count as worthwhile knowledge take place?
2 How is this *selected* knowledge presented to the learner?

Answers to these questions may lie in the dispute surrounding the nature of knowledge. Basically, there are two opposing views concerning the nature of knowledge. One view assumes a direct correspondence between reality and knowledge, and asserts that knowledge is *discovered*, the other claims that knowledge is *socially constructed* and may be understood only by reference to the social, cultural and historical context in which it arose.

THE FORMS OF KNOWLEDGE

There have been many attempts of late to derive a theory of knowledge to aid curriculum design.[7,8] Perhaps the best known is that advanced by Paul Hirst,[9] who claims that all human knowledge may be differentiated into a number of 'logically distinct' *Forms* on the basis of four criteria.

1 The characteristic basic concepts.
2 The characteristic structures by which these concepts are related.
3 The characteristic ways by which knowledge statements are tested.
4 The characteristic techniques and skills for exploring experience.

Using these criteria, Hirst identifies about *seven* Forms of Knowledge:

Mathematics and formal logic
The physical sciences
The human sciences, including history
Moral understanding
The religious form of knowledge
Philosophy
Fine arts

For Hirst, the central aim of education is the development of mind, so that a curriculum organized on the basis of the Forms of Knowledge represents the most appropriate way of achieving that goal – because it introduces children to the *various ways of knowing*.

A number of distinguished educationists have argued that an effective teaching strategy requires that learning experiences should be designed in such a way that they reflect and illustrate the conceptual and methodological structure of the disciplines. Jerome Bruner may be taken as representative of this tradition of curriculum design.

> The curriculum of a subject should be determined by the most fundamental understanding that can be achieved of the underlying principles that give structure to that subject. Teaching specific topics or skills without making clear their context in the broader fundamental structure of a field of knowledge . . . makes it exceedingly difficult for the student to generalize from what he has learned to what he will encounter later . . . has little reward in terms of intellectual excitement . . . (and produces knowledge) that is likely to be forgotten.[10]

SOCIALLY-CONSTRUCTED KNOWLEDGE

Directly opposed to Hirst's theory is the view that knowledge is the product of the interaction of individual minds with experiences, resulting in a highly *personal* system of interpretations and rationalizations. On this theory, knowledge develops through social processes, as individuals categorize experience and infer meanings. Thus, the status of knowledge as an *objective* entity is severely questioned. Statements about curriculum content are then seen not as statements about objective entities, but as particular views of the world advanced by particular groups of individuals, or (as Blum puts it) as 'products of the informal understandings negotiated among members of an organized intellectual collectivity'.[11]

The sociology of knowledge has a long history. In *History and Class Consciousness*, published in 1923, Lukàcs asserted that consciousness, and consequently knowledge of all kinds, is the product of interaction between men, reality and *interest*. This third variable is just as powerful as the other two in limiting and determining the kind of knowledge that different groups in society acquire. Lukàcs believed that 'under ideal conditions' reality *is* accessible to man's rational appraisal, but that in practice *both* classes in society (the 'dominant' and the 'oppressed') will, because of their different *interests*, attain only a partial understanding of reality (a 'false consciousness', as he calls it). In *Ideology and Utopia* (1936), Mannheim reasserted this theory of the social construction of knowledge, but he exempted scientific knowledge, which he regarded as 'disinterested knowledge' unrelated to its context of production and capable of a direct relationship with reality. Writers in the modern tradition of the so-called 'new sociology' – especially Keddie,[12] Esland[13] and Young[14] – deny special status to scientific knowledge and reject the distinction between academic knowledge and common-sense knowledge drawn by philosophers such as Karl Popper.[15] They argue that *all* knowledge is socially constructed, that we do not know the world as it really is, but only as mediated through the conceptual framework we have. This framework is a human construction, which could have been different and is relative to the social system. Clearly, the way we see the world is partly influenced by the way we have been brought up ('socialized'), by our language and by our experiences, but these writers suggest that it is *totally* determined by these factors and that all knowledge and all kinds of truth are simply 'institutionalized conventions'. Thus, they lead us to a theory of 'cultural relativity' in which a particular view of reality is neither right nor wrong. In other words, 'truth is as you see it!' They refuse to allow limiting features in the nature of reality: the validity of arguments, the truth of statements, and the correct application of concepts to experience are to be explained *only* in terms of the socially dominant group. Hence, different groups could legitimate different standards of validity, truth and correctness. It is only a short step from suggesting that all knowledge is socially constructed, and therefore arbitrary, to suggesting that the *criteria* by which we decide on truth and falsehood are also socially constructed and could, therefore, be altered. Thus, rationality itself becomes merely a convention and the rules of logic and argument are shaped and selected in accordance with the purpose of the argument or the intentions of the arguer. C. W. Mills had argued in similar vein when he asserted that 'the rules of the game change with a shift of interest'. Zones of knowledge (as he called them), because they are human constructs, have 'careers' in which *the norms of truth change*.

> Criteria, or observational and verificatory models are not transcendental. There have been, and are, diverse canons and criteria of validity and truth, and these criteria, upon which determination of the truthfulness of propositions at any time depend, are themselves, in their persistence and change, open to socio-historical relativization.[16]

At the other extreme is Phenix's view that the disciplines are perfected, *absolute* forms of knowledge, existing independently of man.

> The structure of things is revealed, not invented, and it is the business of enquiry to open that structure to general understanding through formation of appropriate concepts and theories. Truth is rich and varied, but it is not arbitrary. The nature of things is given, not chosen.[17]

Whilst not wishing to accept Phenix's proposition that 'the nature of things is *given*', we believe that there is a point at which it makes no sense to ask if things could be conceived otherwise. There *are* limiting features in the world. There *are* events in the world subject to cause and effect. There *is* some degree of stability and order. If there were not, we couldn't perceive it. The way we discriminate and explain must be *partly* due to stable features in our environment and *partly* due to cultural influences. Richard Pring sums this up quite succinctly when he says that choosing to distinguish between cats and dogs may be a consequence of our particular cultural environment, but *being able* to distinguish between them says something about cats and dogs.[17]

SOCIAL CONTROL

Whilst rejecting the extreme position advocated by the 'new sociologists', it is still possible to use the theoretical framework of socially-constructed knowledge and the notion of *social control* as an explanation for *why* the science curriculum changes in a particular way.

Sociologists of knowledge assert that all groups in society attempt to legitimate and disseminate the knowledge which best suits their interests. As Karl Marx reminds us, the groups with the most power, the ruling groups, are in a better position to succeed in establishing their particular version of reality.

> The ideas of the ruling class are in every epoch the ruling ideas: i.e. the class which is the ruling material force of society, is at the same time its ruling intellectual force. The class which has the means of material production at its disposal, has control at the same time over the means of mental production . . . hence among other things (they) rule also as thinkers, as producers of ideas, and regulate the production and distribution of the ideas of their age; thus their ideas are the ruling ideas of the epoch.[18]

However, to suggest that the imposition of a particular view of the world by a ruling group implies both a huge conspiracy of manipulation on the one hand, and large scale human subservience and passive acceptance on the other hand, is to grossly over-simplify the complex interactions in society. We are all born into a specific social and historical context, with its already existing ideas and interactions; we live within an 'ideological matrix' which influences and determines our whole consciousness, so that we acquire a set of beliefs, values and practices which we accept as 'common sense'. This view of society is then reinforced and stabilized through institutions such as schools, so that it appears to be the only way the world *can* be. Thus, the education system may be an important aspect of the social control mechanism.[19] It is inappropriate to enter into a discussion of the concept of social control here, but it is worth noting (as Donajgrodzki[20] points out) that the identification of social control processes at work does *not* imply that the control element is the major or the only factor, or that the 'controllers' and 'controlled' are aware of the process. A particular interest group may, of course, make a conscious and cynical use of education, or any other social structure or institution, but that group is just as likely to have a genuine passion for its cause and to assign itself motives for its actions, which only later appear to have been false. This would appear to be the state of affairs at the time of the great changes in the school science curriculum in the mid-nineteenth century. It may also be happening now!

THE SCIENCE OF COMMON THINGS

The earliest attempt to include science in the curriculum seems to have been Charles and Elizabeth Mayo's *Object Lessons*, designed for 'the cultivation of habits of accurate observation, correct description, and right judgement upon the things of nature and art'.[21] Following the publication of textbooks written by the Mayos (*Lessons and Objects*, 1831, and *Lessons on Shells*, (1832)) and backing from the Home and Colonial Infant

School society, Object Lessons quickly became established as the basis of science lessons in the early years of a child's elementary schooling. In the 1840s a small but influential group of clerics existed, who saw the teaching of science as essential for the moral and religious salvation of the labouring classes. Notable among them was the Rev. Richard Dawes, who became Rector of Kings Somborne in 1837 and, with the help of a government grant, opened a National Society school there in October 1842.[22] This village school soon achieved remarkable educational results, in large measure attributable to the use of secular reading books with a large scientific content and to the teaching of science as applied to 'the understanding of common things'. The first favourable reports from HM Inspectorate appeared in 1845[23] and, in 1848, the Minutes of the Committee of Council on Education contained a long account of the organization and teaching of the Science of Common Things by the Rev Henry Moseley.[24] From this time, Dawes found a staunch ally in Moseley, who applied himself to the diffusion of Dawes' curriculum scheme.

In the early 1850s more well-defined support for the teaching of science in elementary schools became apparent, possibly due to the Great Exhibition of 1851, when it was realized that British manufacturers compared unfavourably with those from overseas. Layton[3] describes how the supporters of the movement for science education recognized three priorities if science were to be firmly established in the curriculum: well-designed and inexpensive apparatus and books; suitably trained teachers; and a sound administrative framework. A government grant scheme for the purchase of school science apparatus and books, promoted by Moseley, went some way to meeting this first priority. Moseley's influence was also crucial in meeting the second priority, when he was instrumental in establishing the requirement that all students in training schools should study science. Additionally, grants were made available to supplement the salaries of lecturers who showed skill in adapting topics in science for elementary instruction. The third essential resource for the establishment of science in the curriculum was a sound administrative framework. Much of the basic groundwork had, of course, already been done by Moseley through his work for the Committee of Council. Further impetus was supplied in 1853 by the creation of the Department of Science and Art, with Dr Lyon Playfair as Head of Science. Playfair strongly endorsed the view that science should be introduced into elementary education, and early signs were that much fruitful work would be done in cooperation with the Committee of Council on Education.

By 1854, with the three essential resources necessary for the development of Dawes' scheme reasonably satisfied, the movement seemed poised for success. Journals such as *Educational Expositor* carried many articles discussing and suggesting further developments for the scheme.

Suddenly, in mid-decade, when all seemed set for a significant advance, several crucial changes occurred. Dawes was moved to the Deanery of Hereford where, even though he retained his interest in education, much of his time was taken up with his new duties. In 1855, a year after influencing grant regulations favourable to science and introducing a large amount of physical science into the examinations of training schools, Moseley was appointed resident Canon of Bristol Cathedral, being replaced as Inspector with special responsibility for the Church Training Colleges by the Rev Frederick Temple, who within two years had revised the scheme of examinations for students, reducing the amount of mechanics and demoting physical science from its prime position to one of several *optional* subjects. By 1859 mechanics had disappeared as an examination subject and the number of teachers able to claim grant aid for scientific apparatus had been drastically reduced. The most vital resource of all for the continued success of the science of common things movement, the supply of trained teachers, had been virtually halted. In the administrative sphere a significant change of priority was apparent. Playfair, a strong supporter of the Dawes schemes in the early years of the decade, shifted his ground significantly regarding the most appropriate kind of science for the elementary school curriculum. The aims and objectives of science education were moved firmly into the affective domain, with prime place being afforded to 'love of nature', for which natural history and the 'sciences of observation' were regarded as the most appropriate vehicles. In 1858 Playfair left the Department of Science and Art to resume his academic career as professor of chemistry in the University of Edinburgh. By 1859, with a new and very limited system of claiming grant aid for science teaching, the role of science in the curriculum had been severely curtailed. With the Revised Code of 1862, following the Report of the Newcastle Commission, all financial assistance towards science in elementary schools was withdrawn. It is worth noting that in assessing the state of popular education the Commissioners rather surprisingly, did *not* seek the views of Dawes or Moseley. The result of these new regulations was that science disappeared from the elementary school curriculum, and did not reappear until 1882.

The question of particular interest in this article is *why* this change should have come about. The 'social Darwinist' explanation given by Layton – that better and more acceptable alternatives had become available, may appear reasonable from a common-sense viewpoint, but does not stand up well to close historical scrutiny. Rather than failing, the experiment with the Science of Common Things was showing signs of marked success, children were successfully learning science! Hence it would be more correct to say that it was *abandoned* rather than it failed, and that its abandonment represents an attempt at social control. It is reasonable to ask, therefore, *to whom* the new science curriculum alternative of *pure laboratory science* was 'more acceptable'? It is reasonable to ask *whose interests* were furthered by the introduction of this alternative and why this group's interest was being threatened by the success of the Science of Common Things?

THE EMERGENCE OF PURE SCIENCE

During the early 1850s the traditional orthodox conception of a classics-based liberal education, which set apart the aristocracy and gentry from the rest and restricted the entry of the emergent middle class to the ruling order, was beginning to come under attack. An important and forceful essay by Herbert Spencer[25] on the relative merits of various branches of knowledge directly questioned some of the basic assumptions of this classical education, and put forward a case for the inclusion of *science* in the curriculum. He suggested four main 'areas' in which scientific knowledge had a greater 'worth' than any other form of knowledge.

1 It cultivated a superior type of memory.
2 It was superior in cultivating judgement.
3 It was superior in instilling moral discipline, through its appeal to reason.
4 It was essential for developing a religious culture – science could not be separated from religion without harmful effects to both.

Spencer and Hershel[26] were adamant that the science promoted in schools should be 'practically useful' in various professions, manufactures and businesses, but such an emphasis was roundly condemned by Whewell, who considered that it would inhibit scientists in moving towards 'laws of a more exalted generality and higher speculative beauty'.[27] Such an attitude is representative of the increasingly prominent advocates of education in *pure abstract science*. Robert Hunt, Secretary to the Society of Arts, argued that whilst the practical aspect of science was of 'some importance', it is the study of *abstract science* that 'refined and elevated human feelings'. He claimed that any idea of measuring the value of science in terms of its utility was degrading it from its 'far higher and holier ends'. By training the young to 'estimate truth by its money value' and by seeking scientific knowledge for 'purely mercenary ends' we would ensure that scientific knowledge advanced no further. He suggested, instead, 'more noble' ends for science education:

> I would venture to impress upon all teachers of the young, not to attempt to teach science in all its details, but to excite curiosity, stimulate inquiry and quicken the powers of observation.[28]

His concluding words presented a view of science designed to advance it for serious consideration as a component of a liberal education:

> . . . by allowing the young mind to expand itself over the fields of nature 'like a wild bird of the wilderness', to embrace within its flight the whole truth in its illustration of creation's great phenomena, by ascending from practical science to the high poetry of science, we shall produce a nobler being.[28]

The opposition to the teaching of the Science of Common Things and the promotion of Pure Abstract Science for inclusion in the curriculum for liberal education of the upper classes merged with the movement for the improved status of natural history. In this context the work of Henslow[29] and T. H. Huxley are particularly important. The views of many eminent scientists of the time were represented in a report presented to the British Association by its Parliamentary Committee.[30] Under the chairmanship of Lord Wrottesley, this committee undertook a survey of opinion among scientists on what they saw as the most effective measures to be adopted in improving the position of science. On the basis of the report (presented in 1857), Wrottesley drew up twelve resolutions to be submitted to Parliament. Implicit in the resolutions was the value of *pure science* – prestige for abstract science was deemed to be essential for the progress of science. Of the four resolutions directly concerned with education, none was concerned with science at the elementary school level. It may be assumed from this that Wrottesley and his committee either (i) considered science at the elementary level to be unimportant, or (ii) considered that developments at this level were already satisfactory and needed no further comment. It is *our* view that the report implicitly reflected a growing awareness of a serious problem: that developments in science at the elementary level were not only 'satisfactory' as far as science *learning* was concerned, but were highly *successful*, and that social hierarchy was being threatened because there was no corresponding development for the higher orders. Giving the labouring poor access to a particular form of knowledge, seen as a very important resource, and at the same time denying this resource to their superiors was coming to be regarded as a very dangerous state of affairs. Wrottesley himself expressed his concern over elementary school science in a section of his book on the 'present condition of England'. He comments on the impressive grasp of scientific principles in schools for the labouring poor compared with the lack of any science in the curriculum of grammar and public schools, and describes in detail an incident in a pauper school where he asked a class for the explanation of the principle of a pump:

> . . . a poor boy hobbled forth to give a reply; he was lame and hump-backed, and his wan emaciated face told only too clearly the tale of poverty and its consequences, unwholesome and scanty diet in early years; but he gave forthwith so lucid and intelligent a reply to the question put to him that there arose a feeling of admiration for the child's talents combined with

a sense of shame that more information should be found in some of the lowest of our lowest classes on matters of general interest than in those far above them in the world by station.[31]

Wrottesley's conclusion confirms the worst fears of the upper classes concerning the education of the lower orders:

It would be an unwholesome and vicious state of society in which those who are comparatively unblessed with nature's gifts should be generally superior in intellectual attainments to those above them in station.[31]

Similar views, showing the depth of the disquiet, were expressed by many other influential individuals. In an article in the *Edinburgh Review*, A. C. Tait (who followed Arnold at Rugby and later became Archbishop of Canterbury) expressed concern that the education of the poor was making such good progress that the higher orders were being left behind. Consequently it was 'absolutely necessary for government to attend to education of the rich'. He predicted a complete overturn of the social order if 'the son of a labourer possesses better knowledge than the son of the squire'. It is interesting to note that he also makes direct reference to Dawes at Kings Somborne and to the undesirability of the children of labourers, being educated with the sons of the higher orders.

The principal goal of the Science of Common Things was intellectual development of children, the acquisition of scientific knowledge and the provision of experiences for the exercise of reason, speculation and imagination. Improvements in the moral and religious condition of the children of the poor were assumed to follow as a matter of course once self-confidence and integrity of thought had been achieved. By giving a prominent place in the curriculum to applied sciences such as mechanics and agricultural chemistry, education could be related to a culture which was familiar to the labouring classes. Furthermore, the restricted linguistic experiences of so many elementary school children need no longer be an insuperable obstacle to the growth of rationality. As Layton remarks:

Here was no crumb of upper-class education charitably dispensed to the children of the labouring poor. Instruction was related to a culture which was familiar to them and provided opportunities for the use of reason and speculation by drawing upon observations which pertained to everyday life. *Understanding and the exercise of thought were not the prerogative of the upper and middle classes.*[3] (our italics)

As a consequence, the upper classes felt threatened. Influential scientists of the day, men such as Owen, Hooker, Lyell and Faraday, advanced the view that the ruling class was in danger of losing its position through lack of scientific knowledge. These views are evident in the *Report of the Public School Commission* set up in 1861.

In a political point of view, it is not only an unhealthy but also a dangerous state of things in some respects, that the material world should be very

> much better known by the middle classes of society than by the upper classes.[32]

If it was considered such a 'dangerous state of things' that the new middle class had access to a form of knowledge denied to the upper class, how much more serious must have seemed the 'state of things' when the *lower* orders were seen to be becoming superior in scientific 'intellectual attainments to those above them in station'. By the middle and late 1850s a campaign backed by the *Times* newspaper had been mounted on two levels. On the one hand it advocated the merits of *pure science* as a component of the liberal education of the higher orders, on the other it advocated a *halt* in the scientific education of the lower orders, whom it saw as being 'over-educated'. The higher orders had realized that those below them in the social hierarchy were gaining access to scientific knowledge which might be used as a resource in future socially undesirable activity. Since, however, the continuing insistence of the higher orders on a classics-based liberal education excluded science to a large degree, it was in their interests to exclude science from the education of the poor. It is suggested that this, and *not* the appearance of 'better alternatives', was the reason behind the abandonment of the Science of Common Things. From this perspective it is possible to speculate that the Revised Code of 1862, which finally removed science from the elementary school curriculum, was the institutionalization of these beliefs legitimated on administrative and financial grounds. The curriculum proposed for the elementary schools was a watered-down classics curriculum, containing *no science*. Clearly, a curriculum based on 'general training' offered the possibility of more direct control. Prominent amongst the advocates of this 'new' curriculum was Joshua Fitch, appointed Principal of the British and Foreign School Society Training College in 1854, and promoted to the Inspectorate in 1863. His Elementary School curriculum comprised reading and writing, arithmetic, English grammar (the 'classics of the poor'), a little geography and history. A knowledge of common things was not to be obtained by the direct study of science, but through 'country walks, star gazing and domestic experiences'.

> If children go into the world ignorant of common things, it is not for the want of technical instruction about them; but either because their daily life has been confined to a narrow and unlovely world, their homes are wretched, and God's fairest works kept far out of their sight (circumstances over which we have but small control), or else because their powers of observation and of thoughtfulness have been insufficiently developed; and this is a defect which I believe would be more truly corrected by the good and sound teaching of arithmetic, geography, grammar, history and the Holy Scriptures, than by all the catechisms and manuals of miscellaneous information ever written.[33]

When science eventually reappeared in the curriculum of the elementary schools, some twenty years later, it was in a very different form from that advocated by the liberal reformers. Objectives were now firmly in the affective domain: the principal goal was 'love of nature', which was considered necessary for ensuring success in later stages of a scientific education. Pure science had become accepted as the *correct* view. This marks the start of the conception of science education as it is known today. The 'new' view was described in some detail by Professor Roscoe in an address to commemorate the opening of new buildings at Owens College, Manchester. He argued for 'the educational value of original research', which he saw as 'personal communication with nature for its own sake'. Through this type of scientific enquiry, which was value-free and disinterested, 'habits of independent thought and ideas of free enquiry are thus at once inculcated'. In claiming that the purpose of science education is to select and supply future scientists of talent to the universities, he described the teaching of science in schools as 'the means of sifting out of the great mass of the people those golden grains of genius which are now too often lost amongst the sands of mediocrity'.[34] This new view of science was designed to develop an elite who conformed to the image of the 'pure scientist' rationalized by the higher orders. Science had been allowed into the curriculum once more, but only on terms which effectively excluded the mass of the population from any meaningful scientific education. In this way it was ensured that the resource, available to all in theory but only accessible to the higher orders in practice, no longer posed a threat to the social hierarchy. As far as the elementary schools were concerned, the science component was to be natural history. As long ago as 1854, T. H. Huxley had defined scientific method as 'extended and applied common sense'.

> Science is nothing but trained and organized common sense, differing from the latter only as a veteran may differ from a raw recruit.[35]

For Huxley, biology was the experimental science which best exemplified scientific method and was ideally suited to the disciplining of the mind. Moreover, biology was ideally suited to the promotion of 'a love of nature'.

THE CURRENT SITUATION

The major thesis of this article is that the way in which school science is perceived today is *not* the end result of 'inevitable progress' in the disinterested search for truth. Rather, it is *socially constructed*, being the product of particular sets of choices made by particular groups of people at particular times. Its final form represents the triumph of a particular interest group. In providing a way of understanding nature that by definition *excludes* knowledge of the natural world as it is experienced by the mass of the population, the conception of school science that we have today was not designed to achieve the full potential of the majority. Hence it is unsuited, in its present form, to a common curriculum in comprehensive schools.

Michael Young has argued that science teachers continue to see the main purpose of science education as the supply of future scientists, with the result that two very different kinds of school science courses have arisen: academic science and non-academic science – 'the former claiming credibility from the professional scientific community, and the latter through notions of 'relevance' and immediate interest for pupils'. Thus, 'relevance' and 'intellectual credibility' have come to be regarded as incompatible, and even mutually exclusive; O-level and A-level courses have become increasingly abstract whilst courses dealing with the outside world and the environment have been reserved for the non-examinable or, at best, for CSE. The inevitable consequence of this dual policy towards science education is the emergence of two classes of citizen: the scientifically literate and the scientifically illiterate. According to Young, curriculum decision-makers have social control motives in wishing to create a large scientifically illiterate workforce, 'who see themselves as dependent on experts in more and more aspects of their life'. He argues that those in power see it as desirable that 'except in the specific context of their work, and possibly in leisure pursuits such as car maintenance, our increasingly technologically dominated world remains for the majority as much a mystery as the theological mysteries of feudal times'.[36]

Jenkins[37] has attempted to discern some social control element in the nature study movement of the early twentieth century and Millar[38] claims to have detected similar concerns in the proposals of the Newsom Report and the influential Scottish Education Department's curriculum paper *Science for General Education*. Millar claims that these documents betray a concern with social control both *within* the classroom and outside (for example, in industrial relations), which determines both the content and the teaching methods employed.

> As soon as a course module is refined to the point where its use in the class keeps the pupils occupied, enables a satisfactory staff-pupil atmosphere to develop, and therefore permits the teacher to feel unthreatened by an incipient loss of control, it is endorsed as 'satisfactory'. . .
>
> The hope here is clearly that a 'scientific' attitude to information, characterized by a desire to consider all sides of a question, to keep an open mind, to hold a point-of-view subject to experimental verification, will be transferred to areas which are far removed from the school science area.[38]

It is tempting to look for social control mechanisms operating during other periods of significant change in the science curriculum. What motives lay behind the other important curriculum changes described by Uzzell,[1] Layton[3] and Jenkins[2]? Were there social control factors at work during the great changes brought about by the Nuffield courses in the 1960s? What lay behind the General Science movement in the mid-twentieth century and the more recent attempts to promote integrated science? Which interest groups are promoting the current drive to increase the number of girls taking up careers in science, and why? As we enter a new phase of curriculum development in science we need to ask two questions:

1 *Whose* view of school science is being adopted in the curriculum?
2 *Whose* interests are being promoted by the particular view of school science that is adopted?

All proposals present a *particular* view of science. For example, the Association for Science Education's *Alternatives for Science Education* includes the following statements:

> . . . a good science education should seek to develop a range of intellectual skills and cognitive patterns which would help youngsters to handle the problems of growing up in, and integrating with, a society that is heavily dependent on scientific and technological knowledge and its utilization . . . provide opportunities for explaining, and therefore understanding, the nature of advanced technological societies, the complex interaction between science and society, and the contribution science makes to our cultural heritage.[39]

The document goes on to urge teachers to 'provide opportunities whereby youngsters can gain a sense of social meaning and identity' and sets out six 'personal and social aims of science education for all'. Typical of these is the aim identified by the ASE as *science in the world of work*: 'The development of an understanding of the way in which scientific and technological ideas are used to maintain an economic surplus'. Similarly, one is tempted to look for social control intent in the ASE policy statement *Education through Science* when it sets out the aims of science education for *all* in the following terms:

> . . . the development of an appreciation and understanding of the ways in which science and technology contribute to the worlds of *work, citizenship, leisure* and *survival*. We would include under this heading an understanding of the way scientific and technological ideas are used to create and maintain an economic surplus, facilitate participation in democratic decision-making in a technological society, enrich and sustain a wide range of leisure activities and pursuits, and enable the individual to utilize scientific ideas and technological processes in the context of increasing self-sufficiency, the conservation of resources and the utilization of alternative technologies.[40]

At least three of the six aims of science education listed in *Education through Science* could be regarded as having a social control intent:

1 'The attainment of a perspective or way of looking at the world . . .'
2 'The attainment of a basic understanding of the nature of advanced technological societies, the interaction between science and society, and the contribution science makes to our cultural heritage.'
3 'The realization that scientific knowledge and experience is of some value in the process of establishing a sense of personal and social identity.'[40]

In view of the foregoing discussion one is tempted to ask:

1 *Whose* 'way of looking at the world' is being advanced?
2 *Whose interest* is being promoted by the curriculum?
3 *Whose* view of society is to be projected?

REFERENCES

1. Uzzell, P. S. 'The changing aims of science education', *S.S.R.*, 1978, 210, **60**, 7–20.
2. Jenkins, E. W., *From Armstrong to Nuffield* (John Murray, 1979).
3. Layton, D., *Science for the People* (Allen & Unwin, 1973).
4. Turner, D. M., *The History of Science Teaching in England* (Chapman and Hall, 1927).
5. Uzzell, P. S., 'The curriculum: whence, why and whither', *S.S.R.*, 1981, 223, **63**, 343–8.
6. Layton, D., 'The educational work of the parliamentary committee of the British Association for the Advancement of Science', *History of Education*, 1976, **5**, 25–39.
7. Phenix, P. H., *Realms of Meaning* (McGraw-Hill, 1964).
8. King, A. R. and J. A. Brownell, *The Curriculum and the Disciplines of Knowledge* (Wiley, 1966). Schwab, J. J., 'The structure of science', in Ford, G. W., and L. Pugno, *The Structure of Knowledge and the Curriculum* (Rand McNally, 1965. Broudy, H., *Building a Philosophy of Education* (Prentice Hall, 1961).
9. Hirst, P. H., 'Liberal education and the nature of knowledge', in Archambault, R. D. (ed), *Philosophical Analysis and Education* (Routledge & Kegan Paul, 1965).
10. Bruner, J. S., *The Process of Education* (University of Chicago Press, 1960).
11. Blum, A. F., 'The corpus of knowledge as a normative order', in Young, M. F. D. (ed), *Knowledge and Control* (Collier-Macmillan, 1973).

12. Keddie, N., 'Education as a social construct', in Jenks, C. (ed), *Rationality, Education and the Social Organization of Knowledge* (Routledge & Kegan Paul, 1977).
13. Esland, G. M., 'Teaching and learning as the organization of knowledge', in Young, M. F. D. (ed), *Knowledge and Control* (Collier-Macmillan, 1973).
14. Young, M. F. D. (ed), *Knowledge and Control: New Directions for the Sociology of Education* (Collier-Macmillan, 1973).
15. Popper, K. R., *Objective Knowledge* (Oxford University Press, 1972).
16. Mills, C. W., 'Language, logic and culture', *American Sociological Review*, 1939, **4**, 670–80.
17. Pring, R., *Knowledge and Schooling* (Open Books, 1976).
18. Marx, K. and F. Engels, *The German Ideology*, 1845, quoted in McLellan, D., *The Thought of Karl Marx: An Introduction* (Macmillan, 1971).
19. Barnes, S. B., *Interests and the Growth of Knowledge* (Routledge & Kegan Paul, 1977). Berger, P. and T. Luckmann, *The Social Construction of Reality* (Penguin, 1967). Johnson, R., 'Educational policy and social control in early Victorian England', *Past and Present*, 1970, **49**, 96–119. Mulkay, M., 'Knowledge and utility: implications for the sociology of knowledge', *Social Studies in Science*, 1979, **9**, 63–80.
20. Donajgrodzki, A. P. (ed), *Social Control in Nineteenth Century Britain* (Croom Helm, 1977).
21. Mayo, C. and E. Mayo, *Practical Remarks on Infant Education* (Home and Colonial School Society, 1849).
22. Ball, N., 'Richard Dawes and the teaching of common things', *Educational Review*, 1964, **17**, 59–68.
23. Committee of Council on Education, *Minutes 1844–5*, Report by Rev J. Allen.
24. Committee of Council on Education, *Minutes 1847–8*, 7–27.
25. Spencer, H., 'What knowledge is of most worth?', *Westminster Review*, 1859, XVI, 1–41.
26. Herschel, J. F. W., *Preliminary Discourse on the Study of Natural Philosophy* (The Cabinet Cyclopaedia, 1830).
27. Quoted in Layton, D., *op. cit.*, p. 46.
28. Hunt, R., 'On familiar methods of instruction in science', *Lectures in Connection with the Educational Exhibition* (Society of Arts, Manufactures and Commerce, 1854).
29. Chapter 3 of Layton, D. (1973) is devoted to J. S. Henslow.
30. Layton, D., 'Lord Wrottesley FRS, pioneer statesman of science', *Notes and Records of the Royal Society of London*, 1968, **23**, 230–47.
31. Lord Wrottesley, *Thoughts and Government and Legislation* (John Murray, 1860).
32. Report of Her Majesty's Commissioners appointed to Inquire into the Revenues and Management of Certain Colleges and Schools, and the Studies pursued and Instruction given therein (HMSO, 1864), Vol. 4, Part 2.

33. Fitch, J. G., *The Relative Importance of Subjects Taught in Elementary Schools* (Bell and Daldy, 1854).
34. Roscoe, H. E., 'Original research as a means of education', in *Essays and Addresses, Owens College, Manchester* (1874), 21–57.
35. Huxley, T. H., 'On the educational value of the natural history sciences', lecture 1854, republished in Huxley, T. H., *Man's Place in Nature and other Essays* (J. M. Dent, 1906).
36. Young, M. F. D., 'The schooling of science', in Whitty, G. and M. F. D. Young (ed), *Explorations in the Politics of School Knowledge* (Nafferton Books, 1976). (Chapter 17 in this volume).
37. Jenkins, E. W., 'Science, sentimentalism or social control? The nature study movement in England and Wales, 1899–1914', *History of Education*, 1981, **10**, 33–43.
38. Millar, R. H., 'Curriculum rhetoric and social control: a perspective on recent science curriculum development', *Europ. J. Science Education*, 1981, **3**, 271–84.
39. *Alternatives for Science Education* (ASE, 1979).
40. *Education through Science* (ASE, 1981).

17 The schooling of science

● M. F. D. Young

Young is concerned about the gap between science teaching and what he sees as the proper role of science in society.

He reflects on a diminution in school science and the danger (described by Matthews) of trivializing science by overloading it with projects and social implications.

Young provides a few historical examples of unenlightened aims for science teaching and goes on to claim that 'relevance' is still downgraded, that 'academic' science cannot be achieved in comprehensive schools, that doing leads to learning, and that one should talk mainly about science itself, not only about its abuse.

At the end, the author claims that the postulated dichotomy between 'pure' and 'applied' science arises not only in schools but also in 'a society in which men have become increasingly separated from the products of their labour, mental and manual'. He concludes that 'the transformation of school science, and the separations that characterize it, then becomes a part of a much wider struggle for the realisation of a socialist society'.

Despite a decade of unprecedented investment in curriculum innovation, school science displays many of the manifestations of a continuing 'crisis'. Closure of degree and teachers' certificate courses through lack of applicants, and further education colleges with science departments which only remain viable by accepting an overseas student intake of up to 90 per cent are but two examples. At the school level we have fears expressed that one outcome of comprehensive reorganization could be that 'the teaching of physics in schools may be a dying activity . . . the subject could even disappear'[1] and that 'the shortage of good physics teachers [would] not be quite so alarming . . . [were we to] concentrate our scarce manpower on the older secondary school pupils who could better appreciate the intellectual content'.[2] The price that we are being asked to pay for preserving school physics then is a withdrawal from most junior and middle school science, and therefore, in effect, from any science at all for many pupils.

Another aspect of this crisis is considered by Matthews, who reviews the various attempts to attract more pupils to science by an emphasis on projects and the social implications of science. These can, he suggests, 'trivialize teaching with the attendant dangers of disturbing the supply of competent scientists'.[3] In other words, attempts to make science more 'relevant' merely confound the problem which is, according to Matthews, almost echoing the words of the Dainton and Swan Reports that 'it is vital that society maintains a supply of highly qualified scientists . . . and that . . . science education in schools represents an important stage in this process'. Thus problems in science education are not just problems of curriculum reform and more 'relevant' courses, nor of philosophical arguments about the nature of science, but problems which have their origins and their resolution in a particular kind of society and its transformation. In other words, the failure of science teaching to enable science, a major human activity, to become more than a minority pursuit, though related to the historical emergence and persistence of current practices in science education, cannot be understood in terms of them alone. This chapter is divided into four parts:

1 A sketch of aspects of the way school science was established in the nineteenth century, and how contemporary curriculum innovations have been developed within that framework.
2 An attempt to indicate how prevailing traditions of school science are reflected in and reflect the much wider separation of science and technology in society as a whole.
3 An examination of some of the practices of teachers that sustain prevailing conceptions of school science, of alternatives to them, and possible constraints on the alternatives being realized.
4 Conclusions and implications.

1

> Science emerged later as a branch of education and its assimilation into the existing institutions and structures was not achieved without some noticeable exercises of accommodation.[4]

This view of the incorporation of natural science into the school curriculum is taken by David Layton, who offers us a valuable account of this process of 'accommodation' in the late nineteenth century, complementary to his earlier study of the demise of 'the science of common things'.[5] In particular he describes how one conception of 'pure' laboratory science was established which enabled school science to be justified in terms of the prevailing tradition of liberal education and its devotion to 'the discipline of the mind, the attainment of habits of controlled attention and the exercise of reasoning powers and memory'. Thus Chemistry and Physics could comfortably claim a place alongside the Classics and Mathematics. Likewise, the purpose of introducing science into the secondary schools was never in doubt to such leading advocates as H. E. Roscoe, the first President of the Association of Public School Science Masters (the precursor of our Association for Science Education); school science was, for Roscoe, as Layton quotes him, to be 'the means of sifting out from the great mass of the people those golden grains of genius which now are too often lost amongst the sands of mediocrity'.

A consequence of this accommodation was, as Layton puts it, that 'the application of science to everyday life had (by the 1870s) disappeared . . . the learner was slowly inducted into the ways of the scientist – a particular type of scientist also – the ''pure'' researcher'. Largely through the method of government recognition and financing of laboratories, the separation of school science into separate 'subjects', physics, chemistry, and biology, became firmly established before the end of the century, as did for quite other reasons the exclusion of geology. Furthermore, the models of 'subject' teaching which dominated (and in many ways still do) experimental work were part of this process. As Layton describes it, school chemistry became the 'easily organized and easily examined exercises in qualitative analysis . . . [in which] packets of powder were sent out [to the schools] and packets of paper were returned when the pupils had completed the routine of taking the solution through the charts'; if anyone asked 'why?', 'training of the faculties of observation and reasoning' would doubtless have been the reply.

Likewise in physics pupils were offered 'a starvation course on the precise measurement of physical quantities . . . [for, as an influential text of the time began] ''Physics is essentially the science of measurements'''. Of course, many things have changed, but even in the Nuffield era 'the emphasis has remained on abstract . . . ''technically sweet'' science, dissociated from its applications and implications'.

Before turning to the attempts to revitalize science teaching which have emerged since the early 1960s, it is important to ask the question 'Why did school science emerge in the way it did?' Is it adequate to see it as an accommodation to existing educational structures, as Layton does? I suggest we need to try and grasp both the innovations Layton describes and the structures they confronted in terms of their wider political and economic significance. Alternative traditions of science education in which scientific knowledge was conceived, among other things 'as an instrument in the pursuit of political independence and social emancipation', had, Layton writes, become 'casualties in a process of natural selection as the educational environment had become progressively more sharply defined'.[6] The problem with this kind of social Darwinist view is that it treats a *social* process, selection, as *natural*, rather than as an outcome of certain activities and interests in particular historical contexts. This is indicated in Layton's reference to the views of science on the one hand in terms of 'the disinterested pursuit of truth', and on the other, particularly by those involved in the Great Exhibition, as 'the producer for the industrial market place (so that science was to be studied for the economic benefits it would yield)'. The question of economic benefits of science points to a concern with the character of the economy at the time and to the importance of considering the demise of the attempts to implement a science curriculum 'as practice' and the success of the science curriculum 'as fact'[7] in the context of changes in Victorian capitalism.[8]

The political economy of school science remains to be written and in particular the response by the Nuffield Foundation to the ASE proposals in the early 1960s which were followed by the setting up of the Industrial Fund for the Development of science teaching in the private sector. All I want to do here is to suggest that, as in the nineteenth century contexts described by Layton, more recent curriculum innovations in science actually acted as a constraint on certain of the possibilities that science teachers might have developed. I am not suggesting that this was either intentional or always directly experienced by teachers, but that it can be seen as a way of looking at how certain possibilities get closed off, how certain frameworks for action become seen as almost in the order of things. The following are illustrative of some of the ways this process may work:

(a) In characteristically linking all the early projects to O and A level, the new materials sustained and affirmed an existing distinction between academic and non-academic science – the former claiming credibility from the professional scientific community, and the latter through notions of 'relevance' and immediate interest for pupils. 'Relevance' and intellectual credibility have come to be seen in opposition, so that courses concerned with glass making, ceramics, photography and the environment are either treated as 'for the non-examinable', or as only warranting at best a CSE grade 3.

(b) The corollary of this is that the one set of materials which at least makes some attempt to set its activities in a non-school, non-lab world – Secondary Science – is viewed as an unsuitable base for O level, even by its originator, 'as it lacks a strong enough chemical component' – echoing the dominance of a view of school science as 'knowledge to be transmitted'.

(c) The failure of academic science (pre- and post-Nuffield) for the majority is explained either in terms of its conceptual difficulties or in terms of the pupils' lack of ability. 'If one teaches science to average classes in a comprehensive school . . . one is unlikely to have met any pupils whose thinking goes beyond the concrete operations stage'.[9] An example Shayer gives is understanding density, though how one might

identify such an understanding might tell us more about school physics than a pupil's ability; was it an ability to memorize a definition, or calculate from a ratio of mass to volume, or to know, for example, why one might put a hydrometer in a car battery? What is never considered is the 'non-subject' but scientific and technological knowledge which pupils often have (and teachers sometimes lack), or even more, the actual social relations between teacher and taught, and how they may 'produce' the lack of understanding that is attributed by many researchers as well as teachers to low ability.

(d) 'Innovations' in school science have confirmed it as laboratory knowledge and as distinct from technology as workshop or factory knowledge, despite their practical inseparability. It is only in the academy that so called 'pure' science is practised, and even there the claim of 'pure' science as disinterested has little foundation as university departments compete for a more generous allocation of government or business funds. The pure/applied distinction obscures the way in which the practice of scientists is inextricably linked to the productive labour upon which they depend for their livelihood. We have therefore the absurd situation of Project Technology, largely avoided except in ritual statements by school science educators, being set up as a separate attempt to upgrade craft, metal and woodwork, and thus somehow infiltrate the school knowledge order (we have no grounds for doubting parallel outcomes of the Nuffield 16+ Project, as it becomes incorporated into the no-man's-land of the Certificate of Extended Education). This helps to obscure the possibility that the very separation and hierarchy that the curriculum projects have sustained between science and technology may be responsible for the drop out of so many children from serious scientific work. One experiment described by Hoskyns calls into question the opposition between supposed interest or relevance and intellectual credibility – why else were regular truants turning up only for physics, learning the kinetic theory in working diesel engines, electronics in building hi-fi equipment, and optics through photography. As one boy said about building circuits: 'Building helps you understand. If you're just given a piece of paper, you wouldn't know, because you wouldn't know what went into building it'.

(e) Under the assumption of learning theories that emphasize how learning takes place through doing, most of the projects neglect the social character of learning and have failed to examine, except in a very superficial way, the activity of science teachers at all. All too easily *doing* becomes equated with following worksheet instructions *for* doing, and the emphasis on resources implies the teacher as a stimulus without whom nothing will take place. Thus pupils are assumed only to really *learn* when stimulated by a teacher, and the teacher's traditional didactic style has been replaced by a view of him as a kind of puppet master lead-

ing his pupils through the routines of the syllabus. Asked whether it helped to talk, a boy from the physics class referred to above replied 'If everybody talks about what they are doing and how they're figuring it out, everybody takes an interest in everybody else' – a view of learning very different from that espoused by most producers of curriculum project materials, and one rooted, albeit in a limited context, in a view of knowledge as men collectively objectifying their experience of the world, and taking responsibility for it.

(f) In the one project (SCISP) that considers 'science and society' questions, these are raised primarily as debates about the uses and abuses of science and the pro- and anti-science lobbies. Science teaching in general has tended to close off the opportunity for pupils to grasp science as a social practice, rather than as a body of knowledge, through the selective nature of the assumptions and choice within syllabuses, and the form that topics take. These are presented as given and necessary (though sometimes revised from above), and quite independent of the teachers and pupils themselves. Hine gives many interesting examples of this process in school physics; he writes:

> 'Doing' heat includes such trivia as dropping hot objects into cool liquids, discussing hot water systems (but not as genuine technological problems), and the clinical thermometer . . . the calculation of the energy required to produce a hot bath . . . [though] the concept of a society dependent on particular energy slaves, for instance, is not included.[10]

This section has sketched aspects of the historical and contemporary character of school science that confronts teachers who consider strategies for change. The traditions of science teaching that have emerged in the last century are expressions of wider contexts and act on those contexts. It is to these features of science as a crucial force of production and determinant of the division of labour that I turn in the next section.

2

Science teaching, as my earlier discussion suggested, began and continues with its main purpose to maintain the supply of future scientists. This has two interrelated, and in effect self-justifying outcomes – the mass scientific and technological ignorance of a people in an increasingly technologically dominated society, who see themselves as dependent on experts in more and more aspects of their life, and a community of scientists who see the knowledge which they are responsible for producing and validating as *necessarily* not available to the community at large. Arguments about the inherent difficulties of science, the inherent limitations of science teaching,[11] or the innate inabilities of the majority can, of course, be refuted 'in theory'. The problem is more serious, because increasingly they are going to have to be disproved 'in practice'. I'd like to take two examples – the first of which draws on material from Clutterbuck's 'Death in a Plastics' Factory'.[12] Everyone is familiar with the PVC of cables, pipes and plastic macs. Evidence has recently appeared that over-exposure to the monomer vinyl chloride from which PVC is made can lead to a rare and fatal liver cancer; large sums have recently been invested in production plants which require too high a degree of exposure, and not surprisingly further large sums would be required to modify the plants to reduce it to a safe level. The health of PVC workers has in this case become a trade union issue – a political struggle between management and workers. However, the unions face certain problems which take us back to the failure of science education for all but the specialist few. Lacking knowledge of the physiological processes involved, of the technology of a plant they had no part in designing, and in particular, the technology of very accurate detectors no one had yet designed, they remained largely dependent on experts.

In this case, if it had not been for a BSSRS group, the workers involved would have had no reason to question that the existing level of risk was unalterable, which raises quite different notions of relevance to those espoused by, for example, the Schools Council.

As high technology industries find decreasing markets for their products, the familiar outcomes are for management to lay off workers who respond with factory sit-ins demanding the 'right to work'. In some cases, of which Lucas Aerospace is an early example, the shop stewards have broadened the basis of their demands to put forward a programme which includes alternative production priorities (solar cells, electric cars, medical equipment, etc.) as well as alternative modes of production.[13] The significance of this, as with the industrial health example referred to above, is that the majority of the Lucas workers involved will have left school with only the minimum of education in science and technology. So long as production is hierarchically organized and some conceive the technology for others to operate, the problem is masked. Once, as in Lucas and other examples, there is pressure for participation of wide sections of the work force in production decisions, the training of specialized technologists and the unavailability of the basic principles underlying the technology to shop-floor workers become a constraint on the possibility of alternative modes of production, but also potentially a dynamic for change.

Both these examples point to the way traditions of science and technical education are being challenged, not just through the failure to recruit students but in the changing production contexts of which they were originally an expression. I want therefore to turn to a more detailed consideration of the practices by which prevailing traditions of school science are sustained – or, to put it another way, how science teaching expresses those wider features of the division of labour referred to in the examples which I have described.

3

It is inescapable that most of those who become 'successes' in school science are systematically denied the opportunity to grasp science as an integral and inseparable part of social life – as an expression of man's historical attempts to transform the natural world, rather than a mere body of knowledge about nature external to man. The 'failures', equally systematically, leave school to become part of the mass of scientific illiterates, who may in their work learn enough technology to supervise and repair complex machines but will never learn about the social relations of which the designing and manning of machines is a part.[14]

Except in the specific context of their work, and possibly in leisure pursuits such as car maintenance, our increasingly technologically dominated world remains for the majority as much a mystery as the theological mysteries of feudal times. How is this achieved in school science? To ask this question is not to suggest that science teachers are alone responsible or that an awareness of the assumptions underlying school science would lead to any sudden transformation – school science is far too embedded both in the way school knowledge has been institutionalized and in the wider context of the emergence of compulsory schooling. It is rather to point to some of the 'within school' processes that would need to be transformed if a very different model of science education to that established in the late nineteenth century were to develop.

The development of state schooling since the nineteenth century can be seen as an intervention into aspects of the everyday lives of the majority of the people in the interests of social control and economic productivity. This, as accounts such as Layton's and others show, was more visible in the nineteenth century, and was not a feature peculiar to school science.[15] The separation of science as a specialized activity is no less a feature of contemporary schooling. Aspects of this process in contemporary science teaching and the way it reproduces features of the social division of labour outside school will now be considered.

(a) School science separates science from pupils' everyday lives, and in particular their non-school knowledge of the natural world. It is learnt primarily as a *laboratory* activity, in a room full of special rules, many of which have no *real* necessity except in terms of the social organization of the school. An almost classic example of this process of alienation is illustrated in how the teacher in this transcript specifically sets science

apart from everyday life and all other school work (this is the very first time a first-year class enters a secondary school science lab).

> It may well be the first time you've done science and there are a whole lot of different things about working in a lab than there are in all the other classrooms in the school . . . you have to work with certain kinds of rules which are different . . . later we'll give you a list of them which you can put in your folder . . . there are things that are potentially dangerous . . . we've got gas taps here . . . those of you who've been in a kitchen do not need to be told this (so abstracted from the real world is the teacher that he can even imagine that *some* kids may never have been in a kitchen!).

The rules the teacher recounts all present a view of the lab world as a closed one, which finishes at the end of the lesson period. Some kids, of course, don't take over this 'separation' and bring in things from home – something, no doubt, they've learnt to do in primary school.

Apparatus and diagrams often affirm this separation – one only has to think of the relation between the traditional textbook diagram of a domestic hot water system and a child actually trying to understand the particular one in the house he lives in. An instance of this separation, which dramatized the problem for me, was a physics teacher who had worked through a whole term on optics, including telescopes and microscopes, and later found that one of his pupils, who had achieved nothing in school physics, had actually designed and built a telescope at home, taken readings of stars, and photographed an eclipse of the moon.[16]

That this separation is expressed in the interaction between teachers and pupils is illustrated by an analysis of two transcripts drawn from a first-year lesson, in which I was particularly concerned to explore the variety of ways in which school science as a conception of 'knowledge to be transmitted' underpins the teacher's talk and his way of listening to pupils' questions and responses. There are a whole variety of other practices, from what I would call the 'subject habit' of sequence making from lesson to lesson and the reconstruction of 'how it was', to the way science teachers formulate for pupils what they are going to do that might have and need to be considered.

Any teacher (or pupil) response is embedded in a theory (of a lesson, learning, science, etc.), which alone can provide for the particular as opposed to the multitude of senses that might be given to any question, but which is never available to the pupils. Their responses, their way of making sense, cannot therefore be treated by the teacher as reasonable accounts, unless by habit, chance or tradition, pupils are able to guess the teacher's sense.[17] For the teacher, then, appropriate pupil knowledge is only produced if pupils pick up that which teachers do not make available. In other words, if he produces the reply that the teacher's theory, not his question, calls for. Likewise, the procedures of making sense that the pupil engages in in producing responses, whether or not appropriate, are not available to the teacher. This raises some problems for typical notions of 'education as cultural transmission'; though science teachers are widely concerned to improve their teaching, the ways in which pupils generate recognizably effective displays of competence bear little or no relation to the practices teachers recognize as 'efficient'.

I'd like to turn briefly to the transcript extracts, with the question in mind as to what kind of practical 'theories' the pupil and teacher responses might be embedded in. Teacher 'theories' are not treated as a topic by teachers, no more are pupil theories. Both, however, can be understood as being used as a resource through which sustaining talk about school science is not a problem for either teacher or pupil.

A1 (Teacher): It will be what you call the pea shoot . . .
Comment: Teacher's account involves a theory of the classification of different parts of the pea.
A2 (Pupil): What kind of pea is it?
Comment: Teacher's theory not necessarily available; pupil's question involves another theory, concerned with the classification of different types of pea. (This possibility arose not from reading the transcript myself but in working through this bit of transcript with the teacher collaborating with me who explained the pupil's question in terms of pea classification – as, if you like, a pervasive feature of the folk biology of West Indian culture.)
A4 (Teacher): It's a dried pea, probably a dried pea that you can buy in a shop.
Comment: Pupil theorizing (in A2) not recognized – so teacher, in terms of his resource (knowledge of the structure of the pea), closes rather than explores the pupil's question, displaying to the pupil 'that there are *no* kinds of dried peas', or that, if there are, they are not relevant to his concerns as 'knowledge transmitter', and therefore not part of school science.
B1 (Teacher): Have you ever seen examples of when (soil) is produced?
Comment: The teacher's question involves 'ecological' relevance criteria to enable him to treat earth inside the worm in the context of its normal habitat.
B4 (Boy): No, I just seen holes in the grass.
Comment: The pupil also has an 'ecological' theory, but with different relevance, he describes the holes or burrows worms make.
B5 (Teacher): Have you ever seen anything else that might tell you there was a worm on the grass?

Comment:	The teacher listens, but in terms of his theory does not hear pupils saying 'holes' as appropriate.
B10 (Boy):	Leaves.
Comment:	The pupil displays further knowledge of 'worm life', which teacher through his relevance criteria does not appear to notice.

One problem raised for me by my interpretation of the transcript relates to the conventional wisdom that calls for relevance for the so-called less able child, where relevance is associated with assumed links to pupils' everyday life. The teacher, in this case, can be understood as invoking a theory of relevance which links worm casts to football fields. A quite different notion of relevance might involve the project of discovering pupil relevancies, their theories of the natural world, which are, even from these short transcripts, potentially available. This is quite different from accepting pupils' 'theories' uncritically or assuming that all pupils are potential Einsteins, but it would involve transforming typical conceptions of a lesson and of teaching, and accepting an inbuilt unpredictability of outcomes through the following of pupil initiatives rather than attempting to guide pupils to fit in to the teacher's prior plan of the lesson. This would inevitably confront the teacher with problems not resolvable within the classroom or lab alone, and would raise very concretely questions about timetables and school organization.

I have attempted a partial analysis of how pupil and teacher talk in school science might be made sense of by invoking the 'theories' that each uses as resources in the interaction but which are not themselves made explicit. This is then one possibility of displaying these resources, assumed by participants, which sustain and thus become recognizable as school science. I have suggested that in terms of his conception of school knowledge, the teacher does not recognize the pupil as himself a theorist. This can be seen as an aspect of treating science as an objectively available body of knowledge, and how its selective recognition is unproblematic except in terms of 'getting it over'.

What constitutes school science would, I suggest, be very different if teachers were to see themselves *and* pupils as scientific theorists. It would be, if you like, an attempt to de-alienate scientific knowledge, to recognize that knowledge is inextricably linked to its production by people, in a political context, not only in the school, which is dominated by a 'culture of positivism' which locates knowing in methods, not persons.

(b) School science, reflecting the individualism that is often seen as an inescapable part of scientific discovery, separates pupils from each other and any sense of link with others who have engaged in similar problems. Newton's laws of motion, for example, are learnt as disembodied 'facts',

separated from their relation to Newton as a man who like ourselves lived at a specific historical time with all its conflicts and troubles. This is not just a plea for adding the 'history of science' to school science but rather a questioning of the whole way in which a concept of scientific knowledge, as something for the individual to adapt to, is confirmed by science teaching practice.

(c) From its establishment, school science has sustained a separation of knowledge from its use. When the applications of some scientific understanding are referred to they are treated as a kind of appendix or set of properties; the density and reactivity of chlorine, for example, is followed by its use in bleaching and hygiene – as if uses did not embody in this case a whole history of public health regulations and state intervention into the contaminated water systems that were the by-products of Victorian capitalism. Even if a lesson starts with a concrete example of pupils' life experience – the way camping gas cookers work, for instance – the *real* problem is learning Boyle's Law and how volumes of gases change under pressure, not the practical problem of storing butane. It is difficult for pupils not to learn that it is deriving and doing calculations from Boyle's Law that is real science, whatever the teacher's intentions. In this way potentially exciting scientific discoveries, which provide ways of solving real problems and transforming aspects of our environment, become self-justifying and, for many, boring and difficult and pointless. Too often science educators see this difficulty as either intrinsic to the subject, a failure of his or her teaching, or a lack of ability of the pupils concerned. The abstract and mathematical character of physics is treated as an unchallengeable representation of scientific truth, widely expressed in the way the subject is examined and the status given to 'theoretical' physics. The possibility is hardly considered that this particular notion of 'truth', and its inhibiting social consequences for the divorce of science from technology, does not rest on any foundations of our understanding of nature, but on the emergence of a society in which mental and manual labour are increasingly separate. This is not to dismiss mathematics but to suggest that, in the schooling of science, the abstract certainties of mathematical models become more important than asking why we, whether scientists or others, might want such certainties and for what purpose.

It is perhaps not surprising that a science that is proud of its 'irrelevance' to human problems, and dismisses the technology which it informs and on which it depends, should have indirectly encouraged, among other things, an ultimately self-defeating anti-science, anti-technology counter-culture.

(d) School science separates pupils and teachers from themselves as people, by presenting it as the 'school subjects' – physics, chemistry and biology – forgetful not only of their history but of the physics,

chemistry and biology of ourselves and how we relate to our environment. This is perhaps best illustrated in biological and medical education. School biology is increasingly characterized by a reductionism to molecular levels of explanation. This reductionism, a relatively recent phenomenon of school biology is a reflection of much current research practice. What is involved is not a viewing of man's consciousness as interrelated with his biology, but an essentially passive view of man increasingly subject to control by genetic and other experts.[18] Not so dissimilar is Laing's account of his medical education in which as a future doctor he learnt to dissect bodies as if he too were not a body.

(e) In the process of schooling science, it has progressively been separated, in assumptions, organization and promotional hierarchies of the school, not only from technology and pupils' and teachers' everyday lives but from the range of other inquiries and activities within the school – history, art, politics, music and Literature. It is as if the particular way in which science was established, which, as Layton's example of the exclusion of geology illustrates well,[19] was more concerned with the protection of a particular social order than opening up ways in which the natural world might be understood and transformed, had become accepted as a kind of inevitable reality, rather than the product of particular historical circumstances.

In developing this critique of science in schools I have wanted to emphasize the assumptions about knowledge that have been embedded in the process of its schooling and the links between this process and changing political and economic circumstances. Equally it would be inaccurate to deny the 'real' progress that has taken place. There are more opportunities for children to question, to *do* rather than *see* experiments, to test ideas, in at least an overtly more open way, with more emphasis on thinking for oneself and less on the reproduction of textbook answers. The possibilities as well as the limitations of these changes within the given school context are well illustrated by an example of the Nuffield A level Physical Science course in practice.[20] In the school where I spent some time observing, the sixth form students spent one double session a week on their project and the rest on normal teaching. This double session was unlike anything I'd seen in a school lab before – even a sixth form. Staff and students drifted in and started various activities – without prior knowledge it was difficult, unlike in a normal class, to tell who was teacher, pupil or lab technician. The pupils were engaged in various stages of a variety of projects from examining the degeneration of albumen during the shelf life of eggs, to a study of the various strength properties of resin bonded fibre glass which is used for splints for those with broken or deformed limbs – particularly in African countries where rickets is widespread. From time to time a pupil would go up to a teacher and they would discuss the problem. Though the teacher might be able to point to an alternative method or technique or a useful reference source, it was the pupil who took the initiative and who knew more about the particular project at hand. In a less rigidly authoritarian school structure, the teachers too would doubtless have been engaged in projects of their own. But then, to put it crudely, teachers are supposed to transmit the knowledge created elsewhere, not actually to *create* knowledge themselves. Later in the week I sat in on several of the same group's non-project classes. The girls all came in, and sat in a row in the front bench facing where the teacher would be when she arrived. Except for a few whispers, they sat in silence, waiting for the teacher to come. She was friendly, not much older than her pupils, and obviously got on well with them. 'We are going to start by revising the periodic table', she began, 'What can you tell me about group 1?' Silence – In the next forty-five minutes, by relying largely on two of the girls, she was able to extract from them an account of the patterns of periodicity of the elements. The point I want to make is *not* that this was bad teaching, or that the teacher and pupils did not have a good relationship – they did.

I want to emphasize the difference between the two situations the girls and teacher found themselves in. Comparing the project class, which took up about one sixth of their time, with the typical non-project class I described, the initiative and responsibility was almost completely shifted from learner to teacher. A group of intelligent and responsible students who coped with complicated theories and sophisticated apparatus in their projects were transformed, in the interests of covering the syllabus, into passive, ignorant receptacles, feeling that there was no way that they could assert their control over the situation, and retain their identity as senior members of the school. I give this example in some detail as I think it illustrates the limited character of what have been called innovations in school science – even within their own terms.

This is not to claim that projects are in any sense a crucial strategy for liberating school science, for no methods are free from the possibilities of being coopted within an existing order. It is rather to point to the kind of contradictions within the existing contexts of school science that might be the basis of wider strategies for change.

4

CONCLUSIONS

Science education was envisaged, as David Layton tells us, by some early nineteenth century radicals like Richard Carlile as undermining dogma and leading to social emancipation.[21] The process and practice of the schooling of science, for all its changes, has, as I have tried to show, become almost the opposite – 'necessarily dogmatic' according to Jevons and many others, and producing technological domination rather than emancipation. This paper has largely been limited to the processes within education – the ways they have been part of a wider process of economic and political domination have been little more than hinted at. Inevitably oversimplifying, I would summarize what I have tried to say by suggesting that the schooling of science has produced three kinds of people, whose interrelations have up till now led to opposition to any attempts to realize the emancipatory potential Carlile saw. They are:

(a) 'Pure scientists', whose relations with nature are at best those of abstracted understanding. This is not to deny the discoveries that have been made, but to state that the purposes that have given meaning to the scientists' pursuit of truth have been success in and the sustaining of the scientific establishment.

(b) The 'applied scientist' whose identity is fundamentally pragmatic – given something to be done, he will work out how to do it. Ends are given, but no one asks by or for whom. Just as the pure scientist, from his early training, absolves himself from the uses to which his discoveries are put, rather than seeing that the discoveries themselves are inescapably linked to an economy on which he depends for support, so the applied scientist accepts that others define the goals that he has to achieve rather than seeing that his own means or technology itself presupposes a social order, set of priorities or goals.

(c) The identifiable failures of school science – the anti-science anti-technologists who can see science *only* as domination rather than that science as domination is itself a historical product, and the mass of people whose schooling teaches them that science is a specialized activity over which they neither have nor could have any control.

These 'successes' and 'failures' of school science have emerged from a society in which people have been separated from their knowledge of the natural world, which is experienced as external to them. The schooling of science, therefore, has begun with the knowledge, not the people, who have been expected to adapt to it. If, however, we start with a concept of man as part of nature *and* acting on nature, and that this acting on or appropriating has historically been in terms of particular purposes, then the abstracted pure scientist, the technologist, applied scientist, the anti-science intellectual and the mass of the scientifically ignorant are not just products of the schooling of science. We can see them as identities that have emerged in context of the history and development of modern capitalism – a society in which men have become increasingly separated from the products of their labour, mental and manual. The analysis and transformation of school science, and the separations that characterize it, then becomes a part of a much wider struggle for the realization of a socialist society. A radically different school science may not be possible in our society as it is, but unless we develop a critique that involves strategies for transforming it, any wider change in the social relations of production is likely to replace one form of domination by another.

NOTES

1 R. Schofield, 'Schools and Physics', *Physics Bulletin* (May 1975).
2. B. Woolnough, 'Happy facts about Physics', *Times Educational Supplement* (26 September 1975).
3. P. S. C. Matthews, 'Has Science Education a Future?', *School Science Review* (1975).
4. D. Layton, 'Science or Education?', *University of Leeds Review*, vol. 18 (1975). The quotations on the following pages are also taken from the same source.
5. D. Layton, *Science for the People* (London, George Allen & Unwin, 1973).
6. D. Layton, 'The Educational Work of the Parliamentary Committee of the British Association for the Advancement of Science', *History of Education*, vol. 5, No. 1 (1976).
7. M. F. D. Young, 'Curriculum Change: Limits and Possibilities', *Educational Studies*, vol. 1, No. 2 (1975). Reprinted in M. Young and G. Whitty (eds), *Society, State and Schooling* (Brighton, Falmer Press, 1976).
8. C. Green, Review of Layton (1973), *Radical Science Journal*, No. 2/3 (1975).
9. M. Shayer, 'Conceptual demands in the Nuffield O Level Physics Course', *School Science Review*, vol. 54 (1972), p. 186.
10. B. J. Hine, 'Political Bias in School Physics', *Hard Cheese*, No. 4/5 (1975).
11. J. Ravetz (*Scientific Knowledge and its Social Problems*, London, Oxford University Press, 1971) writes: 'these inherent limitations of the school teaching situation . . . must be recognized' (p. 207). He nowhere attempts to explain why they should be 'inherent'.
12. This account is based on an earlier draft of Charlie Clutterbuck's 'Death in a Plastics Factory' which appears in *Radical Science Journal*, vol. 4 (1976).
13. A good account of the Lucas Aerospace Combine Shop Stewards Committee proposals and some of their political implications is given by Dave Elliott in Nos. 12 and 13 of *Undercurrents*.
14. H. Braverman, *Labour and Monopoly Capital: The Degradation of Work in the Twentieth Century* (Monthly Review Press, 1974), and A. Gorz, 'Technical Intelligence and the Capitalist Division of Labour', *Telos*, vol. 12 (1971). Reprinted in M. Young and G. Whitty (eds), op. cit.
15. P. Corrigan and S. Frith, 'The Politics of Youth Culture', *Cultural Studies* 7/8 (1975), and D. Steed, *History as School Knowledge* (MA dissertation, University of London Institute of Education, 1974).
16. I owe this example to Anthony Hoskyns, Sir William Collins School, London.

17. This idea is also developed in Rosalind Driver's 'The Name of the Game', *School Science Review* (1975). I am grateful for a number of perceptive comments by Rosalind Driver on an earlier version of part of this paper – particularly her references to the 'Commodity knowledge' assumption of the 'Patterns' model of learning used by SCISP, and of the various independent learning schemes that have been developed claiming to 'solve' the problems of mixed ability classes.
18. This point is from a talk on 'Reductionism in Biology' by Jonathan Cooke of the Medical Research Council Unit, Mill Hill, though he is not responsible for extending its implications to school biology.
19. D. Layton (1975) quotes a witness to the Public School Commissioners as follows, 'the theory of geology could not be received by mere boys without violent disturbance to their religious beliefs'.
20. I am particularly grateful to Mr B. J. Hine for opportunities to see and discuss the teaching of the Nuffield Physical Science Course.
21. Richard Carlile, 'An Address to Men of Science' referred to by Layton (1976). See also Note 15 above.

GLOSSARY

PVC	Polyvinylchloride
BSSRS	British Society for Social Responsibility in Science
SCISP	Schools Council Integrated Science Project

18 History of science in the science curriculum: an historical perspective

• W. J. Sherratt

Proposals to establish development groups to stimulate and strengthen the teaching of the history of science and technology in school syllabuses have recently been accepted by the Education (Research) Committee of the Association for Science Education. This acceptance may well become a further landmark in developments that stretch back nearly one hundred years. This chapter discusses some of the factors underlying the early calls for history of science in the science curriculum of the English secondary school, and the roles seen for the historical material that were advocated up to the Second World War.

AWAKENING OF INTEREST

> It is desirable . . . to introduce into the teaching some account of the main achievements of science and of the methods by which they have been attained. . . . There should be more of the spirit, and less of the valley of dry bones. . . . One way of doing this is by lessons on the history of science. . . .[1]

The British Association's Report of 1917, *Science Teaching in Secondary Schools*, was one of several investigations into school science teaching during the first two decades of the twentieth century. This report, which attached particular importance to teaching science as 'a body of inspiring principles' and as 'a truly humanizing influence', is a landmark for history of science in school education. It is the first major British report to give prominence to history of science in the school curriculum. It clearly showed distinct roles for the history suggested. And it marked a peak in a growing interest in the use of historical material in school science courses.

Up to the closing years of the nineteenth century mention is hardly ever made of history of science in the secondary school curriculum. Many of the prominent advocates of school science – men such as Herbert Spencer, Thomas Huxley, John Tyndall and Canon Wilson – frequently showed interest in and knowledge of historical matters; but they made no sustained calls to introduce history of science into the schools. Likewise, nineteenth-century schemes of work, school science syllabuses and reports had little or no place for such matters. However, from the closing years of the century onwards allusions to history of science in the school curriculum are to be found with a steadily increasing frequency, and by the turn of the century it seems that some science teachers were using historical material in their courses. In 1903 the Rev A. H. Fish, of Arnold House School, Chester, described his science course which had 'evolved over the last fifteen years of teaching'. The lessons, which he described as 'very successful', closely followed the history of physical science and were accompanied by a good deal of biographical matter. Each lesson was grouped around one or two historical experiments '. . . surrounded as far as possible with the historical conditions under which they were originally performed'.[2] Four years earlier Florian Cajori's *A History of Physics* had been reviewed with the recommendation that:

> every teacher of physics and every library in schools should possess a copy . . . nothing is more stimulating to students of science than familiarity with the methods and results of great investigators.[3]

Oliver Lodge, physicist and first Principal of the new Birmingham University, believed that throughout physics teaching it was desirable to intermingle the facts of science with human interest and to elicit admiration for the 'pioneers of science'. He argued that the early stages of science were sure to be something like the early ideas of the child, and commended to science teachers the writings of Newton, Young, Fresnel and Carnot.[4] In *School World*, a monthly magazine for use in secondary schools edited by Richard Gregory, various references were made to possible uses of historical material in school science courses. Authors of articles and books on pedagogy increasingly referred to its potentialities. Especially prominent in this increasing awareness were Gregory and T. Percy Nunn, both of whose earlier writings were clearly reflected in the 1917 report *Science Teaching in Secondary Schools*.

FACTORS BEHIND THE UPSURGE OF INTEREST

During the decades around the turn of the century steps were being taken which would eventually lead to the recognition of history of science as an independent academic discipline. By the end of the nineteenth century a substantial body of literature on the histories of the sciences had been built up; the first University Chair for the subject was created in Paris in 1892; at the 1900 Paris International Congress of Historians Paul Tannery organized, for the first time, a separate section for history of science. The early years of the twentieth century saw the study being taken seriously by a significant number of scholars and becoming fashionable in certain quarters; fashion often plays a part in attracting people to a cause. Furthermore, when science was finding a place in the school curriculum during the closing decades of the nineteenth century much science teaching was done by classics masters. These masters with a background of classical studies and a probable awareness of Matthew Arnold's views on history of science in education[5] may well have been attracted by science histories. However, the most fundamental factors underlying the upsurge of interest seem to have been the attacks then being made on science, the unease of teachers about the existing science teaching, and the contemporary interest in the intellectual development of the individual.

1 *Attacks on science*

Nineteenth-century supporters of science education had argued for its inclusion into the school curriculum on the grounds of its utility and ever-increasing influence on everyday life, and because it gave a mental training at least as good as that given by the classics. But these arguments were not accepted uncritically. It was widely recognized that the goods upon which Britain's prosperity depended relied increasingly upon the application of scientific principles, that these principles should be diffused throughout the community, and that science must play a part in education if Great Britain was to maintain her position in the world. However, some people were quick to point out that it did not follow that every citizen need be a trained scientist; the well-being of the community also depended on other specialists – farmers, shipwrights and teachers – yet it did not follow that 'we must all study agriculture, naval architecture and pedagogics'.[6] It was argued that science did not give a good general training to the mental faculties; the training was in a restricted area and suitable only for scientists. Science itself was bitterly attacked, criticised as being no more than a cold-blooded, depersonalized and dehumanized intellectual feat, concerned only with things and not with people. The progress of science was seen by some as having no beneficial, or even a detrimental effect on the character, as destroying the mystery of the universe, as making the rainbow cold, even as being harmful to civilization. Various people rejected science as a means of learning about human nature, human society and culture.

The obvious counter to such attacks was to assert that science was truly a cultural and humanistic study, and to emphasize those aspects of science which supported this assertion. Hence the importance attached in *Science Teaching in Secondary Schools* and in the *Thompson Report*[7] to the humanizing influence of science. Many people saw history of science as a prime means of demonstrating the humanistic and cultural aspects of science.

2 Disquiet among science teachers

The *Thomson Report* summed up feelings that had been steadily increasing among science teachers during the previous decade. It asserted that both the content and the method of teaching secondary school science were in need of urgent reform. In its belief that science courses were too narrow and restricted the report echoed the views of those teachers who regretted the lack of an overall and comprehensive view of science. As regards teaching methods, it believed that too much emphasis on the laboratory was detrimental to other important aspects. Although the Thomson committee considered laboratory work essential, it deplored the waste of time caused by the insistence that individual pupil experiments were always preferable to teacher demonstrations. Again the committee was in accord with the sentiments of a number of teachers. From the nineteenth century onwards many teachers had wished to emphasize the experimental side of science and to give some understanding of its nature and methods. The heurism of Armstrong[8], which naturally focused attention on scientific method rather than on scientific knowledge, achieved both of these desires. However, from the early years of the twentieth century there was some reaction against measurement studies and the excessive use of heurism. It was not uncommon to find science teachers who no longer wished to rely purely on experimental work to teach about the methods of science.

This mood of unease within science teachers was paralleled by changes within history of science itself. There it was being argued that the study should not be of the histories of the individual sciences but a treatment of science as a whole; all of science should be included, an overall and comprehensive view was needed. This attitude seems to have been transferred to school science courses where, it was said, histories of science could 'enable a comprehensive view of science to be constructed' and 'do much to counteract the narrowness of view which sometimes accompanies specialization'.[9] At the same time the startling discoveries made in physics were forcing upon scientists new conceptions of the meaning of laws and theories of science, of the nature of science, and of its methodology. These discoveries were helping to arouse a new interest in examining the philosophical basis of science with the writings of Ernst Mach and Pierre Duhem marking a new and sustained interest in historical analysis by philosophers. Thus school teachers were now provided with the example and with further historical material for descriptive teaching of the nature of science and its methods.

3 *Parallelism between intellectual and historical development*

Early in the twentieth century, with faculty psychology increasingly under attack, there was a good deal of interest in the intellectual development of the individual. During the previous century several authors had argued that the history of mankind was indicative of the several stages through which every child passed to maturity.[10] This belief in parallelism, which was taken up around the turn of the century by Oliver Lodge, Benchara Banford, Percy Nunn and others, naturally focused attention on the history of science. During the succeeding decades the supposed parallel between individual and historical development was frequently used to justify the use of the historical method and the inclusion of historical material in school science courses.

Science Teaching in Secondary Schools recognized three especially conspicuous motives which had prompted men to understand nature. It called these the wonder, utility and systematizing motive, and related them to children of various ages. According to the report, at about the age of eleven children responded 'most surely and actively to the direct appeal of striking and beautiful phenomena', the wonder motive; from about twelve to sixteen the utility motive assumed mastery; the full advent of adolescence was necessary for the systematizing motive to have the first opportunity of predominance. Some twenty years later, again influenced by Nunn, the *Spens Report* described these motives as rhythms or successions of phases which were exhibited in the history of science as a whole, were constantly repeated in its smaller parts, and were exhibited in the changing interest a child had in a subject. Using history of science to illustrate these phases the report described how the history of electricity began in the eighteenth century:

> with a period of wonderment and delight in marvellous and bizarre phenomena for the first time brought to light . . . it passed to the exploitation of electricity in the service of man . . . and was completed by the contemporary phase – initiated by the great work of Clerk Maxwell – in which the physicist seeks to construct a picture of the whole material world in terms of electrical entities.[11]

In between these two reports several books on pedagogy discussed the same theme.

Discussion on the parallelism between intellectual and historical development seems to have been a further factor in the upsurge of interest in history of science in the early part of the twentieth century.

ROLES SEEN FOR HISTORY OF SCIENCE IN THE SCHOOL CURRICULUM

Many roles, some highly idiosyncratic, were suggested for history of science in school courses during the first half of the twentieth century. History of science was seen as a source of simple experiments for illustrating fundamental scientific principles; it was a means of understanding modern complexity by teaching from the simple to the complicated; it was useful for aspects that did not lend themselves to an experimental treatment; it was thought valuable when the time was limited (and criticised as too time-consuming); it was able to provide a moral training. It could even supply the teacher 'with a possible method for presenting the subject [science] when all other is lacking'.[12] But from the early years three roles were argued most frequently. History of science was a means of demonstrating the cultural and humanistic aspects of science; it was highly suitable for teaching about the nature and methods of science; it could counter over-specialization.

1 *To demonstrate the humanistic and cultural aspect of science*

The assertion that science possessed a cultural value and exerted a truly humanizing influence became the argument used most commonly to promote the claims of science in the school curriculum during the first half of the twentieth century. For many decades there had been widespread agreement among science teachers that their courses needed humanizing and needed to emphasize the cultural aspect of science. But there was no consensus of opinion on how this should be achieved. Nor was there precise agreement on the meanings of the terms. Consequently, the use of history of science was only one of the several suggested ways of meeting the humanizing and cultural requirements.

The words humanistic and cultural were closely linked and often considered synonymous in the minds of people in the nineteenth and early twentieth centuries. For a good deal of the nineteenth century the narrow classical interpretation of humanism – pertaining to classical studies, Latin and Greek language and literature – dominated the secondary schools and universities. In the second half of the century the work of Darwin, Spencer and Huxley profoundly influenced this prevailing concept and helped to develop scientific humanism, a humanism based on scientific discovery, the empirical approach, and rational evaluation of human relations. Increasingly this scientific humanism took on implications far wider than the natural sciences themselves: it became a movement aimed at the total reform of the educational process; scientific ways of thinking and acting became extended over a field wider than science itself; science was seen as one aspect of a total cultural or social system leading to man's progress.

The classic nineteenth-century debate between traditional and scientific humanism came in the writings of T. H. Huxley and Matthew Arnold over the relative importance to education of the natural sciences and the more traditional humanities. Both Huxley and Arnold agreed that humanism, whether classical or scientific, was concerned with promoting human culture, and that culture meant knowing the best that has been thought and said in the world. Their writings in this debate, especially those of Arnold, clearly show that humanism and culture involved history of science, and that history of science had a definite place in education:

> . . . by knowing ancient Greece, I understand knowing her as the giver of . . . the guide to a free and right use of reason and to scientific method, and the founder of our mathematics and physics and astronomy and biology . . . By knowing modern nations, I mean . . . knowing also what has been done by such men as Copernicus, Galileo, Newton, Darwin.[13]

Here lay the seed for the later advocates of history of science to counter the criticisms that science was inhuman and lacked a cultural value.

The most common and basic historical interpretation placed on the term humanistic aspect of science was little more than a truism. Science was an activity carried out by human beings, thus by including in science courses something of the lives and works of past scientists, courses would become humanized. A consequence of this interpretation was that scientific biographies became the most common type of historical material associated with school science courses during the first half of the twentieth century. F. W. Westaway, in his monumental and highly influential *Science Teaching*, talks about how the imagination of the young may be kindled by a knowledge of the long and patient struggle associated with the great names in science, 'the series of lucky accidents, bold hypotheses, painstaking studies, the failures, disappointments and the successes', of how boys like to read of the quarrels of the great men of science, and of how biographies show that science has transcended national boundaries.[14] Percy Nunn in *The New Teaching* says:

> The prime contribution of the heroes of science to the world's cultural wealth is not the scientific method but the scientific life . . . Our proper aim, then, is to make our pupils feel . . . what it is to be . . . inside the skin of the man of science, looking out through his eyes as well as using his tools, experiencing not only something of his labours, but also something of his sense of joyous intellectual adventure.[15]

An important aspect of many such writings was the appeal to make biographical detail more than a narrow description of the lives and works of scientists. There were suggestions of setting the historical facts into the wider context of their contemporary intellectual and social background, and an emphasis on evaluating a period from within. Nunn had spoken of getting inside the skin of a man and looking out through his eyes. H. H. Cawthorne, a science teacher in the 1930s, reiterated this approach.

> The boy should project himself into the life of the scientist . . . He may be Gilbert of Colchester . . . he must be made to feel that he is living in the age following Columbus; he must be conscious of the spirit of discovery which surrounds him . . .

Cawthorne had no time for mere details of lives and encyclopaedic sequences of facts.

> If a study of the life and work of Davy [is as below], then the subject were better left alone: 'Davy Sir Humphrey (1778–1829) – while at Bristol he respired 20 quarts of nitrous oxide – he electrolyzed gypsum in solution, and solid potash (isolating potassium for the first) – he predicted Ba, Sr, Ca, Mg, Si, Al and Zr – he explained the nature of chlorine and . . . and . . . lamp.'[16]

A survey of school science textbooks of the period reveals a good deal of the type of material that Cawthorne would have wished left alone; if they contained any biographical material most frequently it was little more than a series of names, dates, pictures, and a few historical achievements. Occasionally some school science texts appeared with historical material that provided more genuinely a cultural background. Such a work is R. G. Mitton's *Mechanics and Hydrostatics*. Nearly one-quarter of the chapter on the motion of falling bodies is devoted to science from the Middle Ages through to Newton. The following chapter, on Newton's laws of motion, begins with a brief outline of the life and work of Newton. This material includes comments on the state of science during the Dark Ages, the preservation of Greek learning in the libraries of cloisters, the telescopic discoveries of Galileo, and Newton's discoveries in mathematics and optics. None of this material is immediately relevant or necessary for an understanding of the motion of falling bodies or Newton's laws of motion. The tone and width of the writing suggest that the author placed some value on the cultural aspect of the background material. Significantly, Mitton was at the time a master of Clifton College and acknowledged a debt to E. J. Holmyard, the General Editor of the series.[17]

Away from the school science textbooks the picture was brighter. Both the increasing number of specialized history of science journals and educational journals such as *School Science Review* carried at regular intervals biographical articles more in keeping with the sentiments of Cawthorne; additionally there was a spate of books of scientific biographies, often addressed to the general reader and young student, many of which were highly readable and authoritative. It can fairly be said that if any science teacher wished to humanize his courses by including scientific biographies suitable and adequate material was available, especially if he went outside school science textbooks.

A wider interpretation of humanistic embraced phrases such as the romance of science and the cultural aspect of science. Notable for his suggested use of historical material to bring out the romance of science was F. W. Sanderson, Headmaster of Oundle School from 1892 to 1922. Sanderson, who put into practice many of his suggestions, believed that the function of the science teacher was to open out ideals and inspire pupils with a love of the natural world. He believed that groups of pupils should prepare historical exhibitions with experiments and demonstrations to illustrate the lives and works of great investigators. The basis of these exhibitions, which would be left in working order and used for teaching purposes, would be books from the classics of science together with original papers. Sanderson was particularly keen that pupils should read original papers.

> Read Archimedes . . . Read Faraday's papers . . . mark the long processes of experiments . . . the diversity of methods, the trials and failures, uncertainties, doubts and suggestiveness, the atmosphere of discovery . . .[18]

But the success of Sanderson's methods was not universally agreed. Shortly after his death in 1922, Armstrong commented that although the boys from Sanderson's school were full of enthusiasm they had insufficient knowledge of the fundamentals of science and were undisciplined thinkers. In 1944 the *Fleming Report* stated that although Sanderson had introduced the firstly really drastic changes in the curriculum that the public schools had ever witnessed, they had little effect on the other public schools.

The relationship of science to modern culture was seen in the twentieth century as profound and important with science playing a significant and active part in shaping both the intellectual and material changes that were occurring in contemporary society. Moreover, modern culture was recognized as the accumulation and synthesis of varying contributions made by science and technology. This had a particular relevance to the educational value of the history of science; people argued that to appreciate and understand how and why modern culture and society came to their existing state it was necessary to know and understand the ideas and achievements of the past. Attempts seem to have been made, especially in the 1930s, to encourage science teachers to consider the social consequences of scientific discoveries and to use history of science to do so but seemingly with few practical results. In 1942 Humby and James pointed out that schools had failed to demonstrate to future citizens that scientific discoveries were social activities with social consequences:

> . . . science is taught as a collection of laws and facts rather than as a constantly growing body of knowledge with social implications of vital importance . . . pupils too rarely realize . . . that the pursuit of scientific knowledge is a social activity, that science has the power to affect society and society the power to direct science. The relation between science and history is taught, if at all, in the most uninteresting and irrelevant way. The social repercussions of science are relegated to a few isolated industrial applications.[20]

2 *To teach about the nature and methods of science*

The late nineteenth-century resurgence of interest in the philosophy of science has already been noted. This resurgence was reflected throughout the succeeding decades in the many suggestions made for using historical material to teach about the nature, methods and philosophy of science. When authors wrote of the nature and methods of science they frequently had quite specific goals in mind. Pupils needed to see that scientific enquiry involved the forming of inferences and hypotheses, with their testing and possible overthrow; they should understand the transient nature of scientific laws, theories and truths; they should appreciate how a scientific truth differed from a religious truth; they should be aware of some of the theories which dominated contemporary scientific thought, and realize how these theories and theories in general grew; they should be conscious of how theories unified apparently disconnected facts and often suggested fresh problems to attack; they should note the paradoxical aspect of some of the great men of science, radical in the introduction of their own new ideas yet frequently conservative in later resisting new 'truths'; they should be presented with science not as a collection of facts but as a method. History of science frequently provided the material to achieve these goals.

Archer Vassall, who wanted pupils to be familiar with 'typical instances of the overthrow of generally accepted theories', cited as examples Galileo's rebuttal of Aristotle, and the problem of combustion and phlogistic theory. Vassall let the pupils perform relevant experiments, watch demonstrations, then hear a lecture on the history and overthrow of the theory. In the same report I. M. Drummond wrote that pupils should realize how great theories grew and unified apparently disconnected facts, with 'an historical treatment of the molecular and atomic theories helping towards such a realization'.[20] Her ideas on the teaching of astronomy have more than a little resemblance to what was to appear nearly fifty years later in Nuffield O-level physics! In the early 1920s Eric Holmyard argued that not only was the historical method an appropriate way to teach the nature of science, but it was the *only* way in which a clear understanding of the nature of a scientific truth could be successfully achieved. Holmyard believed that the average boy had difficulty in understanding that the word of science was not final and absolute, that the 'truth' of science and the 'truth' of religion were totally different conceptions. Perhaps he had his tongue in his cheek when he argued that to allow a boy to believe that the word of science was final could affect his whole character, but he was quite explicit in his statement that the historical method was not one of several equally good schemes of teaching chemistry. It was the only method.[21]

Several examination syllabuses of the inter-war period did ask for some understanding of the nature and methods of science. But a sample of the corresponding science examination papers shows that it was rare for questions to be set on this theme.

3 *To counter over-specialization*

The British Association's *Science Teaching in Secondary Schools* asserted that:

> History and biography enable a comprehensive view of science to be constructed . . . (and) supply a solvent to that artificial barrier between literary studies and science which a school timetable usually sets up.

A year later the *Thomson Report* stated that a knowledge of historical matters could overcome the unfortunate situation,

> that many of the ablest boys who enter the public schools pass on to the universities ignorant of science and with little or no idea of its importance as a factor in the progress of civilization or of its influence on human thought;

it believed that courses with an historical content would be profitable to both science and non-science specialists and '. . . would do much to counteract the narrowness of view which sometimes accompanies specialization'. On numerous other occasions during the first half of the twentieth century, history of science was suggested as a means of providing an overall and comprehensive view of science, and as a way of countering the related issues of excessive specialization and the division between the arts and the sciences in the advanced stage of schooling.

In the pre-matriculation stage the problem was seen more as a lack of width in the science courses rather than scientific subjects being studied to the total exclusion of the arts. In the early years of the century boys' schools concentrated mainly on physics and chemistry and girls' schools on biology, all in a very restricted form. A criticism of such courses was that they seeemd to be planned as if the sole object was to lay the foundation for specialized study of science at a later period even though most pupils would never make such a study. As suggested earlier, it may be that the calls to use history of science as a means of providing the desired overall and comprehensive view sprang from the type of history of science advocated by Tannery and later Sarton. Both urged that the study should not be of the histories of the individual sciences but a treatment of science as a whole; all of science should be included as indeed should all history; an overall and comprehensive view was needed. But to talk in such general terms was a good deal more simple than to construct science courses on such a basis. If such a construction was ever attempted it was not widely publicised. Although all seven of the suggested schemes of work in *Science Teaching in Secondary Schools* made some reference to history none used it to give an overall and comprehensive view; comprehensiveness came from including some astronomy, physics, chemistry and biological science within their own separate compartments. And as the time progressed calls for such a use of history of science seemed to die away. During the inter-war period the main responses to calls for wider pre-matriculation science courses were the establishment of General Science, and for botany to be replaced by biology and taught increasingly to both girls and boys. On the other hand, calls for history of science to counter post-matriculation over-specialization and act as a bridge between the arts and the sciences persisted throughout the whole of the period under consideration.

Prior to World War I sixth-form work and advanced courses were largely uncertain or non-existent in a great many of the grammar schools. It was only after the war with the increase in the number of grammar school pupils, the changes in the examinations available, and the establishment of special grants that sixth-form work and advanced courses were increased and strengthened.

The intention in both the Higher School Certificate, introduced in 1917, and the new grant regulations was for some degree of specialization supplemented by more general studies. However, some people feared that the hopes of a balanced curriculum catering for the differing needs of sixth-form pupils would not be fulfilled, and developments appear to show that such fears had justification. Higher School Certificate imposed on many schools a heavy burden of academic work often quite unsuitable for those pupils not going on to some form of higher education. Standards demanded in main courses seemed to be driven steadily upwards, partly because of university requirements and competition between schools. Many teachers valued and defended a high degree of specialization, seeing it as the best means of maintaining standards and ensuring the intellectual development of their pupils. In many cases the sciences were studied to the total exclusion of the arts, and vice versa. Furthermore, there was often a narrow concentration within the science subjects themselves. It was against such a background that calls were made for history of science to be used as a possible way of countering excessive specialization and bridging the gap between the sciences and the humanities.

As a field of knowledge history of science could be seen as both a science and a humanity, a means of giving a literary appreciation to scientists, scientific knowledge to non-scientists, and demonstrating the cultural aspect of science to both sides. The *Thomson Report* in 1918 suggested details for the contents of such courses. At the third annual meeting of the Science Masters' Association history of science figured in a discussion on post-certificate science for non-specialists.[22] In the opening paper given to a 1923 conference on science teaching in schools and colleges Sir William Tilden regretted the specialization in modern courses and urged that time be found for history of science.[23] There were calls for history of science to be used in a similar role in the universities. At the Second Congress of the Universities of the Empire, held in 1921, Cecil H. Desch spoke of the place of humanities in the education of men of science and saw the role of history of science in education as a link between the sciences and the humanities;[24] a theme he repeated at the 1926 British Association meeting at Oxford. A. E. Heath, a university teacher, believed that honours degrees caused many science teachers to become too highly specialized at the expense of wider issues, and called for a sound knowledge of both the physical and biological sciences together with a knowledge of history and philosophy of science.[25] Further such examples abound. Perhaps it is true to say that during the inter-war period the role advocated most frequently for history of science in education was that it could act as a bridge between the two cultures and counter over-specialization.

It has been argued[26] that during this period women teachers, who dealt with a smaller proportion of university entrants than did men, expressed more serious doubts about intensive specialization than did their male counterparts. Those doubts may well have been one of the factors underlying their interest in the history of science, an interest which, on the basis of reports of annual meetings of the Association of Women Science Teachers, was possibly greater than the interest shown by science masters. This is an area which may well be worth further investigation.

NOTES AND REFERENCES

1. BAAS, *Science Teaching in Secondary Schools*, 1917, 18–19. This report was drawn up by a committee chaired by Richard Gregory and consisting almost entirely of teachers with secondary school experience. After a brief consideration of the existing methods and scope of secondary school science teaching, it gave seven schemes of work as specimen courses.

2. Fish, A. H., 'Science in a liberal education', *School World*, 1903, **5**, 354 ff.
3. *School World*, 1899, **1**, 157.
4. See, for example, Lodge, O., *Pioneers of Science* (Macmillan, 1893) and *School Teaching and School Reform* (Williams and Norgate, 1905).
5. See the discussion on the humanistic and cultural aspect of science.
6. Livingstone, R. W., *A Defence of Classical Education* (Macmillan, 1917).
7. B. Educ., *Natural Science in Education (Thomson Report)* (HMSO, 1918). This report was produced by a government committee chaired by the physicist J. J. Thomson. It gave special consideration to the position of science in secondary schools and universities.
8. See Brock, W. H., *H. E. Armstrong and the Teaching of Science* (Cambridge University Press, 1973).
9. *Thompson Report*, p. 78.
10. These included Pestalozzi, Froebel, Comte, Spencer and Zoller.
11. B. Educ., *Spens Report* (1938), p. 162.
12. Cawthorne, H. H., *Science in Education* (Oxford University Press, 1930), p. 69.
13. Arnold, M., 'Literature and science', *Discourses in America* (Macmillan, 1885), pp. 91–2.
14. Westaway, F. W., *Science Teaching* (Blackie and Son, 1929), pp. 11–12. Westaway, teacher, headmaster and HMI was the author of several books of which *Science Teaching* was perhaps the most influential. In this work he was quite explicit that whether or not science was taught on an historical basis, some definite instruction in the history of science should be included in every science course (p. 378). During World War II, Westaway was much concerned about the apparent indifference of scientists towards the world's urgent problems. This he attributed to the high degree of specialization in the schools which had forced scientists away from the humanities. He expressed the fear that 'during my professional career, I advocated the claims of science teaching much too strongly and I am now quite sure that the time often devoted to laboratory practice and to the purely mathematical side of science, more especially chemistry and physics, was far too great'.
15. Nunn, T. P., 'Science', John Adams (ed.), *The New Teaching* (Hodder and Stoughton, 1919).
16. Cawthorne, op. cit., pp. 78–9.
17. Eric Holmyard showed interest in both the natural sciences and history while a student at Cambridge: he read chemistry, physics, botany and zoology from 1908 to 1910, history 1910–11 and chemistry 1911–13. His early teaching career was at Bristol Grammar School and Marlborough College. While at Clifton College from 1920 to 1940 he spent a good deal of his time writing both school chemistry texts and on the history of science. His *Elementary Chemistry* sold over half a million copies between 1925 and 1960. Although in the Preface to his *Higher School Certificate Inorganic Chemistry* he stated 'the allotment of space to individual topics is roughly in proportion to

the frequency with which these topics appear in the examination papers', he recognized that the cultural aspect of science was seldom reflected in examinations but that it should appear in school textbooks. He did a good deal to encourage others to write textbooks which included some history and he vigorously urged the introduction of historical material into school science courses.

18. Wells, H. G., *Sanderson of Oundle* (Chatto and Windus, 1924), p. 242.

19. Humby, S. R. and E. J. F. James, *Science and Education* (Cambridge University Press, 1942), p. 49.

20. *Science Teaching in Secondary Schools*, pp. 31 and 58 ff.

21. Holmyard, E. J., 'The historical method of teaching chemistry', *S.S.R.*, 1923–4, 20, **5**, 227–33.

22. 'Post-certificate science for non-science specialists', *S.S.R.*, 1921–2, 11, **3**, 119–25.

23. 'Conference on science teaching in schools and colleges', *S.S.R.*, 1922–3, 15, **4**, 158.

24. Desch, C. H., 'The place of the humanities in the education of men of science', Alex Hill (ed.), *Second Congress of the Universities of the Empire, 1921, Report of Proceedings*, pp. 25–30.

25. Heath, A. E., 'The philosophy of science as a school subject', *S.S.R.*, 1919–20, 4, **1**, 131–4.

26. Edwards, A. D., *The Changing Sixth Form in the Twentieth Century* (Routledge and Kegan Paul, 1970), p. 35.

19 Curriculum rhetoric and social control: a perspective on recent science curriculum development

• R. H. Millar

This chapter outlines an approach towards interpreting the influence of social factors on the directions in which secondary school science curricula have developed. In particular, the influence of the institutional context of comprehensivization on emerging science curriculum materials in Britain in the 1960s is explored. From a survey of curriculum writings of this period, it is suggested that authors have access to a matrix of tacit notions (cultural resources) involving, among others, the mentality of the learner, the nature of science and of the work of the scientist, and the style of appropriate science instruction. It is argued that the way in which these resources are deployed suggests a concern on the part of curriculum authors with issues of social control, both in society at large and within the schools themselves.

INTRODUCTION

The period since the mid 1950s has seen the emergence of a very large number of proposals for new school science curricula. That the phenomenon transcends national boundaries is clearly shown by the compendium published by the International Clearinghouse on Science and Mathematics Curricular Developments. The seventh report of the International Clearinghouse published in 1970 (Lockard 1970) lists over 200 such projects. About half of these are American in origin; the others come from a variety of industrialized and Third World countries. The appearance of this plethora of new curricula contrasts with the comparatively stable situation which had obtained for the previous half century. What reasons can be found for such a widespread simultaneous perception of the shortcomings of existing curricula? Which goals are these new curricula intended to achieve more efficiently than their predecessors?

To some extent, of course, the recent curriculum developments (from about 1962 onwards) are products of the prevailing atmosphere of change created by influential earlier curricula – notably those of the Physical Sciences Study Committee (PSSC), the Chemical Bond Approach Project (CBA), the Chemical Educational Materials Study (CHEMS), and the Biological Sciences Curriculum Study (BSCS), all originating from the United States. The very extent of the curriculum 'avalanche' which has ensued suggests, however, that the style of these early innovations, and indeed the very notion of science curriculum innovation itself, resonated particularly well with the social and political context into which they were launched.

This chapter concerns itself with the rhetoric which has surrounded these new curriculum proposals, rather than with their content. Statements about objectives and aims have come to be accepted as the vehicle through which much of the curriculum author's strategy is conveyed. Whilst curriculum content is constrained by what is, and is not, possible within the classroom, the associated rhetoric is relatively free from such limitations and is, thus, perhaps, a more fruitful source of insight into the attitudes both of its authors, and, of course, of its readers (insofar as the authors are in touch with their audience).

In terms of numbers of new science curricula, Britain is in the vanguard of the movement. In this chapter I wish to suggest that this enthusiasm for curriculum innovation in Britain can be made intelligible, at least in part, in terms of the wider social framework, both in British society as a whole, and in the narrower context of the classroom. In doing so, I will be deploying my own descriptive categories on the rhetoric which surrounds these innovations. Categorizations already exist, of course. The educational debates of the 60s and 70s have led inevitably to the 'pigeon-holing' of certain constellations of apparently opposing views. Terms such as 'progressive' or 'traditional', which may initially be conceived as descriptive, soon acquire pejorative overtones. The very choice of descriptive labels can imply a moral evaluation of the rhetorical position described. More significantly, the language itself can appear to endorse the objectivity of one particular interpretation of this debate, by contrasting the 'altruistic' stance of the 'progressive' with the more 'selfish' and 'élitist' 'traditional' position. I wish, instead, to sketch the outline of an explanatory scheme which deals more even-handedly with the differing positions which actors adopt. By identifying a *common* concern of the participants in this educational debate with questions of control in society and within educational institutions, some preliminary steps may be taken towards an understanding of the directions in which science curricula are currently moving.

THE TWO MENTALITIES

Shapin and Barnes (1976, 1977) have recently analysed the debates which surrounded the introduction of science into the school programme in England in the early nineteenth century. They have attempted to relate the statements of significant actors to the concerns of the interest groups to which the actors belonged, rather than looking for 'some objective ''educational problem'' which wise contemporaries perceived' (Johnson 1970). Shapin and Barnes (1976, p. 231) have argued that:

> All pedagogical writings . . . tend to be developed on the basis of particular conceptions of the constitution of the mind, the nature of thought, and the relationship of knowledge and thinking. Such conceptions may take the form of explicit psychological theories, or they may be informal, taken-for-granted models and pre-suppositions to which appeal is routinely made as arguments proceed.

From early nineteenth century rhetorical writings on education, they suggest that the educational debate is conducted within a framework of tacit and widely-shared assumptions concerning types of mentality. In particular, they delineate two common 'models' of mentality, which they term 'gnostic' and 'banausic'. The former is associated in the rhetoric with the thought of the 'higher orders' in society, the latter with that of the 'lower ranks' (the banausoi). Three contrasts between gnostic and banausic thought are identified.

The first sets the *intellectual, verbal* and *abstract* qualities of gnostic thought against the *sensual* and *concrete* nature of banausic thought. (A subtheme of this dichotomy is the contrast between gnostic *profundity* and banausic *superficiality*.)

The second contrast is between banausic *simplicity* and gnostic *complexity*. These are represented in the writings of the time as appropriate to the situations of, respectively, the worker/artisan and the man of letters. The complexity of gnostic thought is portrayed as *harmonious* and *stable*, in contrast to the *unbalanced* and *volatile* thought of the banausoi.

Finally, the *active* use of thought by those of a gnostic mentality is set against the *passive* banausic mental processes.

The scheme may be usefully summarized as shown in Figure 1.

Shapin and Barnes argue that there was a widespread consensus in the use of these notions of mental type and that they were deployed as a rhetorical resource consistently by authors with a wide divergence of interest. In writings relating to the education of adults, the two mentalities are

	Gnostic	*Banausic*
Thought	Intellectual	Sensual
	abstract	concrete
	profound	superficial
	verbal/symbolic	non-verbal/non-symbolic
	Complex	Simple
	harmonious	unbalanced
	stable	volatile
	mediated	direct
Responses to input	Active	Passive
	volitional	automated/mechanical
	purposive	lacking in purpose

Figure 1

assigned to the two main classes of society (as perceived by the writers themselves). When dealing with child pedagogy, however, Shapin and Barnes (1976, p. 240) note that *all* children are 'initially characterised as possessing a banausic mentality'. However, the education of children of the 'higher orders' aimed to transform this mentality into a gnostic one; whilst the education of the children of the 'lower orders' sought no such transformation.

These ideas were current in the debate about whether science should be introduced into elementary education in England in the late 18th and early 19th centuries. They were held both by the conservative writers who wanted little or no education for the working classes *and* by reformers who worked for the introduction of science. Shapin and Barnes see both groups as interested in social control. In their account, the conservatives feared the results of educating the masses, whilst the reformers were experimenting with types of control, since they feared that to do nothing would lead to social disorder and anarchy: the experience of the French Revolution may have been a significant factor in producing both these attitudes.

THE CONTINUING AVAILABILITY OF THE 'MENTALITIES' RESOURCE

I want to consider the extent to which the tacit rhetorical resource of the 'two mentalities', which Shapin and Barnes describe, is still available to writers today. The intervening century and a half has seen a change in the tone of educational writings. The contemporary banausoi (if they exist!) could scarcely be described as: 'Beings who have hardly ever once . . . made a real effort to direct and concentrate the action of their faculties on anything abstracted from the objects palpable to the senses . . . The abstracted, contemplative, and elevated ideas of the celestial happiness are far above their apprehension' (Foster 1826). However, a rather similar idea can be expressed as follows:

> At the level of knowledge and understanding, those thinking processes which are in the highest categories have been introduced for only experiential purposes in the early years and it is possible that the least able pupils *may* not be able to work at this level of generalisation and abstraction even at the end of their school careers. Equally the desire for objectivity in the assessment of different possibilities *may* be too difficult an attitude to develop in some of the pupils with whom this report deals (Scottish Education Department 1969).

Shapin and Barnes (1976, p. 231) state that in the period they consider, 'writers frequently laid bare their assumptions and cognitive models, as well as their goals and interests, in an unusually clear and distinct fashion'. The contemporary polemicist is certainly more circumspect as regards his goals and interests; but the passage above would appear to indicate that, while he feels obliged to be more guarded in his tone, he still has access to cognitive models like the 'two mentalities' model.

The two groups within the school to whom the gnostic and banausic labels are now assigned are not *primarily* distinguished along class lines. The pupil following an academic-certificate course is seen as the future (perhaps, even, the present) possessor of a gnostic mentality: the 'less-able' or 'non-certificate' child is the permanent banausos. Only insofar as these categories correlate with social class (as normally defined) do the mentalities carry their original 'class' connotations.

Kershaw and Scott, writing in *School Science Review* in March 1975, describe their ROSLA group of pupils in terms reminiscent of Shapin and Barnes's banausoi:

> These pupils considered themselves a captive group characterised by low motivation, slowness of thought, learning and perception. They also possessed limited powers of retention and recall . . . emotional, restless, distrustful of teachers and authority, and lacking in personal organisation and self-discipline . . . Many of these pupils become easily bored, giving rise to the associated behavioural problems in school or in later life.

These comments appear in the context of a plea for a modular science course for such pupils. The picture of the pupil presented is here used to support the case for such features of the course as: regular regrouping to avoid the possibility of lengthy pupil-teacher or pupil-pupil mismatches; pupils' experiencing a variety of teachers and approaches; the modular approach enabling staff to develop their own modules; and an emphasis on education for leisure. However, the *uses* of the 'mentalities' resource will be discussed in due course; our present concern is merely to establish the continuing availability of the resource itself.

Discussions of methods suitable for mixed-ability group teaching draw on aspects of the 'mentalities' model. It is argued that such methods:

> . . . aim to provide extra *depth* for the brighter children . . . in the Further Work questions at the end of each sheet. All the children get *through* the same course, they don't all take it to the same depth. (Kamm 1970)
>
> Bright children will not be distinguished by how far they get *through* the course, but by the *depth* to which they study the topics in the course. (Banister 1970)

The profound/superficial dichotomy seems implicit here.

The greater need of the banausoi for concrete experience is often allied to an endorsement of practical classes. The success of such methods with non-certificate classes has been seen by some teachers as:

> . . . one of the main points made by those who try out practical-type lessons. The pupils enjoy them, are enthusiastic and excited, particularly those of lower ability. (Marking 1970)

The writings of individual teachers and educationalists demonstrate the continued availability of the idea of distinct mentalities as a cultural resource; but they do not so clearly demonstrate how the resource can be used, since most individuals have only limited opportunity to make recommendations or instigate wide-ranging changes. For that reason, I wish now to turn to official curriculum publications; to show that these are also able to draw on the idea of mentalities; and to consider what use they make of this resource in their arguments.

CURRENT USES OF THE 'MENTALITIES' MODEL

In developing the remainder of this argument, I want to consider centrally the document *Curriculum Paper 7: Science for General Education*, produced in 1969 by the Consultative Committee on the Curriculum of the Scottish Education Department. The publication of this document has had considerable influence in Scotland on actual classroom practice and has stimulated significant research effort. Closely related to this curriculum paper, however, is its predecessor, *From School to Further Education* (1963), known as the Brunton Report (Scottish Education Department 1963). The English 'equivalent' of the Scottish Brunton Report is the Newsom Report, *Half our Future* (Ministry of Education 1963), to which I will also make some reference. Newsom and Brunton considered the education of the less-able pupil in England and Scotland, respectively. The remit of *Curriculum Paper* 7 was:

> to carry out a comprehensive review of the present curriculum in science in –
> (1) the first two years of secondary education
> (2) the later years of secondary education for non-academic pupils with particular reference to the implications of the report *From School to Further Education*.

The curriculum paper states certain objectives of the curriculum, both cognitive and affective, and observes: 'Different learning experiences for pupils with different cognitive styles are appropriate for achieving the same objectives' (Scottish Education Department 1969, paragraph 49). The term 'cognitive style' is particularly value-free; the implicit pigeon-holing according to mentality type which is found in the Brunton Report or the Newsom Report often carries more pejorative overtones.

These documents deploy models and distinctions very strongly reminiscent of those described by Shapin and Barnes. Their first contrast (between the 'concrete' and the 'abstract') is particularly evident. For instance, the Brunton Committee, writing in 1963 of the 65% of Scottish secondary pupils who do not follow courses leading to the Ordinary or Higher Grade of the Scottish Certificate of Education state: 'As a general rule, they are not interested in academic learning and prefer physical activity to thinking; their mental activity is stimulated by real things and happenings in the physical world rather than by ideas and concepts'. The same concrete/abstract dichotomy is familiar to the authors of Schools Council *Working Paper 1*: 'The Newsom pupil commonly finds it easier to think in concrete rather than abstract terms, and . . . comes somewhat slowly to a generalisation or theoretical idea' (Schools Council 1965).

In the particular context of science teaching, this leads the Newsom Committee to conclude:

> The need for practical work . . . is probably much greater for our pupils than for the abler ones. An abler pupil can generalise . . . from a few examples and apply his general conclusion to other situations, but our pupils need a greater variety of experience before generalisations can begin to form in their minds (Ministry of Education 1963, paragraph 429).

This need for concrete experience, and the corresponding difficulty in arriving at generalization, are seen as producing a passive attitude to knowledge. To quote the Schools Council authors again: 'Relationships upon which significance will depend, which may arise spontaneously in the minds of their abler fellows, will need to be made abundantly manifest to . . . pupils . . . of lower ability' (Schools Council 1965).

There is evidence here of a certain urgency; the 'relationships' between different cognitive contents in the curriculum *must* be seen by the pupils. The Newsom Committee betray the same anxiety when they pose the rhetorical question (regarding 'their' pupils): 'If they are slower at seeing connections and arriving at generalisations than others, is it not all the more necessary that they should be shown that the connections exist?' (Ministry of Education 1963, paragraph 439).

Shapin and Barnes's second dichotomy (between 'simplicity' and 'complexity') is also available to the Brunton Committee. In contrast to the harmonious sequential development of an academic course with able pupils, 'a strictly formal and logical development of a subject is not essential to the pupils who are our concern; more often than not it serves only to confuse them and hinder their progress' (Scottish Education Department 1963, paragraph 91).

As a result of this unbalanced and confused hold on knowledge, the less-able pupil is characterized as lacking in a sense of security, liable to be influenced by his surroundings and by his desire for immediate success:

> The less their ability, the less well do they meet demands for sustained effort; they respond best to tasks which yield quick results and most of them do not look far ahead (Scottish Education Department 1963, paragraph 14).
>
> Many of these boys and girls lack a sense of security; this becomes as often as not the key to their whole pattern of behaviour, the background to their thoughts and actions, and lays them open to the less creditable influences of modern society (Scottish Education Department 1963, paragraph 143).

The idea of distinct mentalities, then, has not become an obsolete rhetorical resource over the last 150 years. However, we should not expect that the resource is necessarily used nowadays in pursuit of the same ends as those it once served, nor should we suppose that other additional resources have not been invoked to do service in support of the goals and interests which contemporary educationalists pursue.

ASSOCIATED IDEAS

What then is the matrix of assumptions into which these ideas about mentality are now seen to fit? It is perhaps already clear how the imputed slowness of the less-able child to arrive at generalizations, and his/her need of concrete objects, is used to justify an increased emphasis on a practical approach to the teaching of science. This emphasis is reinforced by the adoption of a particular philosophy of science and of scientific method. The Newsom Committee appear to adopt an inductive view of science, of theoretical inferences arising from controlled observation of the minutiae of situations:

> What are the essentials of the scientific method? To see, to wonder why, to attempt explanation, to test these by taking a closer look, is a common

enough sequence of experience. The scientist repeats this process deliberately and in a controlled situation, learning to look closely, record accurately, and say clearly what inferences have been made (Ministry of Education 1963, paragraph 422).

The authors of *Curriculum Paper 7* have built this sequence of observation, formation of hypotheses, and testing of hypotheses into their suggested course structure, stating that: 'Science teaching in secondary education is seen by us as a three stage organisation, the first part of which is observational in nature, the second a more interpretive approach with some quantification of concepts, while the third is a generalisation and further refinement of concept' (Scottish Education Department 1969, paragraph 7). In their curriculum 'An attempt has been made to expose pupils to many other aspects of the work of the scientist; the apparatus at his disposal, the experimental methods he uses, the different processes of thought by which he arrives at his conclusions' (Scottish Education Department 1969, paragraph 8).

The methods the scientist uses are automatically prefixed by the description 'experimental'; and the authors feel able to invoke without qualification the idea that the procedures of the scientist in arriving in 'knowledge' are clearly discernible and enumerable. This is a world-view in which the term 'thinking scientifically' has a meaning which does not require clarification since it carries a definite meaning for the authors, and, by implication, for their readers. Thus they are free to state that one of 'the broad aims of science education should be that pupils acquire . . . an ability to solve problem situations and think scientifically' (Scottish Education Department 1969, paragraph 8).

It would be the task of a much longer and more detailed paper to seek to analyse the models of the scientific method implicit in the various curriculum writings of the recent past. For our present purpose, we should note that the implicit model of scientific activity adopted here leads to a concentration on *method* rather than on *content*. Hence, as is argued in paragraph 70 of the same publication, 'teaching in science moves further away from an emphasis on content towards ways of working and thinking'.

This naïve 'common-sense' view of science is also one in which an idea such as 'objectivity' can be freely used without discussion. Hence, *Curriculum Paper 7* (in paragraph 8) advocates, as another 'broad aim of science education', 'that pupils acquire . . . an ability to observe objectively'.

In the section dealing with non-certificate pupils in secondary years 3 and 4 (paragraph 60), the objective is stated in more explicit terms: 'Pupils should acquire . . . an attitude of objectivity to all decisions and assessments required of the individual'.

Another general strand of argument in the same paragraph of *Curricu-*

lum Paper 7 is its emphasis on attitude objectives: 'For the group of young people we are asked to consider, we would further conclude that in terms of relative importance, it is probable that success in attitude formation is more important than success in some of the specifically cognitive objectives'.

The taxonomy of Bloom and his co-workers (Krathwohl, Bloom and Masia 1965) provides an accepted framework for stating such attitude objectives in an explicit form. Some clearly desirable goals when so stated, appear to be uniquely attainable through a suitable science education programme. Attitude goals of this kind as set out in *Curriculum Paper 7*, are listed in Figure 2.

As general objectives we would wish pupils to acquire,

in attitudes

(9) Awareness of the inter-relationship of the different disciplines of science.
(10) Awareness of the relationship of science to other aspects of the curriculum.
(11) Awareness of the contribution of science to the economic and social life of the community.
(12) Interest and enjoyment in science.
(13) An objectivity in observation and in assessing observations.

Objectives for the second cycle:
Pupils should acquire,

in attitudes

(11) Awareness of the relationship of science to other disciplines of knowledge.
(12) Awareness of the importance of science in the working, leisure and social aspects of the community and society in general.
(13) An interest and a willingness to participate in science-related leisure pursuits.
(14) Willingness to conform to and an interest in propagating sensible rules for safety and good health for the sake of the community, as well as of the individual.
(15) An interest in and a willingness to participate in conservation of the natural environment.
(16) An interest in gathering information about science through all the media of communication.

(17) An appreciation of man's responsibility to use science for the benefit of society.
(18) An attitude of objectivity to all decisions and assessments required of the individual.

Figure 2 Statement of objectives

As mentioned earlier, *Curriculum Paper 7* deals with two distinct groups of Scottish pupils: *all* the pupils in the first two years of secondary education; and that group in the third and fourth years who 'for a variety of reasons, may not wish to continue in school beyond the statutory leaving age and whose needs are therefore much more practical, and related to the daily life they are very soon to be involved in' (Scottish Education Department 1969, paragraphs 20 and 60). The first group of five objectives (see figure 2) is recommended as suitable for *all* pupils in years 1 and 2; the second, more detailed group, refers to the older, non-academic pupil.

It is, however, striking that none of these detailed objectives is in any clear way related to any of the syllabus content which the curriculum paper outlines, a point which other commentators have noted (Brown 1976). At first sight, such a disjunction between syllabus objectives and content may appear surprising: however, from the perspective adopted in this paper, the objectives are taken to have a rhetorical rather than a pedagogical function; their correspondence with the content may then be expected to be, at best, fortuitous.

It would thus appear that, unlike his nineteenth-century counterpart, the contemporary writer does not feel able to use the idea of mentality type in a direct and unmediated way. His purposes are served by a rather more complex web of assumptions, relating a more sensual and concrete mode of thought to a need for 'practical' forms of science teaching; this is then supported by the uncritical adoption of a common-sense view of science which permits the unproblematic use of concepts like 'scientific thinking' and 'objectivity'. This essentially 'rational' activity called 'science', which is seen as commending itself by the methodical way in which it generates reliable knowledge, is to be transmitted to pupils *as a method*. In addition, satisfactory pedagogy will seek to develop desirable attitudes towards science itself, since science is such a central feature of the cultural landscape. Attitude objectives are also invoked, relating both to societal, vocational and leisure interests.

CURRICULUM AND CONTROL

What, then, are the fundamental concerns of these curriculum reformers, and how do they make use of this array of rhetorical tools? To approach a tentative answer to this question, it is necessary to look at the context in which the new curricula have emerged.

The period during which these curricular ideas were published was marked by growing dissatisfaction with some of the effects of a selective educational system. Most especially, this was seen as producing a large disaffected group of children, labelled by schools (and by themselves) as failures. Academically, this group was seen as failing to achieve even those more limited goals of which it was regarded capable. Socially, its members were implicated in a variety of anti-social behaviours inside and outside school, and demonstrated a reduced, or frankly non-existent, level of respect for those in positions of authority or esteem. Within the schools, the same disaffected group was seen as potentially responsible for a breakdown in the established order.

The perceived social climate within the schools was not unlike that which the early nineteenth-century educational protagonists saw in the wider society of their day. Shapin and Barnes portray the educational reformers of that period as wishing to experiment with methods of social control. The same idea can be invoked to explain much of the current imperative towards curriculum change. For while it is easy to see how the views of those whose response to the educational situation of the mid 1960s was to return to 'traditional' methods and approaches can be interpreted in terms of an underlying concern with social control, I want also to suggest that the proposals of the curriculum 'progressives' evidence a similar concern. Like the early nineteenth-century progressives, their ideas reflect a perceived need to *experiment* with new forms of control.

It is when one considers how they can contribute to social control within the classroom that the advantages of the new curricula over the old become most apparent. In working on the development and teaching of suitable courses for non-certificate pupils in years 3 and 4 of the secondary school, one notices how little the evaluation of such materials by the teacher as 'successful' or 'unsuccessful' depends on criteria related even remotely to science, or to any measured or measurable cognitive development. As soon as a course module is refined to the point where its use in the class keeps the pupils occupied, enables a satisfactory staff-pupil atmosphere to develop, and therefore permits the teacher to feel unthreatened by an incipient loss of control, it is endorsed as 'satisfactory'. There is no need to find out whether the pupils are learning anything at all *before* making the evaluation. Now it is clearly true that in the absence of such an atmosphere, and with pupils who are bored and restive, little or nothing 'educational' can be achieved. The converse, however, is not necessarily true or self-evident. I wish only to make the point that a 'controlled' classroom is tacitly taken as meaning that the curriculum element in question is working 'satisfactorily'.

One must then ask: what types of science course tend to achieve this sort of 'success'? Those which do are invariably almost completely practical; visual material and books are colourful and rely on diagrammatic rather than verbal presentations; films are useful if not over-used; projects and work outside the classroom can also help. And these are precisely the recommendations of much of *Curriculum Paper 7*.

For practising teachers, the classroom itself is, I would contend, the principal arena in which the imperatives of social control will make themselves felt. For other educationalists, the use of the curriculum seen from the wider perspective of society will also be important – as it is also important for many teachers. If, however, new curricular suggestions are felt to contribute to social control *both* in the classroom *and* in wider terms, their acceptability will be correspondingly increased. Figure 2 gives some indication as to how these concerns are perceived. Thus all pupils (that is, including the future scientists and technologists) should be helped to acquire such attitudes as: 'Awareness of the contribution of science to the economic and social life of the community'; and 'Interest and enjoyment in science'.

Many commentators of this period hoped that a reorientation of science education along the directions to which these (and similar) objectives point would help to arrest 'the present drift of able students away from the sciences' (Scottish Education Department 1969, paragraph 18).

However, the objectives for the non-certificate third and fourth year (banausoi) point towards slightly different concerns: the profitable use of leisure; the promotion of socially-desirable behaviour; the development of a *positive* attitude to science and technology. It might be suggested, therefore, that concern with this particular group is not *primarily* a concern with the production of *scientific* manpower. The emphasis is rather on the inculcation of attitudes which are regarded as desirable in the unskilled or semi-skilled worker of the future. By emphasizing scientific *method* (as opposed to *content*) in science courses, some behaviour traits (such as careful observation, clear recording of results, perseverance, steadiness, and so on) might be expected to carry over into the work situation. An 'objectivity' in approaching issues, if it can be encouraged in the science class, will perhaps produce a worker who is less emotionally involved in immediate situations, but is capable of distancing himself from a question and considering it more dispassionately. There must be few situations in which an unskilled worker is routinely required to make use of such an ability (if he possesses it) in the course of his daily job. If the job is sufficiently varied for problem situations ever to arise, it is more likely that they will either be referred 'upwards' for solution, or solved by the tacit application of skills acquired as part of the learning of the 'craft', rather than by recourse to a simplistic hypothetico-deductive scientific model remembered from schooldays. In some areas, however, an 'objectively'-thinking worker would be most desirable (at least from the employer's point of view): '[the pupil] has a great need for information of an objective and unbiased kind, for example, about industrial relations' (Scottish Education Department 1963, paragraph 80).

The hope here is clearly that a 'scientific' attitude to information, characterized by a desire to consider all sides of a question, to keep an open mind, to hold a point-of-view subject to experimental verification, will be transferred to areas which are far removed from the school science arena.

In addition to these 'work-attitudes' which the new science courses might hope to develop, a related objective is to foster in pupils a positive attitude to, and evaluation of, the whole scientific (and technological) enterprise. Such an attitude to science is naturally desirable in the pupil whose future job is likely to be influenced by scientific innovation (not always in ways which he might desire). It is, too, an area in which science educators are likely to become increasingly anxious: the last decade has seen a marked increase in writings critical of the whole culture of science, and of its impact on the material, social and mental environment of those who live within technological societies.

Finally, the objectives related to leisure and 'use of leisure' seem like the contemporary manifestations of a concern which has a very long pedigree. Even a casual glance at educational writings shows that educationalists have always had a healthy dislike for the ways in which the 'uneducated masses' choose to spend their leisure time. When increased leisure is widely seen as an 'inevitable' future development, the concern is correspondingly greater, particularly with regard to those groups in society who seem to be making singularly undesirable use of what leisure they currently possess. This concern with the use of leisure illustrates clearly the educationalists' preoccupation with social control, in the sense in which that term has been used in this paper.

For the term 'control' has not been taken to imply direct or even conscious manipulation of others, but to reflect, rather, the striving of individuals through their participation in a debate to advance a conception of society and of social organization which they themselves espouse. Terms like 'social control' can all too easily become, themselves, pejorative in overtone. No such evaluation is intended here. This paper is, itself, subject to analysis in the same terms as those it employs. It is offered merely in the belief that it is better to proceed with some awareness of those social forces which act as partial determinants of our actions, than to aspire to a detached and unrealistic 'objectivity'.

REFERENCES

Banister, I. A. 1970, Teaching science to mixed-ability groups. *School Science Review*, Vol. 177, No. 51, p. 947.

Brown, S. 1976, *Attitude Goals in Secondary School Science* (Stirling Educational Monographs No. 1, University of Stirling: Scotland).

Foster, J. 1826, *An Essay on the Evils of Popular Ignorance* (London); quoted in Shapin and Barnes (1976) – see below.

Johnson, R. 1970, Educational policy and social control in early Victorian England. *Past and Present*, Vol. 49, p. 119.

Lockard, D. 1970, *Seventh Report of the International Clearinghouse on Science and Mathematics Curricular Developments* (University of Maryland: USA).

Kamm, M. D. 1970, Teaching science to mixed-ability groups. *School Science Review*, Vol. 179, No. 52, p. 439.

Kershaw, I. and Scott, P. J. 1975, Science for pupils of low educational attainment. *School Science Review*, Vol. 196, No. 56, p. 449.

Krathwohl, D. R., Bloom, B. S. and Masia, B. B. 1965, *Taxonomy of Educational Objectives – Handbook II: Affective Domain* (Longman: London).

Marking, J. 1970, Practical programmes. *School Science Review*, Vol. 179, No. 52, p. 440.

Ministry of Education 1963, *Half our Future – Report of the Central Advisory Council for Education (England)* (H.M.S.O.: London).

Schools Council 1965, *Working Paper No. 1: Science for the Young School Leaver* (H.M.S.O.: London).

Scottish Education Department 1963, *From School to Further Education* (H.M.S.O.: Edinburgh).

Scottish Education Department 1969, *Curriculum Paper 7: Science for General Education* (H.M.S.O.: Edinburgh).

Shapin, S. and Barnes, B. 1976, Head and hand: rhetorical resources in British pedagogical writing, 1770–1850. *Oxford Review of Education*, Vol. 2, pp. 231–254.

Shapin, S. and Barnes, B. 1977, Science, nature and control: interpreting mechanics institutes. *Social Studies of Science*, Vol. 7, pp. 31–74.

20 Core science – educational necessity or academic pipe dream?

• M. Waring and B. Schofield

Mary Waring and Beta Schofield consider a common core curriculum. They identify 'social justice' and 'the safeguarding of essentials' as two arguments for its establishment, arguing that there is a need to give equality of access and improve efforts to provide for diversity of interests and talents. Identifying a core curriculum is dependent upon value judgements and is influenced by vested interests. The authors describe the arguments of 'outside' vested interests for including science in the core curriculum and discuss the problems that have to be faced. They also explore the relations between common core and options in the 11 to 16 curriculum.

The idea of a common core curriculum has gained much support during the last few years as various groups – some of them very strange bedfellows indeed – have thrown their weight behind it. Support appears to be based, in general, on two major considerations, namely social justice and the safeguarding of essentials. Both are, surely, educationally valid, and so to dismiss the idea of a core curriculum on the grounds that anything commanding widespread support is thereby not worthy of serious consideration is to trivialize discussion of matters that might well be important.

Egalitarian ideals of equality of opportunity, *via* equality of access to *common* schools offering a *common* culture by means of a *common* curriculum, have been around for some time now, although it is only in the last twenty years that the first of these, the common school, has become any sort of reality (to the extent that it is in any case possible in a system with a flourishing private sector). A common curriculum offering a common culture has obvious attractions as a democratic device, for it seems to promise all children, regardless of their social origins or genetic endowment, a common stock of knowledge and understanding and a shared tradition of values, attitudes and norms.

But social justice also requires that we acknowledge the existence of individual differences, for, whether children are born equal or unequal, whether they develop differences or have difference thrust upon them by home environment and/or early school experience, it is an indisputable fact that, by the time they reach secondary schools, they exhibit a considerable diversity of interests and talents. Few egalitarians would argue that it is socially just to minimize these differences via a totally common curriculum. Social justice would seem to demand, instead, that teachers try to cope with the differences in such a way that *every* child has a taste of success, and *every* child has an equal opportunity to prove himself unequal in one or more ways. At present the majority of comprehensive schools appear to operate upon the principle of mixed ability teaching of a common curriculum to years one and two, rather than a common core. This base is then followed by a system of options, or by banding or setting from the third year, when issues of specialization and choice become more urgent. But, since certain options lead to GCE examinations, others to CSE and the rest to no public examination whatever, it is inevitable that options acquire differential status, and that the divisiveness of streaming and setting does not disappear. They may be less obvious where a really wide range of options is available, but this is workable only in very large schools and it is precisely these schools that are being hardest hit by falling rolls. There are some comprehensive schools in which a common core extends right into the fifth year, but little is known about the ways in which they do or do not make allowance for individual differences, about their successes, and about their failures and their problems.

Egalitarianism, then, is one pressure operating in favour of a common core curriculum, although it offers no clear guide to the actual constitution of that core. This is the point at which the second set of pressures enter, that is, concern over safeguarding essentials. It is clear that the idea of a common core is attractive as a means to this end, however 'essentials' are interpreted. For the various manifestations of the 'back-to-basics' movement, with its concern for 'standards', the interpretation is a narrow one. In spite of this fact, the movement has been very successful during the 1970s in fomenting press and public criticism of education and of educational standards. As economic recession has deepened and as inflation has risen, so these criticisms have become linked (i) to concerns about whether or not effective use is being made of public resources and, in particular, whether schools are giving value for money. Central to this aspect of the debate have been the twin themes of 'accountability' and 'responsibility' and one outcome has been the establishment of the *Assessment of Performance Unit* to find ways of determining accountability. A 'protected' core has clear attractions on this score; (ii) to Britain's need to survive economically in a highly competitive world. Many of the pronouncements made in connection with the 'Great Debate' charged the schools with having failed society, making them a scapegoat for our economic ills. Too many children, it was claimed, could not read, write or add; schools were unable to control them or even to keep them on the premises during school hours. Such claims were later 'substantiated' by selective quotation from the HMI reports on primary and secondary schooling.[1]

The climate of concern over 'standards' has also encouraged those who favour greater central control of the curriculum so that, first, leaks and then firm statements from the DES about their intention to take on, once again, some responsibility for the content of the curriculum, received a sympathetic response from many outside the schools. The pill was sweetened by the fact that this responsibility was to be confined to part, not all, of the curriculum, that is, to the identification of a 'core' or 'protected' part, common to all schools, but it continues to be viewed with suspicion by the professionals.

Identification of a core, argued the Secretary of State's discussion document *A Framework for the School Curriculum*[2] (published in January 1980), would 'ensure that all pupils, whatever else they do, at least get a sufficient grounding in the knowledge and skills which, by common consent, should form part of the equipment of an educated adult'. Whether or not the DES should be so empowered is, of course, a highly contentious issue, but it is not our present concern. Ensuring standards and fitting children for life in adult society – surely the major function of the common core – would indeed seem to represent educational necessity. But obtaining 'common consent' on the constitution of the core is another matter altogether, for the whole exercise of identification is quite inescapably founded upon values and value judgements, and it will also be radically affected by vested interest. It is for these reasons that many educationists have argued that the possibility of a centrally-defined, mandatory core is a pipe dream, and that individual schools will need to accept responsibility for defining and implementing an appropriate common core, preferably one based upon common principles. This may well become a logistical necessity if other Local Authorities follow Devon's recent decision to link staffing with curricular requirements (and, presumably, with priorities firmly geared to 'balance'), in place of pupil/teacher ratios, as in the past.

It is an interesting and, to us no doubt, gratifying fact, that complete unanimity appears to have existed so far about the need to include science in the common core, even though the extent and breadth of core science is open to dispute. For example, the Secretary of State's paper suggests that some 10 to 20 per cent of the total timetable should be given to science; the HMI's view of 'balance' clearly differs.[3]

Why is science so widely assumed to be an essential core subject? We are not concerned here with any attempt at 'objective' assessment, nor with what we as science teachers believe, but with the reasons offered by others whose vested interests lie elsewhere. Whether the arguments are 'right' or 'wrong', whatever their source, it seems that, in general, science is viewed as an essential part of the core curriculum for one or more of the following reasons. (These are, in fact, not entirely separable, but it is done here for the sake of clarity.)

1. The need for scientific and technological manpower at all levels of operation, that is, not just for a scientific élite – the 'pure' sciences research worker. This argument is clearly based on economic necessity, and it raises the question of whether or not pupils should be treated as means to industrial and defence ends.
2. The value and interest of science *per se*. This can be interpreted in terms of its role in satisfying children's curiosity now and in the future. For other protagonists, however, the argument is linked to a conception of science as a discipline, a 'way of knowing', and hence as a potential developer of 'mind' and of rational autonomy. Does either make science an educational necessity? Is the 'discipline' argument unrealistic in terms of all pupils and therefore an academic pipe dream? Or is it an elaborate academic defence of high status knowledge and, therefore, an élitist pipe dream (or plot, according to one's stance)?
3. There is a widespread belief that every adult in a post-industrial, democratically-orientated society, and in a world facing acute problems, many of them science-related, needs to have:
   (a) some knowledge and understanding of science and technology;
   (b) some appreciation of their social and historical relations; and
   (c) some experience and appreciation of 'scientific method' and its applicability.

This argument is more immediately utilitarian, but does it make core science an educational necessity? Does insisting that schools teach science to all pupils necessarily mean that pupils will, when they reach adulthood, understand the impact of science and technology on their world, cope with science-related choices and decisions, or recognize where their responsibilities lie? *What* 'science for all' will achieve these, and how? It is surely crucially important for us to raise and to seek answers to a whole range of issues about the nature of core science.

PROBLEMS TO BE FACED

1. *What* science should form core science, and how will it be related to any options? How should it be taught; that is, what means will achieve our ends, with teachers with very different characteristics,

who now achieve their successes by very different means? What, for that matter, will our ends be? While it is fine – and right and proper – for us to set out our ideals, we also have to admit that we really know very little indeed about either appropriate ends, or the means of achieving them; that our attempts are, and always have been, based on many untested assumptions (often obscured by the rhetoric of science education); and that we have got to be prepared to explore core science along many dimensions if we are to find out (a) what these young people can learn, and usefully learn, together, and (b) how this is related to the meeting of individual needs. We will only know what it amounts to when we have done so.

2. How common will core science be? Will a common mandatory model be decided for all schools, or will individual schools be allowed to determine their own pattern of core and options, possibly based upon a set of common principles? How will this be monitored to ensure that it is put into effect?
3. Can the core extend from 11 to 16? There *are* comprehensive schools providing a common core right up to the fifth form. We need to know more about what they are doing, how they do it and with what kinds of success. If the core is to be limited to years one and two, is there any need for change?
4. Should core science be taught as integrated science or as separate sciences?
5. How much time will be given to core science overall, and what will be the relative time-allocation for core and options? How much flexibility is possible?
6. Who will set it up? The DES? (A new paper on the core curriculum is due to be published shortly.) The Schools Council? Examining Boards? ASE? Other bodies? Individual schools? Some sort of collaborative group? How will this affect what goes into it?
7. What sort of development cycle should operate? Central or local development, or some combination of both? Who will produce the resources, often an expensive undertaking, quite apart from professional considerations? What form should they take? How will means-ends relationships be established? Who will ensure adequate time for both development and implementation, as well as communication and support for experiment?
8. Who will finance it? It seems likely that, if it is to be widely implemented, and if teachers and schools will buy and use the resources, then funds might be forthcoming. But again, how might this affect what is produced and how?
9. Arrangements will need to be made in connection with public examinations and certificates. The fact that examination knowledge is often synonymous in the public mind with 'real' knowledge has

important implications for core science. If it is not examined, then it will have low status, and parents, especially parents of academically able pupils, will press for exemption – which could nullify the exercise. Could a system based on examination of both core and options be devised, so that different combinations could lead to different awards to meet differing needs? The Southern Regional Examining Board already operates a flexible CSE scheme based on a number of options. By choosing different emphases or combinations, pupils can obtain awards in either physical science, biological science or combined science, or a double award in physical science and biological science. While it might be argued that the particular system does not ensure the coherence that one might hope to achieve in core science, it does suggest that feasible alternatives might be found, alternatives which could operate equally in the present two-tiered system and in a system of common examinations at 16+.

10. Finally, how might core and options be related to one another? Should core science be the whole apple – that is, all the science that the majority will do? Cores are notoriously indigestible, and there is certainly much in school science that the majority of pupils would find very indigestible. Assuming, for the moment, that core science were to consist largely of 'science' as we know it, it seems clear that basing schemes of work upon concepts would produce immediate problems. Consider a situation in which only those concepts accessible to the entire school population between 11 and 16 were included.

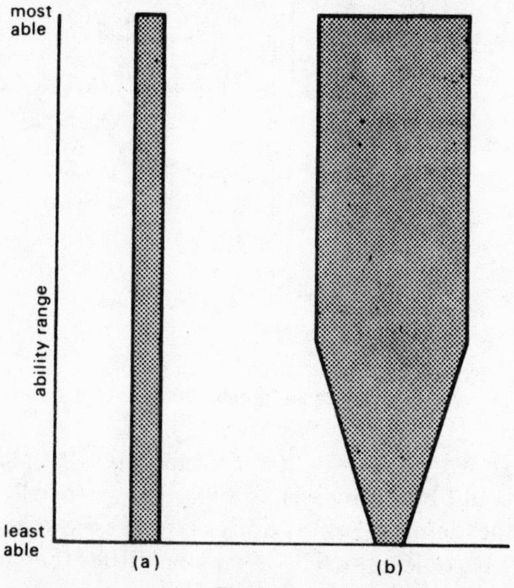

Figure 1

The breadth of the offering would inevitably be very narrow indeed, even allowing for differences of opinion as to what would be feasible (see Figure 1(a)). Simply trying to express a few likely concepts in simple language, using words that would have real meaning for the bottom 30 per cent of pupils, brings one sharply up against the limits. For example, for the current kind of statement relating pressure and volume would have to be substituted something like, 'You can squash a gas so that it take up less room. The more you squash it, the less room you will need.'

The breadth might, perhaps, be increased by choosing those concepts that are accessible to, say, the top sixty per cent, and by being prepared to accept a tailing-off of understanding for the remainder (see Figure 1(b)).

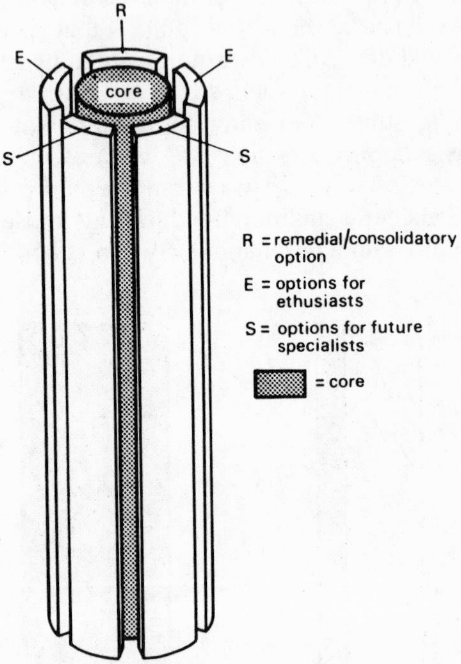

Figure 2. Apple core

This level is, however, below that of Grade 4 (CSE). It is clear that such a curriculum could by no means be regarded as socially just to a large group of more academically able pupils as well as the least able. The offering might well become a mush – a banana rather than an apple!

Basing the core entirely on 'process' objectives might seem a workable alternative, but it would preclude a common system of examining (with far-reaching results). Further, whether all 'process' skills and abilities are equally accessible to all pupils, particularly at the same age, is open to question, and little is really known about ways of developing and fostering them.

It is always possible that a very different conception of core science might be both necessary and desirable and that, with different ends, more school science might be common to all pupils. The possibility should not be lightly dismissed. Nevertheless, really radical change normally requires a revolution, originality almost always working within the framework of tradition. So piecemeal change of the existing system is the most likely prospect before us. Because of this, a structure of core plus options would seem to be essential for core science itself, regardless of whether or not other science options become available outside the core. 'Core and options' in what follows is therefore confined to 'core science', to 'science for all' between 11 and 16.

The simplest arrangement consists of a common core extending from 11 to 16, and a range of options for specialists and/or enthusiasts and, possibly, for consolidation/remedial work. From the timetabling point of view, such a range would make block timetabling a probability, if not a necessity, unless an already difficult situation is to be exacerbated (see Figure 2).

But there are problems. Could core and options be kept in tandem for all pupils throughout the five years? It seems unlikely. For this, and for other obvious reasons, this structure would require early decisions, e.g. to study physics as against rural studies, and there would be few possibilities for later changes of direction for those in difficulty, or for late developers.

A partial remedy might be to have a totally common core for two years, as a base for core and options from Year 3.

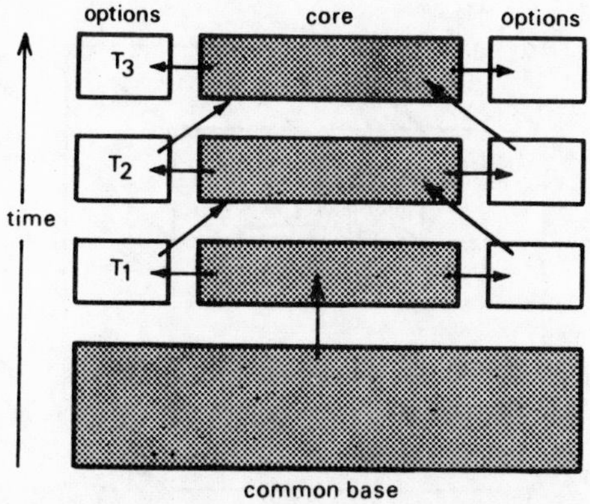

Figure 3. Apple-core jigsaw

Alternatively, core and options could alternate in a variety of ways. Figure 3 shows one such arrangement. This might help to keep core and options in tandem, but structuring would still be critical and so largely inflexible, because experiences needed at time T3, for instance, would have had to be gained earlier in time T1 or T2. Transfer across options would still be extremely difficult. In addition, the time gap between each part of the core and the related part of an option might be large, with the result that many pupils could lose track. Again, what had been done in time T1 could not be used until time T2, because pupils with other options would not have the necessary experiences. Again, the time gap might make options seem to be detached from the core and, perhaps, rather arid.

The next logical step is clearly to break down core/option alternation still further into a framework of modules, each of which would occupy a uniform but brief period of time, expressed in weeks or double periods. Whether they were for specialists, for enthusiasts, or for those needing more consolidation, options would be embedded in the module along with the underlying element of the core. Thus in the whole framework of modules the core would be rather like the pips in a pomegranate.

Each module would consist of core plus related options, the core normally occupying a fairly high proportion of time, although this might vary from module to module. In each, core material would lead straight into options which could cover simple extra consolidation work and more practical experiences for those having most difficulty, through one (or more) options for the majority, to extension work and more difficult theoretical concepts for the most able (see Figure 4).

Modules would fit together to form a coherent framework. Clearly, there are limits to flexibility, since some parts of the work would be dependent upon earlier understanding. Nevertheless, the short-term nature of the modules would make it possible for teachers to use alterna-

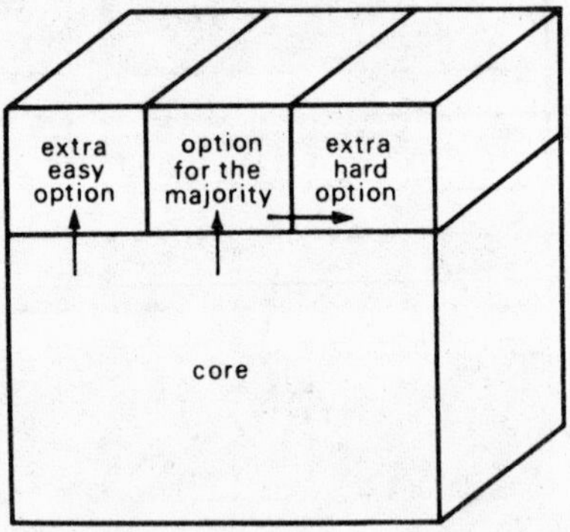

Figure 4(a): Single module

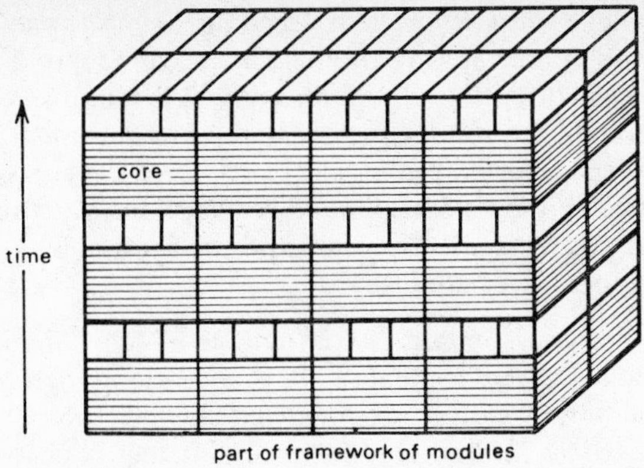

Figure 4(b): Modular framework 'pomegranate'

tive pathways and networks (in the same way as they now use circuses of experiments rather than class sets of experiments), to facilitate resource provision where year groups were block timetabled. Another advantage of this model is that modules could be fitted into existing schemes in piecemeal fashion, greatly facilitating change from one system to another, especially where individual modules were slanted towards one of physics, chemistry or biology.

This sort of model-building is not just an academic exercise. It was used in determining the structure of Nuffield Science 13–16 and has shown itself to be a feasible approach.

WHAT BENEFITS MIGHT PUPILS DERIVE FROM A COMMON CORE IN SCIENCE?

1 If a common core can be made to work, then the shared experiences that it would provide could offer equality of access to shared knowledge and understanding, skills, values, attitudes and norms. For the individual, it could afford a sense of being able to share a good part of the 11–16 science curriculum with all of his peers, in a situation in which academic differences are more muted than at present.

2 A core science curriculum that is planned from scratch with ALL pupils in mind and not from 'above' (that is, the most successful) down, might hold out possibilities:

   (a) of providing better opportunities for developing knowledge and understanding that is useful to all, as well as those information-seeking and information-processing skills that will be important in adult life, if these young people are to be able to take on responsibility for their own learning about matters that have become important to them. Much will depend upon what science is offered to them, and how it is taught;

(b) of providing a more cohesive, coherent and meaningful set of experiences for all pupils; and

(c) of developing a closely linked core/options structure of benefit to all, and in which the least and the most able, as well as late developers, will not lose out.

3 If the core is common (or largely common) to all schools, movement between schools will be facilitated. It is important to remember that British mobility now stands at something like ten per cent per annum.

4 Again, if the core is common to all schools, Further Education and Sixth Form Colleges (the latter now a distinct possibility as a feature of the future) will take in students who have a shared framework of experiences on which to build. This would apply to all students, not merely to those with O-levels.

Core science appears, then, to be a feasible proposition, although this will have to be tested, and tested thoroughly, in a slow process of working out, in which there is a continuing dialogue between the desirable and the possible and in relation to both content and process.

REFERENCES

1. Department of Education and Science (Her Majesty's Inspectorate), *Primary Education in England* (HMSO, 1978); *idem, Aspects of Secondary Education in England* (HMSO, 1979).
2. Department of Education and Science, *A Framework for the School Curriculum* (Proposals for consultation by the Secretaries of State for Education and Science and for Wales) (DES, January 1980).
3. Department of Education and Science (Her Majesty's Inspectorate), *A View of the Curriculum* (Matters for Discussion no. 11) (HMSO, 1980).
4. *Nuffield Science 13 to 16*, General Editor: Beta Schofield (published for the Nuffield-Chelsea Curriculum Trust by the Longman Group Limited – Resources Unit, York).

21 A case against the core

● R. W. West

West, pointing to the similarity in the position of contemporary Labour and Conservative governments towards educational reform, attacks the notion of a core curriculum on the grounds that an insufficient attempt has been made to determine the curriculum appropriate to universal secondary education. Political strategies have two economic dimensions: cost-effectiveness and cost-benefit (the latter in connection with the needs of productive industry). He sees the movement as a trend towards 'basics', one pole of Geoffrey Bantock's 'two-culture' curriculum. In relation to science education, West sees the movement as tending to shore up the 'holy trinity' of biology, chemistry and physics. He is sharply critical of the failure to integrate the natural and social sciences and, citing Edgley, of the crude assertion about the need to link industry to school. He argues alternatively for science studies that concentrate on studies of 'self', society, the environment, self-sufficiency and creativity.

> In order to control a disturbingly high rate of inflation and to ensure adequate resources for regenerating industry, the Government's top two priorities, economic restraint has been necessary . . . Resource constraints were not always taken into account during the period of rapid development in the curriculum and in teaching methods that occurred in the last decade; they must be borne in mind in any proposals for the future.[1]

Those readers with short memories may be a little surprised to note that this quotation from a DES consultative paper on the future of the school curriculum was not written by Mr Mark Carlisle but was penned by his predecessor, Mrs Shirley Williams, in her background chapter to the Green Paper *Education in Schools* (1977). Mr Carlisle, in 1980, of course said much the same thing in *A Framework for the School Curriculum*:

> At the same time curricular policies, and their costs, must be decided in the context of the resources available for public expenditure as a whole and, within that, for education. These issues are of particular importance at the present time, because falling school rolls and the need to limit public expenditure make it the more important to establish priorities for the resources that are available and to redeploy those resources where it would be advantageous to do so.[2]

I have chosen these two quotations as an introduction to this chapter in order to remind readers that the issue of a core curriculum has much to do with reducing the economic costs of state education and is a notion that spans the period 1976–81, during which the country has been ruled by two right of centre governments, of different political labels, which have shared a common concern: the fight against inflation and the resuscitation of an ailing productive industry. Both have cut funding and have expressed a general commitment to greater control of the curriculum.

The Williams-Carlisle strategy has had two important dimensions:

> a cost-effectiveness dimension based on the attempt to simplify the state curriculum by limiting the range of school subjects, to inhibit curricular diversity, and trim away 'fringe subjects'; and
>
> a cost-benefit dimension based on the notion of redirecting the aims, and thus the output, of the state schools towards the needs of productive industry.

A central element in this strategy is the notion of a core curriculum, a notion that I regard as being a dangerous and pernicious nonsense that must be strongly resisted and finally defeated. Before attempting to justify this view I must do two things.

First, I must make it clear that in this paper I do not wish to limit myself to the narrow problems of the science curriculum, and have no intention of suggesting ways and means whereby a core science curriculum can be defined in operational terms. Instead I want to address myself to a question that often gets left off the agenda, namely the case against a core. Secondly, I want to distance myself from any official position I have held in the Association for Science Education and specifically from my role as a member of the Executive Committee, a post which I relinquished in February. In so far as it is possible this paper simply represents a personal position on the issues raised.

I have already stated my strong antipathy towards the notion of a core curriculum – an antipathy based on a deep intellectual and political distrust of any notion that appeals strongly to the soft centre of British society, and a notion for which no one has yet produced a valid educational argument.[3] To this I want to add an additional gloss. After very careful consideration I can see no case for the inclusion of science education *as currently defined* in a core curriculum on the grounds that for a number of reasons I have yet to be convinced that science education *as currently defined*, justifies its inclusion in the school curriculum *as currently defined* let alone in any protected and by definition compulsory curricula of the type and form currently being considered by the DES. However I want to immediately qualify this position in a temporal, but not absolute sense.

In the *short term*, say the next few years, it is important, indeed vitally important, that science teachers present a highly cogent and articulated case for the defence of school science as it is; for its careful revision and evolution; and for the contribution it can make to general education as traditionally defined. I feel that this was one of the central intentions of the ASE Consultative Document, *Alternatives for Science Education*,[4] and is certainly what we have been attempting to do in the 1981 Policy Statement *Education Through Science*.[5] A systematic and active defence of school science will do two things:

> First, it will safeguard the vital man and woman power resources needed for the long term development of the science curriculum; and secondly, it will in the short term, help to underline the impossibility of simplistic notions of a core curriculum. This general impossibility will be further highlighted if all other subject associations fight the case for the inclusion of their subjects in that same core.

In the *long term*, say the next two decades or so, we need to work towards the general acceptance by all parties in the educational enterprise that the school curriculum as we know it has outlived its usefulness, and we have to create a viable alternative that will not be subject based in the traditional sense and which will not therefore include science as currently defined.

Why, in both the short and the long term, is the concept of a core curriculum a dangerous and pernicious nonsense? To answer this question we must look outside science education and reflect on the recent history of the development of the educational system as we now know it. The provision of universal secondary education in this country – in 1944 along tripartite lines and in, and around, 1965 along comprehensive lines – has not led to the creation of an appropriate curriculum for the education of our people. In 1981 we have still failed to create a curriculum appropriate to universal secondary education.[6] Educational development in the United Kingdom in the three and a half decades since the Butler Act[7] has not significantly altered the social fabric of our society; has not led to any consistent improvement in our economic performance; has not radically increased educational opportunity; has not removed or reduced the poverty gap; has not resolved the problems of a multicultural society; and finally, and most importantly, has not created an Open Society. The United Kingdom today strongly resembles the United Kingdom of the 1940s less that sense of radical idealism, commitment to a Welfare State, and concern for the establishment of an egalitarian society that was strongly held in post-war Britain. In a critical sense the educational system, and the process of schooling, has failed to respond to the *real politic* of the post-war years in spite of a massive investment in educational resources; in plant, people and the very real time of the generations of young people who have lived through various stages of educational reorganization. In presenting my case in this way I am fully conscious of the alternative view that the educational system is not, and cannot be, an agent of social change and that educational systems merely reflect and reinforce existing social norms and values. Such a position would not significantly alter my picture of social inertia but would force the reader to look for explanations of that inertia outside the educational system. It also allows those within the educational system to divest themselves of any responsibility for considering any role other than that of servants to society. My perspective assumes that schools and society stand in a dynamic relationship with each other and does not seek to dissociate curricula values from social values; or the manifestations of curricular bankruptcy from their social equivalency.

The recent history of science education can be analysed in a similar manner. The idealism of the 1950s led to the curriculum investment of the 1960s, the crisis of confidence in the 1970s and to what I can only describe after reading the reactions and responses to *Alternatives for Science Education* as a sense of *anomie*[8] in the 1980s. The SMA/AWST report *Science in General Education*[9] presented the case for science for all; the Nuffield and Schools Council curriculum development teams defined that science and defined it in meritocratic terms – real science for the potential scientists and something else, ill defined, for the masses. The publishers and equipment makers supported these proposals to the full and the 'New Era' of science teaching was launched in the 1960s. By the mid 1970s questions were being asked – Shayer, for example, was asking if the new science education fitted current psychological models of the child[10] – and by the late 1970s the ASE in *Alternatives for Science Education* was saying, basically enough is enough:

> That is not it at all.
> That is not what (we) meant, at all[11].

The new ASE policy document, *Education Through Science*, at least in its current form, represents in my view a statement of the future of school science characterized by the same sense of anomie. It is in some respects a presentation of past and future which fails to create from past experience a coherent and radical picture of future action; a science education policy suspended in time, neutered by much of its neutrality; a policy totally in keeping with a society that wants to stand untouched by radical, or reactionary, analyses of its ills. The Thatcher-Benn axis, itself symptomatic of the general problem, seems to generate a sense of not belonging or of not wishing to belong. In policy terms the Association could well find itself in a position which again I can only put in terms used by Eliot:

Footfalls echo in the memory
Down the passage which we did not take
Towards the door we never opened.[12]

It is against this background that I now want to examine the Callaghan – Williams – Thatcher – Carlisle notion of a core curriculum. In one sense I see this as a classic attempt to resolve the problems of educational and societal fit through the application of the *Principle of Reductio ad Absurdum*. If we feel that our *ad hoc a-la-carte* curriculum has patently failed to deliver the goods by producing a better fit between the output of the educational system and societal needs, the answer presented by our politicians is that of reducing the curriculum to the basics – basic literacy, basic numeracy, modern languages (basically French), basic science and a statutory dose of keep fit and spiritually clean. Cut out the nonsense and the frills of education and get to grips with reality. What, we are told, society wants from its schools is literate and numerate scientific linguists with a general sense of spiritual purpose and a propensity to jog. The core curriculum as defined by our political masters requires the state schools, for it says nothing to the Public Schools, to invest their energy and diminishing resources in developing a quite extraordinary product the like of which we have never before seen – a task oriented automaton who can read French and converse in the mathematico – scientific *Lingua Franca* of the mathematics and science curriculum without any sense of history, space, the creative and plastic arts, of music, or any notion of self and society. It of course leaves the Public Schools, and the beneficiaries of the Assisted Places Scheme, free to educate their young as they wish – but that of course has always been so. In 1968 Bantock published an important book entitled *Culture, Industrialization and Education*[13] in which he presented a two-culture model for education. In an important sense I regard *Education in Schools* and particularly *A Framework for the Curriculum* as representing one pole of the Bantock polarity – a narrow, instrumental prescription for reducing educational opportunity for the majority of young people. The other pole is the free curriculum of the non-maintained sector that lies outside the jurisdiction and economic sanctions of the Department of Education and Science. The free curriculum, of course, will continue to espouse the principles of a liberal education and the intellectual skills and qualities required for leadership. Those with a core behind them will at best be equipped to be led.

Now where does science education fit into this picture? Both *Education in Schools* and *A Framework for the School Curriculum* make great play of the need to include science in the core, or protected element, of the curriculum. The inclusion of science is justified in the following terms:

> to provide a basis of mathematical, scientific and technical knowledge enabling boys and girls to learn the essential skills needed in a fast changing world of work;[14] and
> . . . to help pupils acquire knowledge and skills relevant to adult life and employment in a fast-changing world.[15]

The justification is presented more specifically in *A Framework for the School Curriculum* as follows:

> . . . at the secondary stage, for all pupils of all ability levels, it is important that attention should be paid to the industrial and practical applications of science and to links within the school curriculum between science, mathematics and craft, design and technology.[16]

These arguments for the inclusion of science in the core curriculum, which again are interesting in their similarity, beg a basic question raised by one aspect of our fast-changing world, namely that the fastest-changing factor is the rising rate of unemployment. They also raise the important issue of linking school science to the world of work with the clear implication that because the world of work, in either its recumbent or resuscitated state, is technological in orientation workers need a high, or at least higher, level of scientific training in schools. It is also implied that ordinary people in their ordinary adult lives need more science at school in order to cope with the complexity of a fast-changing world. Now there are two fundamental problems with this view of science in the curriculum, namely the *naïveté* of the social analysis and an apparent lack of awareness of the present nature and content of the secondary school curriculum. I would like to take this latter point first.

School science programmes today are normally defined in terms of classical biology, chemistry and physics or some combination of this holy trinity. No major attempt has yet been made in this country to create an effective integration of the natural and social sciences in spite of the obvious relevance of the social sciences to the problems so far discussed. At O and A levels, and to a large extent at the CSE level, the emphasis is on those academic aspects of the three sciences which are needed as the essential underpinning to degree level courses in higher education. Whilst many syllabus writers will genuflect in the direction of other, and more general, educational aims, the centre of gravity and the content 'mass' of the normal O- and A-level separate science syllabus rests on the first degree requirement. It is this close link between school science and university science that legitimates the former as a valid subject for study at the school level. Now this legitimation has not one jot to do with the broader needs of society, the complexities of a fast-changing world, the problems of adulthood or parenthood, or the resuscitation of an ailing industry. If you want to educate young people for parenthood, citizenship, flexibility, and employment and redeployment you cannot do it through the medium of the average O- and A-level syllabuses in biology, chemistry and physics. I have known people with good O- and A-level passes in science subjects get themselves sunburnt, mess up their marriages, go broke, buy the wrong food, spread gastro-enteritis, and generally fail to make much sense of their fast-changing world. An A-level in physics does not enable you to make a better choice of a new car or to fix it when it won't start. An A-level in physics is a measure of a different set of abilities and a general indication, no more or less, of an ability to solve a particular set of intellectual puzzles that have nothing whatsoever to do with the real world of people, politics and the possibilities that exist in the interaction between them. Such qualifications furthermore do not necessarily equip the holder to apply their physics to the real world of industry and commerce, where physics, and the technology derived from and based on physics, is used. It is currently fashionable, in the context of the core curriculum, to rationalize this position by placing the emphasis on the need for a core science syllabus surrounded by a rich choice of options. The core, it is argued, will serve the needs of all and the options will satisfy the differing aspirations of the potential scientists on the one hand, and the parents, citizens, car mechanics, dyers and odd-jobbers on the other hand. Hence we have the core within the core movement; the attempt to define the minimal basic knowledge all good people must have. Now the starting point for defining the 'hard core' of school science tends to be through an analysis of existing syllabuses. Hence the Science N & F Working Parties, with one exception,[17] created their N & F syllabuses by pasting together bits cut from existing A-level syllabuses. There is some evidence that similar strategies are being followed by the Core A-level Working Parties and one has every reason to fear that science syllabuses for the General Certificate of Secondary Education will be culled from the content and assumptions of existing GCE O-level syllabuses in the separate sciences. Is it naive to suggest that panning for gold in a stream laden with the base metal of current syllabuses which in their *entirety* fail to meet general societal needs, is unlikely to lead to the discovery of a philosopher's stone that will enable a distilled sub-part of that inadequate entity to solve our problems? Might it not be more profitable to search for a rather different stream – a stream uncontaminated with the basic grammar[18] of existing syllabus content – a stream of new ideas linked to the problems of *being* in modern industrial and post-industrial societies? Might it not be more relevant to search for a definition of a new science curriculum in the rich pastures of the Brandt Commission Report,[19] *The Limits to Growth*,[20] *Zen and the Art of Motorcycle Maintenance*,[21] *Where the Wasteland Ends*[22] and Faure's *Learning to Be*?[23]

But what of the other dimension of the justification for science in the curriculum of all our future? The justification based on the notion, which I described as naive, that a technologically based industry needs a scientifically trained workforce. I want to consider this notion at two levels. First, I would like to quote from *The Times*, 30 December 1980. Under the headline 'Strike-free Japanese car firms grow rich with new technology' *The Times* reported:

> In sharp contrast to British Leyland's record, two of Japan's leading car manufacturers have not lost an hour of production from labour disputes over a combined operating period of 57 years.
>
> As a result, the Toyota Motor Company, equipped with highly efficient robots, made a profit of $1,200 m (about £500m) last year, produced 3,280,000 vehicles this year and is soon expected to surpass Ford as the world's second largest producer of cars.
>
> The company experienced its last strike in 1950 but since then it has managed to equip its plants with the world's most efficient robots without a hint of industrial unrest. At the same time no worker has been laid off.
>
> 'We have not lost a day's production, not even one hour of production, since 1950 as a result of labour unrest,' Mr Kouji Yada, a spokesman for Toyota, says.
>
> Mr Mitsuya Goto, a spokesman for Nissan, points out that the company's 57,000 employees submitted 473,000 suggestions to improve quality control and productivity last year.

Now the question we have to ask is: 'Has this record of productivity and man-management been achieved through the creation in Japan of a core curriculum with our form of O- and A-level science at its centre?' Of course not. It has been achieved through a highly structured educational system operating within a highly formal, hierarchical and paternalistic society which places a high premium on social conformity. A core curriculum in our schools might in the very long term create a similar effect and we have to ask ourselves: 'Do we need cars (or whatever) that much?'

I think, however, there is a far more profound level at which to analyse the school-industry interface and here I want to rely on a highly perceptive, and provocative, paper by Roy Edgley, Professor of Philosophy at the University of Sussex.[24] Early in the Great Debate,[25] Edgley drew careful attention to a number of pitfalls in the 'link schools to industry' concept of educational reform. In that paper he made two assertions:

(a) that industry is essentially a deskilling process that seeks to create a compliant and subordinate work-force which functions most effectively when operatives function well below their level of general education; and that

(b) 'education is essentially subversive, and its subversive potential can be contained only by the special social institution of schooling.'[26]

In short it can be argued that a tension exists between education and schooling and between living and working, in which education and living are or can be basically liberating processes, whilst schooling and working are constraining and, importantly, de-educative processes. Now this is a very uncomfortable analysis particularly for all of us who work hard at the process of schooling. Nevertheless I suspect that we have to face this analysis square on. To what extent do existing science courses openly encourage lateral thinking, creativity, imaginative insights, the questioning of authorities, or any other form of scholastic 'deviancy'? To what extent is existing content and pedagogy primarily normative in approach and outcome? Would a simplified and *reduced* core of science studies derived from existing syllabuses improve the position or simply create an even greater hardening of the arteries? To what extent would normal productive industry as currently organized welcome a steady influx of scientifically and technologically literate and aware young people determined to do more than make 473,000 suggestions to improve quality control and productivity? Edgley near the end of his paper made the following statement:

> . . . contained only by the special social institution of schooling. Contained but not eliminated; and the tensions take a particularly acute form in the conflict between an expanding education system and a mode of production which, as its own educational content expands, concentrates that content on the side of capital and progressively deskills labour. The conflict is reflected in various attempts at resolution, from the institutional separation between minority higher education and universal schooling to the theories of educationists who reserve real education for an elite and consign to the schools the job of 'socialization', or training of the emotions, or for leisure and hobbies. All bear witness in their own way to the fact that for most people in our society, the work they do, the fundamental activity that takes up half their waking time and decisively shapes their whole life, is not fit for human beings. The real but suppressed question is not how education can convert barbarians into rational autonomous individuals fit for our liberal democratic civilization, but rather whether our liberal democratic civilization, which is the civilization of industrial capitalism, is fit for people: people who, far from beginning life as barbarous egoists needing socialization, begin as social beings and are 'socialized' into alienated individuals.

Finally, Edgley urged education to come to terms with this problem head on and not 'avert its gaze'.[28] In short the educational system must at all costs continue to place central in its aims and objectives the notion of social change and social justice. When Mr Carlisle rewrote Mrs Williams' aims for secondary education he removed the words 'and in the search for a more just social order'.[29]

If it is this sort of issue that we have to resolve in the next decade and classical biology, chemistry and physics as currently defined and practiced cannot meet the demands of the secondary curriculum, what can? I would like to suggest that science studies in the 1980s should be reconstructed along the following lines:

(a) the scientific study of 'self' – a study of the biological and psychological aspects of the process of becoming a person:
(b) the scientific study of society – a study of the interrelationship between the individual, groups and societies;
(c) the scientific study of environment – a study of the interrelationship between individuals, groups, societies and their biophysical environment;
(d) the scientific study of self-sufficiency – a study of the means of production and the efficient utilization of resources;
(e) the scientific study of creativity – a study of problems and the production of solutions.

To redefine the science curriculum in these terms would, I submit, enable us to create a central range of studies that would be relevant to present and future societal and educational issues and also serve as a 'framework' around which it is possible to place suitably modified permutations of mathematics, language, literature, art, craft, music, history and geography; and also appropriate formulations of political, economic and moral education. From this we might begin to create the common curriculum we clearly need – a coherent and linked set of studies firmly placed in the centre of contemporary social needs. I, for one, can see more logic in this than I can for any core science curriculum that continues to extol the unremitting virtues of the amoeba, the mole, and the ohm.

POSTSCRIPT

In March 1981 the Department of Education and Science and the Welsh Office published their curriculum policy paper entitled *The School Curriculum.*[30] Given the strong criticisms presented above of the parent paper *A Framework of the School Curriculum* it seems appropriate to consider the extent to which any of the above comments can now be regarded as redundant.

The School Curriculum presents yet again the aims of education derived from *Education in Schools* (1977) and suggests how, without reference to resources, these aims can be achieved. In an interesting and highly critical editorial (27.3.81) the *Times Educational Supplement* suggested that the authoritative DES view of the curriculum was:

> . . . a 20-page booklet of such triteness as to be almost beyond belief. There is little in it to disagree with, because there is little in it.

More importantly the *TES* saw the booklet as representing:

> . . . the liquidation of commitments to a core curriculum and a defined framework, which Ministers entered into without understanding what was

involved. It is not a very glorious retreat, but at least it gets this tiresome business out of the DES's hair and leaves it to the professionals.

Now whilst I fully accept these comments I think we need to appreciate that when anyone is forced into inglorious retreat one option open to them is that of reforming their battalions prior to launching an effective counter-attack. In this instance the attempt to impose an instrumental curriculum has been rebuffed and the educational community has, possibly without knowing how, beaten off Ministerial directives and control. The danger is that in the euphoria of success the educational system will relax. In spite of the outcome of the Battle of Carlisle much of the above paper remains relevant for unless science education is reformed from within others will reform it for us. I think we need to remind ourselves that what I can only describe as the forces of curriculum law and order are hard at work creating core syllabuses at A-level, defining national criteria for the GCSE, and a new examination structure that would easily result in the centralization of control further and further away from 'the place where the action is'. These changes result from the activities of the 'professionals' and not the men from the Ministry, and little of the debate concerning the aims and objectives of science education for all impinges on their activities. If we are to see a serious attempt to substitute a socially relevant science education for the amoeba, the mole and the ohm I think we also need to note the following quotation from the *TES* editorial quoted above:

> Anybody can mouth uplifting educational aims . . . The really difficult conundrum is how to translate these high-falutin' and sanctimonious cracker-mottoes into practical activities which bring about cognitive and effective learning.

The key issue remains. How, and by what means, can those who want to reconstruct school science education do something more than produce an alternative set of cracker-mottoes? Whilst in the context of the school curriculum the DES may well have lost round one, I am far from convinced that the current definition of school science education won it. I submit that we now have to re-align our forces and further define our purposes as we prepare for round two.

NOTES AND REFERENCES

1. *Education in Schools: A Consultative Document* (HMSO, 1977), p. 6.
2. *A Framework for the School Curriculum* (DES and Welsh Office, 1980), p. 2.
3. See, for a discussion of this issue, Harris, A., 'The impossibility of a core curriculum', *Oxford Review of Education*, 1977, vol. 3, no. 2, and also Wellington, J. J., 'Determining a core curriculum: the limitations of transcendental deductions', *Journal of Curricula Studies*, 1981, 13, no. 1, 17–24.
4. *Alternatives for Science Education: A Consultative Document* (ASE, 1979).
5. *Education Through Science* (ASE, 1981).
6. See, for example, the conclusions of the secondary school curriculum presented in *Aspects of Secondary Education in England* (HMSO, 1979).
7. *The 1944 Education Act*.
8. 'Anomie' is a sociological term with a number of precise, if different, definitions. In this paper I have used it to describe the feeling of lacking any sense of identity or solidarity with other groups and individuals. A sense, perhaps, of total disenchantment.
9. *Science in General Education* (ASE, 1962).
10. Shayer, M., 'How to assess science courses', *Education in Chemistry*, 1970; The analysis of science curriculum for Piagetian level of demand, *Studies in Science Education*, 1978, **211**, 210–23.
11. Eliot, T. S., 'The Love Song of J. Alfred Prufrock' in *The Wasteland and other Poems* (Faber and Faber, p. 40).
12. Eliot, T. S., 'Brunt Norton' from *Four Quartets* (Faber and Faber, 1949).
13. Bantock, G. H., *Culture, Industrialization and Education* (Routledge & Kegan Paul, 1968).
14. *Education in Schools*, op. cit., p. 7.
15. *A Framework for the School Curriculum*, op. cit., p. 3.
16. Ibid., p. 6.
17. An exception in the science area was the *N-level Study in Integrated Science* prepared by a working party based on the University of Sussex and published by the Schools Council as part of the 18+ examination studies (Schools Council, 1977).
18. The term 'a basic grammar of school science' has been discussed by D. H. Jennings, 'Two sets of proposals for UK science education – a university biologist comments', *J. Biol. Educ.*, 1980, **14**(3) 223–30, and by West, R. W., 'Praxis and Possibilities in School Science Education', *J. Biol. Educ.*, 1981, **15**(1).
19. *North-South: A Programme for Survival* (Pan Books, 1980). Report of the Independent Commission on International Development Issues (the Brandt Commission).
20. Meadows, D. H. *et al.*, *The Limits to Growth* (Pan Books, 1974). Report of the Club of Rome's Project on the Predicament of Mankind (1972).
21. Pirsig, R. M., *Zen and the Art of Motorcycle Maintenance* (Bodley Head, 1974; Corgi Books, 1976).
22. Roszak, T., *Where the Wasteland Ends* (New York: Doubleday, 1972; Faber, 1974).

23. Faure, E. *et al.*, *Learning to Be: The World of Education Today and Tomorrow*. The report of the International Commission on the Development of Education.
24. Edgley, R., 'Education for industry', *Educ. Res.*, **20**(2), pp. 26–32, 197.
25. The debate on the standards and performance of the State education system in the UK initiated by the Prime Minister, Mr James Callaghan, at Ruskin College, Oxford in October 1976.
26. Edgley, R., op. cit., p. 32.
27. ibid., p. 32.
28. ibid., p. 32.
29. *Education in Schools*, op. cit., p. 7.
30. *The School Curriculum* (HMSO, 1981).

22 Purpose and values in science education

R. W. West

West uses the concepts of means, ends, goals and roles to expound ideas about science education and teaching. He discusses conflicting goals in, and the differences between, education and training, teaching and examining. This raises questions about the nature of science education policy and suggests ways in which government, HMI, industry and other groups and agencies can be centres of change and reaction. West concludes with a personal statement of values that should be embodied in a science curriculum.

ON THE MEANING OF WORDS

I want to use four terms and to use them in a rather precise and circumscribed manner. The terms are means, ends, goals and roles. Three of these are quite easy to define. Ends can be defined as that which we strive to achieve – a statement of intent, of purpose, of destination. Means is that which we will do in order to achieve that which we strive to achieve – a statement of actions congruent with our statement of intent. Hence we use these two terms when we speak for example of seeking appropriate means to achieve our ends. Goals are the operational statements that represent our targets and which reflect our intentions or our ends. They are the indicators by which we recognize arrival at our destination. Role is perhaps a little more complex to define but I would define it as being the character we play, or the purpose we have as participants in, or observers of, the attempt to use appropriate means to achieve our ends.

MEANINGS IN USE – THE MORAL OF THE MOLE

My end is to reach London from my starting point in sleepy Sussex. My means involve catching appropriate trains, that is those destined for

London (the one going west is for Littlehampton and Portsmouth – a fate only one remove from death). My goals on this journey are to see before me the Post Office Tower, Big Ben, and a placard entitled Victoria and thence, an intermediate goal, by courtesy of Lord Denning, of finding enough cash for a down payment for total ownership of the tube train. My role may be that of worthy traveller; tired businessman; student of communications systems; assessor of British Rail efficiency; or contributor to the newly resurrected commuter taxation system. My goals are fixed by my statement of end, that is, to be in London. My role as I achieve that end can be multifaceted. Be I traveller, student, or assessor my role varies but my end is fixed.

An educational metaphor to reinforce my point. My intention, my aim, *my presentation of intended outcomes* is to enable Johnnie to differentiate between say, a mole and a mole. My goals will be expressed in terms of the known characteristics of little particles in large quantities, or small furry things with a propensity to turn up large mounds of earth.

My means depend upon my role. As teacher, means reflect the act of teaching and I will utilize a series of strategies and tactics commensurate with that role. As assessor, I will utilize a different set of strategies and tactics that relate to the act of assessment as against the act of teaching. As a trainer of intern mole catchers (a different role) my means will differ sharply for I am highly unlikely to mention Avogadro or any large or small number. The role of the trainer of mole catchers, you will note, is still consistent with my earlier statement of ends – to differentiate between a mole and a mole. Here role shift results in goal shift and we begin to see the real interaction between goals and roles and the ways in which ends can affect means. To conclude my metaphor with a devastating statement of the obvious – don't ask a mole catcher to teach the mole, or a chemist to catch one.

ROLE CONFUSION: GOAL CONFUSION

Much is made of the tensions that can exist when teachers adopt the role of assessors, and we know what happens when examiners and examination boards adopt the role of curriculum developers – and attempt to produce national criteria. These are examples of role confusion – the switching of hats while the mind is disengaged or the educational system is in motion. This suggests to me two simple but obvious educational aphorisms: (a) Examiners are requested not to stand while the curriculum is in motion. (b) Curriculum developers shouldn't when the examination system is standing at the station. Now our problem is that in our everyday personal and professional lives we adopt a range of roles in the context of a multiplicity of goals. Consequently we explore and utilize a variety of strategies (means) in the effort to achieve certain ends. My various roles as parent, teacher, researcher, writer, reader, taxpayer, voter, or common man influence very radically my actions, my definition of desirable or attainable ends, and the way I select means. This can lead to the classic problem of role conflict – the situation when while seeking to achieve a given end one of my roles conflicts with another. Thus I might find that my role as parent conflicts with my role as teacher.

But what of goal confusion and how do we construct our matrix of goals? We define our goals by defining our ends – by specifying our intentions and stating the intended outcomes of our endeavours. It is this process that leads to the greatest single level of confusion for often we fail to achieve a match between hopes and conclusions – between intentions and outcomes.

GOALS IN CONFLICT AND ON AVOIDING COLLISIONS – THE CASE OF EDUCATION AND TRAINING

We all sense a clear distinction between 'education' and 'training' but what is the distinction? At the risk, and real risk, of driving a wedge between two legitimate activities may I make the following points.

No matter whether we have in mind the education of the child or his or her training, we need to specify intended outcomes (ends). We need, moreover, to define goals. Now it is traditional to define *education* in terms of broad characteristics, or indices, such as nimbleness and flexibility of mind, grasp of essentials, familiarity with culture, ability to be literate, numerate, articulate, and so on. In short, we define education, tautologically, as the process of attaining those characteristics that are held by an educated man. Training, on the other hand, is again traditionally conceptualized in terms of narrow characteristics, or indices, such as an ability to turn a screw, joint a joint, or drive a car – in short, to perform a skill or a set of related skills. Now I don't feel that the knowledge/skill distinction between education and training is all that helpful because an educated man uses a wide range of skills and a trained man has a store of knowledge and experience. Instead, let us consider an alternative distinction.

Education is, at root, a subversive activity in which the individual establishes the boundaries of his or her ignorance and thus the true nature of knowledge. Before I am misunderstood may I emphasize that one needs to *know* a great deal to define the boundaries of one's ignorance. He who knows nothing or next to nothing is not educated – he is ignorant. Training is, at root, a conformist activity in which the individual establishes a mastery of defined and specific aspects of knowledge, skills and attitudes.

Both education and training involve learning and can be achieved by the processes of teaching. The essential difference is, however, that education involves divergency whilst training is essentially convergent. Much of what we currently label education is, of course, training. We have, therefore, two options. One is to take more seriously our ability to train and become better trainers, the other is to explore how we might become better educators. In practice, of course, we need to do both and be more self-consciously aware which of the two activities it is we are pursuing at a given time. There is no future in setting education and training against each other.

WHEN TO TRAIN AND WHEN TO EDUCATE

The only way we can clarify when we are in the business of training or in the business of education is through the clear analysis of our intentions – our aims, our ends. We cannot achieve this clarity by examining what we do, that is, *how* we teach. It is not a 'how' question, it is a 'why' question. Now I will want to argue that much of our preoccupation in science education in terms of teaching, planning, examining, and so on is with 'how' questions – how best to grade, how best to demonstrate, how best to select that we wish to teach. In short, we focus on the technicalities of means when often we've not explored our ends. 'How' questions cannot be fully resolved without having first established 'why'. I will return to this matter shortly.

WHY TEACH AND WHY EXAMINE?

We teach in order that others should learn in order to become better trained (more competent) or better educated (less ignorant). We examine in order to estimate the success of their learning – which is not unrelated to estimating the efficiency of our teaching. We approach teaching and learning via means/ends analysis, that is, we plan our teaching according to the formal model derived basically from the work of people like Tyler, Bloom and Kerr and so on. This model can be represented diagrammatically as:

aims objectives content pedagogy evaluation assessment.

We plan assessment, or evaluation, or examining on similar lines:

aims assessment objectives content techniques assessment.

The critical role of assessment arises from the existence of assessment as a key element of the teaching model (and, of course, of the curriculum development model). Assessment and evaluation provide the feedback whereby we estimate the *gap* or match/mismatch between intentions and outcomes. Now whilst much attention is given to the middle and ends of these two processes, that is, the means and outcomes – the 'how', and with what results and effects – little attention, other than in terms of formality, is given to the start – the definition of 'why' – the statement of intentionality. As a result the highly purposeful use of sophisticated means in both teaching and examining leads to a purposeless conclusion, or to conclusions the purposes of which are confused and often muddled.

'IN MY BEGINNING IS MY END AND MY END IN MY BEGINNING'

I cannot start out on a purposeful journey without knowing where I am going and why. The problem with 'why' is the problem of values. The central problem in the development of both educational and training programmes is that of defining purpose, of answering the question 'why?'. Why teach? Why educate? Why train? Our problem as science educators in 1982 is a marked lack of consensus as to the *real purpose* of our existence: what we are in the business of and why.

Now a value position is a statement of intention and belief: it involves knowledge, faith and conviction. Above all it involves laying on the line an action position. Our problem is that what we do or intend reflects not only our own personal values but also social values and the social fact that we live in a divided nation imbued with a multiplicity of values, many of which are in conflict. Value positions reflect conditions and norms which are seldom questioned. Values are stated and are defended but are seldom debated, almost never negotiated. *Education Through Science*[1] reflects the failure to resolve conflicting value systems, be they typified as being from the left or from the right, or hard versus soft, or in accord with an open or closed model of society. An essential prerequisite to any debate about the *purpose* of the curriculum – of its content, its organization, its pedagogy, or its assessment – is a debate about ends. The same, of course, can be said about the writing of policy documents. Purpose demands the adoption of clear and unambiguous value systems. A curriculum model that is solely concerned with means, with 'how', is an empty vessel destined to bob aimlessly in the high seas of purposeless activity. It contains a message for those who find it among the driftwood of the beaches: 'I came from I know not where in search of a destiny. Will the finder please tell me where I should go'.

OH, HOW OUR VALUES CONFLICT

It seems to me very appropriate to explore the problem of conflicting value systems by raising certain questions about the nature of science education policy. This in my view can best be done by looking at the underlying values that are represented on the one hand by those bodies and organizations that act as pressure groups for change in the curriculum and, on the other, those pressure groups that act strongly for the retention of the *status quo*. I will first deal with the major agencies for change.

Central government

With the publication of a framework for the school curriculum and the subsequent policy document *The School Curriculum*,[2] government has intervened in what used to be called the secret garden of the curriculum. Incorporated in these important documents are proposals for restructuring the curriculum during the period of compulsory education with an overt move towards the establishment of a core, or protected, curriculum. Science figures prominently in these proposals as it is stated that *all* young people up to the age of 16 should study science. To many science teachers this simple notion represents a very profound pressure for change which has major ramifications at all levels of provision. Not least, it raises the critical question: 'What science studies are appropriate for all young people up to the age of 16?' It is also a pressure for change that is already causing major repercussions at the level of the providing authorities as they begin to work out the staffing and other resource implications of the movement towards 'Science for All'.

Industry and commerce

It has become customary in recent years to talk in terms of the relationship between schooling and 'the world of work' in such a way as to suggest that the needs of industry and commerce are no longer met by the educational system in general and the schools in particular. Thus we are told that young people leaving school are inadequately prepared for the world of work, especially in terms of their general standards of literacy and numeracy. In addition, industry appears to demand greater levels of scientific and technological literacy than heretofore – a demand that is often linked to the pressure to reduce the level of specialization in science studies at 16+. Whilst industry is often categorized as being reactionary in its demands on the school system – a view that can be found in the Cockcroft Report on the teaching of mathematics[3] – it is significant that one of the most positive responses to the ASE consultative paper *Alternatives for Science Education*[4] came from the Education Committee of the Confederation of British Industry. Science teachers on the other hand tended to regard the consultative document as being too radical. In terms of science education the pressure for change from industry and commerce appears to be in the direction of more broadly based studies with a greater emphasis being placed on applicability and capability. In this respect the pressure is not one of back to the basics.

Higher education

The science curriculum in our schools has been the subject of extended scrutiny by higher education and it is important to note that our universities and polytechnics remain critical of the over-specialized nature of sixth-form studies in schools in England and Wales. By implication the same must be said of the courses that underpin A-level studies and the organizational framework of those courses. In spite of the ultimate debacle of the N and F exercise, higher education has not yet rejected the agreement established between the Schools Council and the Standing Conference on University Entrance in 1966 (the three principles) which included the desirability

> . . . to reduce specialization and broaden the scope of study in the sixth form; [and that] . . . a pupil's choice of subject for study in the sixth form and the university, in so far as it narrows his career opportunities, should be made as late as possible.[5]

The local education authorities

Following the publication of *The School Curriculum* and in the light of falling school rolls and the cutback in public expenditure, the local education authorities have become major agencies for curricular change in our schools and have an important role to play in redefining the nature of science education provision. Whilst in some instances changes may be implemented according to the simplistic rules of accounting, there are many other instances where local education authorities are seeking to approach their problems via a systematic review of curricular provision. In such cases science advisers and science teachers are clearly important agents for change.

Her Majesty's Inspectorate

Since the publication of *Curriculum 11–16*[6] in 1977 the Inspectorate, within very finite limits of resource and power, has been actively supporting changes in our approach to the science curriculum. Chapter seven of *Aspects of Secondary Education in England*[7] represents a major critique of current provision and the relevant sections of *A View of the Curriculum*[8] suggest how science might be incorporated in a core or protected curriculum. It remains to be seen how far the Inspectorate has been able to influence the form and content of the DES further guidelines on science in the curriculum that are to be published shortly.

The Schools Council

The Schools Council by its very constitution and *raison d'être* is dedicated to curricular change and has taken many initiatives over the years with regard to the science curriculum. In my view Science 5–13, SCISP, and Project Technology still represent important attempts to reconceptualize science studies although these projects do present problems. The establishment by the Council, with the help of the Association for Science Education, of the Secondary Science Curriculum Review is further evidence of an ongoing commitment to change.

The Association for Science Education

Like the Schools Council, the Association has an honourable tradition of both supporting existing provision and looking towards the future. The recent policy papers *Alternatives for Science Education* and *Education Through Science* continue this process and there is much in *Education Through Science* that, if implemented, would significantly alter the nature and scope of science teaching in our schools. Thus even the simple notion that all schools should have a clearly articulated science education policy would, if put into effect, quite radically change the nature of current provision.

Examination boards

Whilst many would not conceptualize the school examination boards as change agents, the current common examination system exercise has forced the boards to become deeply involved in the debate about the curriculum. Their new position is not of course, unrelated to longer term economic and resource problems, that will arise from falling secondary school rolls and the increasing costs of the examination system. Irrespective of the final fate of the 16+ proposals, I think we will find the examination boards adopting a more interventionist position with respect to the shape and content of the curriculum.

Society

Those of us who wrote *Alternatives for Science Education* know only too well the hazards of speculating on the possible effects of social change on science education provision. Nevertheless there are certain social trends that are likely to affect the nature of curricular change over the next few years and I feel it is legitimate to regard these as pressures for change. Amongst the most important I will simply note the general deterioration of our social climate and the increasing polarity of values; continuing economic decline and concomitant rising unemployment, youth unemployment, and premature adult retirement; and the increasingly high level of incipient racial disharmony. That these 'social facts' exist is not a matter of dispute, what is contentious is the effect these pressures will have, or should have, on the school curriculum in general and the science curriculum in particular.

I would now like to turn from pressures *for* change to a set of equally identifiable pressures *against* change – the forces that try to maintain the *status quo* in terms of schools and schooling.

Central government

Central government acts manifestly for the maintenance of the *status quo* and overtly rejects proposals for change that appear contrary to policies that have never yet been clearly enunciated. Thus whilst urging local education authorities to change the nature of educational provision in accord with newly established economic and demographic imperatives, the government has rejected proposals that appear to threaten 'schools of proven worth' – an equally instant imperative. (Much of the recent DES statement on examination policy at 16+[9] smacks of this same philosophy especially in terms of the use of the concept of 'standards'. Hence the new system may be acceptable if no decline in standards is threatened and providing none of the three parties concerned, *viz* the GCE Boards, the CSE Boards, and the Secretaries of State exercise a veto on any emergent proposals.) It is quite possible that many of the strategies available for the realistic implementation of the policy of 'Science for All' may fall foul of certain sectional interests.

Industry and commerce

Whilst advocating and supporting change at the national level, industry and commerce can be extremely recalcitrant and inhibiting at the local level or at the level of individual industries. The Cockcroft Committee has specifically drawn attention to the rather cavalier way in which examination grades are demanded and then ignored in favour of selection tests. Many schools anxious to broaden their approach to science studies through the mechanism of programmes of integrated science (even to double O-level standard) have been frustrated by employers insisting on O-level physics without having more than a nodding acquaintance with either the content or the standard of O-level physics courses.

Higher education

Acting in the defence of standards including that of the English first degree, higher education effectively scuppered the N and F programme after several years detailed discussion, planning, research, and syllabus development. Subsequently, in a vain and ill-considered attempt to homogenize the entry standards for students to degree courses, they have encouraged the examination boards to create without the benefit of any research and development core A-level syllabuses that may well act as a major constraint to syllabus renewal for decades to come. Finally, the cutback in resource to higher education and the reduction in student numbers is allowing the opponents of the Robbins principle ample opportunity to restore 'true' values in higher education at the expense of innovatory courses and of educational opportunity.

The local education authorities

The LEAs, caught between the pressures from central government and from elected members who voice the fears and aspirations of the more vocal ratepayers, tend often to seek safe or popular solutions to the crisis of the curriculum. In such a climate staffing resources can be easily manipulated to the detriment of innovation and change. Similarly, corporate management especially when dominated by accountants can overlook the niceties of curricular innovation in favour of the apparently cost-effective virtues of traditional courses and approaches.

Her Majesty's Inspectorate

Whilst advocating change, HMI has a marked tendency, justified historically, for being reluctant to point up effective solutions to many of the problems it diagnoses. Whilst one has some sympathy with the posture of assumed neutrality, one acknowledges fully the lead HMI has taken over the effects of the reduction of educational resource on actual provision. Nevertheless, over-guarded and at times over-woolly statements of alternative definitions of school science can, and do, inhibit change.

The Schools Council

Notwithstanding its own response to a framework for the school curriculum entitled *The Practical Curriculum*,[10] the Schools Council still lacks a coherent model of the curriculum and many of its proposals therefore lack the coherence essential for systematic take-up and systematic implementation. I would go so far as to suggest that the single largest failure of the curriculum development movement in this country is that of not hammering out a curricular rationale for universal secondary education. The partnership of teachers, employers and government embodied in the Schools Council can be seen in this respect, therefore, as an inhibitor of change rather than a preserver of the *status quo*.

The Association for Science Education

The ASE, particularly through the mechanism of its 'silent majority', is a powerful agency for resisting change. The Association, over the years, has been ambivalent on N and F, a common examination (not system) at 16+, and backed away from the analysis presented in *Alternatives for Science Education*. Students of textual criticism can have a field day detecting the influence of the forces of reaction if they study in detail the consultative and policy documents, *Alternatives for Science Education* and *Education Through Science* respectively.

Examination boards

Whilst deeply into the change business at the moment, they remain essentially conservative in their attitudes to syllabuses and methods of examining. They have never really accepted Henry Macintosh's challenge of the 1960s to become involved in curriculum development[11] and have responded too readily to administrative convenience on the one hand and selective listening on the other. The recent attempt in some quarters to dismiss the reaction to the 16+ physics national criteria as being something of a bandwagon, is an ample illustration of the noise examination boards can create in their own feedback mechanisms.

Society

Society, of course, is a major obstacle to change and never more so than when the more powerful and influential members of society are in a bit of a fix. Whilst certain of the social pressures I referred to earlier may result in change, others may not. It is in this area that one becomes most aware of ambivalence and uncertainty. How, for example, will the English middle class react to the loss almost overnight of two key planks in its birthright? I refer to the new situation in which its offspring can no longer be guaranteed a job on leaving school or a place in higher education if the children want it. Once the reality of this situation has bitten will we see a backlash and a forceful attempt to re-establish the old mechanisms of the educational class war, *viz* selection, preferential treatment, and a sound academic education; or will we witness for the first time strong middle class pressure to change the norms and values of society and the educational system that supports it?

The analysis I have presented above seeks to illustrate how the very agencies for change are themselves the centres of reaction. Caught between and within these opposing pressures are ourselves – those who teach science or seek to support its teaching. Charged as we are by government and our own Association to define what is meant by 'Science for All', it is we who have to resolve these tensions and come to terms with the inevitable dialectic. One solution is to seek the middle ground and hunt for compromise. We can enter the market place and barter over values and value positions and create a patchwork of provision in which we set the pieces we win against those we lose. This solution will, in my view, leave us debilitated and shorn of resources, for others bred in the market place can handle its dynamics better. The alternative is to create an open debate on the real purpose of universal secondary education, on the nature of the common curriculum, and on the resolution of the problem of educational and social values. Within the context of such a debate we need to delineate the significant contribution education through science should make. The Association should negotiate the true values of science education and not make demands. It must therefore establish where it really stands with respect to its agreed policy aims and negotiate openly from that basis. Unity of purpose in this respect could help unify educational provision and thus help to build bridges between the disparate elements of our deeply divided society. Whilst that unity and agreement does not currently exist I firmly believe that the ASE through its recent policy statement is more advanced in its thinking and therefore better placed to take a lead than any other subject association.

WHERE ANGELS FEAR TO TREAD

In what must be a personal statement and one that cannot any longer be accompanied by Copland's 'Fanfare for the Common Man' may I take a lead and lay my values on the table in the context of developing the secondary science curriculum.

I believe in the sanctity of the child as the embodiment of hope for the future. Education through science must start from the needs of children. In this respect I would endorse Cockcroft's statement that

> We believe it should be a fundamental principle that no topic should be included unless it can be developed sufficiently for it to be applied in ways which the pupils can understand.[12]

I believe in a just and fair social order. Education through science must be centrally concerned with increasing educational opportunity. This principle is also manifest in the Cockcroft Report:

> This situation has arisen because the syllabuses now being followed by a majority of pupils in secondary schools have been constructed by using as starting points syllabuses designed for pupils in the top quarter of the range of attainment in mathematics. Syllabuses for pupils of lower attainment have been developed from these by deleting a few topics and reducing the depth of treatment of others; in other words, they have been constructed 'from the top downwards'. We believe that this is a wrong approach and that development should be 'from the bottom upwards' by considering the range of work which is appropriate for lower-attaining pupils and extending this range as the level of attainment of pupils increases.[13]

I believe that a just and fair social order cannot tolerate ignorance. Education through science must be centrally concerned with education – with making knowledge accessible and usable so that people may become more conscious of that which they do not know.

I believe that a just and fair social order cannot tolerate incompetence. Education through science must be centrally concerned with training – the process of enabling people to act.

I believe in the inalienable right of the individual to dissent. Education through science must assist the individual to exercise choice with responsibility.

I believe that the individual must be protected from arbitrary infringement of his or her autonomy. Education through science must be fair, be just, and avoid arbitrary processes of selection and rejection, the unequal allocation of resources, and the arbitrary grading of children.

I believe in science as a central manifestation of the creativity of man. Education through science must be centrally concerned with science, the purpose of science, the culture of science, and the improvement of science but it must mediate science for and with the common man.

I believe that order cannot be imposed – it must be negotiated. The new science curriculum must be negotiated in the context of education and training by teachers, with society, and for the benefit of children.

I believe that education is a lifelong process. The new science curriculum must be a foundation on which the individual can build throughout life and should involve the formal agencies of schooling, further education, higher education, adult education, and the informal agencies of living in a democratic society.

Finally, I believe that the teaching profession can and will control its own destiny. Education through science and the new science curriculum are both predicated on this assumption. Our task is to act with vigour and with rigour. If we don't, on our epitaph we will read once again

> Footfalls echo in the memory down the passage we did not take towards the door we never opened.[14]

REFERENCES

1. *Education Through Science* (ASE, 1981).
2. *The School Curriculum* (HMSO, 1981).
3. *Mathematics Counts* (HMSO, 1982).
4. *Alternatives for Science Education* (ASE, 1979).
5. *Preparation for Degree Courses* (Schools Council Working Paper 47, Evans/Methuen, 1973), p. 10.
6. *Curriculum 11–16: Working Papers by HM Inspectorate: a Contribution to Current Debate* (HMSO, 1979).
7. *Aspects of Secondary Education in England: a Survey by HM Inspectors of Schools* (HMSO, 1979).
8. *A View of the Curriculum* (HMI Series: Matters for Discussion, No. 11, HMSO, 1980).
9. Draft document from the DES on Examinations at 16+, March 1982.
10. *The Practical Curriculum* (Schools Council Working Paper 70, Methuen Education, 1981).
11. Macintosh, H. G. 'A constructive role for examining boards in curriculum development', *Journal of Curriculum Studies*, 1970, Vol. 2, **1**, 32–9.

12. *Mathematics Counts*, op. cit. p. 133.
13. ibid. p. 133.
14. Eliot, T. S., 'Burnt Norton' from *Four Quartets* (Faber & Faber, 1949).

V TEACHING METHODS IN SCIENCE

The task of teaching science in schools has often been guided by the 'logic' of scientific disciplines, with their emphasis on sound hierarchies of knowledge. Allied to this has been the assumption that the teacher's own store of science knowledge holds the key to successful learning. While the challenges to these ideas have long been apparent, the developmental approach that seeks to match methods to a pupil's individual current capabilities has provided a radicalization of school science. Several important contributions are contained in this section, including those by Rosalind Driver. Driver's personal constructivist approach takes up the view that the learner 'needs to trace the steps from the familiar to the new, from the fact or idea he possesses to that which he is to acquire'. Gilbert seeks to reconcile these methods with the influential recommendations of the Association for Science Education in its 1981 report *Education through Science*. In Chapters 24 and 25 the contributers elucidate the consequences for teaching of the adoption of style that acknowledges the structured views in 'children's science'. The need, it is argued, is to encourage students to express their perceptions and for teachers to support pupils' rethinking of their ideas rather than to correct misconceptions at the first opportunity.

Warren Beasley's concern lies in the relationship between teachers as managers in laboratory settings and pupil behaviour, most particularly their attachment to specific task activity. Beasley concludes that effective teaching (defined by a high level of pupil task involvement) is most likely when teachers retain whole class surveillance, with an emphasis on verbal interaction and teacher-initiated activity.

Chapters 28 and 29 focus attention on those who have been 'missing out' in science education. These include the majority of girls in schools who, it is argued, perceive scientific work as irrelevant. Head argues the need to give science a more 'feminine' image, involving a stronger emphasis on application in case studies of an interdisciplinary nature. Smail, Whyte and Kelly describe the GIST project that involves teachers and allies action research with programmed activities for pupils, using intervention to induce a more positive image for science among girls. This has involved women working in science and technology visiting schools, for example.

23 From theory to practice

• R. Driver

After a discussion of educational aims, Driver considers the contribution of the developmental approach in matching teaching methods to the development of a child's brain and capabilities. A section on structure in science education has some cautionary words about thinking that a clear structure and logical progression of concepts (worthy though they be) really mesh in with a pupil's learning process. In the same vein, it may be difficult for a student to relate experiments to theoretical models. These problems should not be avoided, but do need to be appreciated. Once mastered, the model is more easily retained than the details of the projects. Moreover, models can be presented at levels matched to particular groups of students. It is at least debatable that a bad model is better than no model at all, provided the pupil realizes that he is not to believe in the bad model.

A short section on experimental method states the advantages of learning for oneself and of confronting a model with data. Finally, there is a very useful reminder that learning through experiment is a slow process, and to take advantage of it may mean omitting some topics from the syllabus.

Whenever we plan and teach a science course we make decisions, whether explicitly or implicitly, about the aims of the course. For example, is it to be a course that is appropriate for all secondary school pupils or is it to be a preparation for pupils specializing in science? Is the course to be responsive to the interests and ideas of young people or is it primarily to reflect the structure of the discipline? What image of science does it promote – is it science as a body of knowledge or is there a place for inquiry and speculation on the part of pupils?

The 1981 policy statement of the Association for Science Education[1] lists six aims for education through science which might be summarized as follows:

(1) understanding scientific concepts,
(2) the development of cognitive and psycho-motor skills,
(3) the ability to undertake inquiries,
(4) understanding the nature of the scientific enterprise,

(5) understanding the relationship between science and society,
(6) the development of a sense of personal worth.

The document indicates that all young people at some point in their schooling should have experiences which lead to the achievement of all these six aims, although it recognizes that the needs of different young people may demand different emphases at various times in their schooling.

Developing and teaching courses which reflect this balance is a very real challenge, not least because of some possible inherent conflicts between the aims themselves. This book has explored some of the issues involved in producing a satisfactory synthesis between just two of the aims: the acquisition of knowledge and the use of pupils' own inquiries in the pursuit of further knowledge. The tension between these two components has existed for as long as science has had a place in the school curriculum.

Over the last 100 years documents on the role of science in general education have reflected this tension. In a report, *Natural Science in Education,* published in 1918,[2] the authors make an eloquent claim for science in the school curriculum in terms of the general faculties it develops:

> It can arouse and satisfy the element of wonder in our natures. As an intellectual exercise it disciplines our powers of mind. Its utility and applicability are obvious. It quickens and cultivates directly the faculty of observation. It teaches the learner to reason from facts which come under his own notice. By it, the power of rapid and accurate generalization is strengthened, without it, there is a real danger of the mental habit of method and arrangement never being acquired.

In 1936 the Science Masters' Association published a report, *The Teaching of General Science,*[3] in which it states three main contributions that science makes to general education:

(1) utilitarian or vocational: it helps the pupils in their everyday life, or may be necessary in their future occupations;
(2) disciplinarian: it teaches them to think; it sharpens their minds;
(3) cultural: its inclusion is desirable because it forms an essential part of our social heritage.

Again, the claim is made that science makes an important contribution to the development of pupils' general faculties, although the report later adds a cautionary note:

> . . . we would point out, however, that *experimental* evidence has shown quite definitely that the possibilities of transfer of training are much smaller than had formerly been supposed.

The 'process' aims of science education have also been of concern to American curriculum developers since the 1950s.[4] The curriculum development projects in secondary science which have taken place since the 1950s in Britain and America have attempted to foster the skills of scientific inquiry and to promote an understanding of scientific principles and their application to everyday life.

As I indicated earlier, the traditional synthesis between these two aims has tended to promote an inductivist view of science based on the premise that all scientific knowledge derives from sensory experiences. This perspective has been reinforced over the years by views about child-centred education, as articulated by such people as Froebel, Dewey and Piaget.

Incidentally, it would be incorrect to suggest that psychologists and philosophers of science have been influential in shaping the science in our schools. Rather the community of science educators has invoked such theoretical 'support' as is necessary to give credibility to 'common sense' views about the nature of science and of children's learning. The problems that exist both with the inductivist view of the nature of science and with the 'accretion' view of children's learning have been outlined in earlier chapters. It appears that it is necessary to piece together a new synthesis between content and process in science education which brings together both a different philosophy of science and a new perspective on learning. This involves the recognition that the science that children learn beyond primary school is more than natural history; it goes beyond the exploration and classification of aspects of the environment. Pupils are being introduced to theoretical ideas and conventions of the scientific community, ideas which derive from the imagination and which may in time be suspended.

If this constructivist view of the nature of science is to be taken seriously then it has certain implications for secondary school science courses. This chapter gives a personal view of a number of these implications.

A DEVELOPMENTAL APPROACH TO SCIENCE TEACHING AND LEARNING

Evidence has been presented which indicates that children use a range of intuitive ideas to make sense of their experiences. Some of these ideas, or alternative frameworks, are characteristic of the thinking of many children, and may persist despite instruction. Perhaps it is not surprising to note the similarity between some of the ideas of children and theories that have been important in the history of science itself (for example the caloric theory of heat or Aristotelean views of motion). Daily experiences of phenomena make some interpretations or models more obvious than others. However, it is very easy to view the notions put forward by pupils as naive and simplistic, and to pass them by, perhaps with disinterest. It is perhaps worth bearing in mind that some of these notions were given serious consideration in the scientific community in the past. By referring to the ideas and investigations of past scientists, some of the powerful ideas of young people can be explored in a way that treats them with respect. It has been suggested that, instead of ignoring the alternative frameworks that children have developed, science teaching programmes could benefit by taking greater account of them. By making their theories more explicit in the formal learning situation children are able to explore their implications and make comparisons between one 'framework' or 'theory' and another. They can also be given experiences which serve to develop their ideas or, if necessary, to challenge them. Various science teaching materials have attempted to do this. One of the most well-developed examples is the treatment given to dynamics by the Harvard Project Physics materials,[5] where the Aristotelean view is explored at some length.

Educators have always recognized the need to 'start where the child is'. Ausubel emphasizes this in the distinction he makes between 'meaningful' and 'rote' learning. In practice this is usually interpreted in terms of relating science teaching to experiences which are familiar to children in their daily lives.

However, perhaps in addition, teaching needs to relate to what is familiar to children, not just at the level of the world of events and experiences but also in their world of ideas. If children are encouraged to make their theories more explicit, these can be open for inspection and testing in the classroom. Children's own ideas in fact can provide the necessary raw material to exemplify the plural nature of scientific theory, and act as a starting point for pupils to design critical tests to distinguish between different interpretations.

Underlying this recognition that children's ideas as well as their experiences need to be taken into account in planning courses is a view of the learning process as taking place by conceptual change. The task for educators is to give pupils the experiences which encourage such change to take place. In preparing secondary science courses little attention has as yet been paid to what is known about the development of pupils' thinking. Such projects as Science 5/13 and the Australian Science Education Project have based their sequencing of materials on a Piagetian stage model. In this kind of scheme, ideas which involve the structures of formal operational thought such as arguing hypothetico-deductively, controlling variables or using proportional reasoning are not introduced until the adolescent years.

Shayer and Adey[6] report their analysis of the cognitive demand of a range of secondary science courses in terms of Piagetian levels, and the results of a survey of the levels of thinking of British schoolchildren. The findings indicate a mismatch exists between the logical demands of the science courses analysed and the level of thinking of most secondary school pupils.

Such an analysis may give general guidance on matching the demands of a course to the logical capabilities of the pupils taking it. It can be helpful in giving a general indication of the way ideas can be sequenced for teaching and at what age they might be introduced. However, there is more involved in taking account of children's thinking than simply paying attention to its logical component. In a previous chapter doubt was expressed about the Piagetian matching model and it was indicated that the content as well as the logical structure of a task affects pupils' performance.

In some science topics investigations of pupils' ideas indicate that these develop with age through a clear sequence, and a knowledge of this can be helpful both in deciding at what age to teach a topic and how to organize appropriate experiences for pupils: experiences which will aid their conceptual understanding of that topic. Some of the interesting approaches being tried which are based on this view of learning as conceptual change have been reviewed in earlier chapters. Techniques which are being incorporated into these approaches include providing opportunities for pupils to make their own ideas explicit, encouraging the generation and testing by pupils of alternative interpretations of phenomena, and giving pupils experiences which challenge their current ideas.

THE QUESTION OF STRUCTURE IN THE SCIENCE CURRICULUM

Such a view of learning through conceptual change has implications for the general organization of the science curriculum. In his influential book, *The Process of Education*, Jerome Bruner drew attention to the importance of the structure of the subject to be taught:

> . . . the curriculum of a subject should be determined by the most fundamental understanding that can be achieved of the underlying principles that give structure to that subject. Teaching specific topics or skills without making clear their context in the broader fundamental structure of a field of knowledge is uneconomical in several deep senses.[7]

Much of the science curriculum development that has taken place over the last two decades on both sides of the Atlantic has indicated this concern for structure. The content of science courses has been updated and their structure changed to reflect recent developments in the conceptual structure of the discipline. Paradoxically, this has been coupled with a shift in pedagogy towards a greater amount of practical work; practical work which in most cases is introduced to be illustrative or provide confirmatory evidence for the presented theories. We tend to think that this 'practical' approach makes the subject more 'relevant' and easier for pupils to understand. Yet there is a sense in which the approach is making even more intellectual demands on pupils in that it requires pupils to relate experiences obtained in the laboratory to the theoretical models being presented. The pupils themselves, with or without guidance, need to make the connection between the phenomena and the theoretical constructs: for example, to link the movement of levels of liquids in tubes to the increased motion of invisible particles which 'compose' the liquid, to relate the change in colour of a solution in a test tube to the concentration of hydrogen ions present. It is important to recognize that in science lessons pupils are involved in learning at two levels at once: they are exposed both to new phenomena and also to their accepted theoretical interpretation. Simply because teaching based on conceptual schemes is problematic does not mean it should not be attempted. However, the demands it makes on pupils need to be recognized. If pupils are unable to link the experiences given in the laboratory to the conceptual themes in the course, then the coherence that is apparent to the curriculum writer or teacher may not be obvious to the pupils, who may remember it simply as a series of disjointed experiences. Incidentally, the current debate over teaching science as separate disciplines or as an integrated course may be an irrelevant issue to many pupils who remember their experiences as a sequence of lessons, whatever the subject is called on the timetable. The key question is 'what is integrated by the learner?'

Even though they have difficulty relating the phenomena to the presented theory, some pupils are prepared to suspend judgement, to learn the rules or laws even though they cannot relate them to their experiences. They are able to maintain interest in the belief that at a later date what they are learning will make sense. On the other hand, many secondary school pupils, perhaps the majority, expect more immediate intellectual satisfaction. They are not prepared to wait weeks or even years before theoretical ideas presented in school can be related to their own experiences. Many of these pupils will never continue with their formal science education after leaving school. Such pupils need to be able to 'make sense' of the scientific ideas presented to them in a more immediate way.

School science may be remembered, but recalled as isolated experiences; some activity with glass blocks and pins may be remembered in much the same way as a snatch of a Wordsworth poem or an unrelated fact in history. It has not become part of the young adult's way of understanding the natural world. Unless the theory or formalism presented to pupils is learned in a meaningful way, it is soon forgotten as useful knowledge and not drawn on in the future: pupils revert to their intuitions or earlier frameworks. The problems that this can cause have been illustrated in earlier chapters. Designing a curriculum around major conceptual schemes may mean that most pupils finish their formal education in science neither understanding the theory they have been introduced to nor seeing the illustrative phenomena as particularly relevant or interesting.

If the orientation of science in general education is to help pupils develop a theoretical understanding which enables them to interpret and make sense of everyday experiences, to make pupils more 'at home' in the natural and man-made world they inhabit, then this may mean reassessing the science curriculum at two levels. It means selecting illustrative phenomena not simply because of the support they give to a theoretical idea, but because they are of practical use and everyday interest in their own right. It also means bringing the theoretical ideas within the compass of pupils' understanding.

In many areas of science, phenomena can be interpreted at a range of levels of sophistication, all of which are in some sense useful. For example, in the early years of secondary school, we expect pupils to understand current electricity in terms analogous to fluid flow in pipes. This model is quite effective in enabling us to predict or explain a range of everyday phenomena involving electrical circuitry; in this sense the model is 'right', it is adequate for its purpose. However, older pupils are introduced to a more sophisticated model in which electric current in wires is construed as a drift of charged particles through a lattice structure. This model is only 'better' than the previous one in that it accounts for a greater range of phenomena. A similar shift in the level of theoretical sophistication is encountered in several other topics, for example, in chemical bonding, the wave properties of light, inheritance and the molecular–kinetic theory of heat.

For pupils who have difficulty in understanding the theoretical ideas in science perhaps it is necessary to reconsider the level of theory presented. For example, are we justified in placing so much emphasis in basic science courses on the kinetic–molecular model when pupils have such difficulty in understanding it well enough to be confident in using it? Would it be more appropriate to accept a caloric notion of heat from younger secondary school pupils? After all, members of the building trade, for example, operate effectively in their calculations of heat conductivity of materials in terms of 'quantities of heat' and 'rates of flow'. From the pupils' point of view it is perhaps preferable to have a workable model to interpret phenomena, even if it has to be changed at a later date, rather than to be exposed to more sophisticated ideas which only confuse.

There are those who will oppose such a suggestion, arguing that we should never teach anything that has to be 'unlearned' later. In response, I would argue that such a view simply does not reflect much of our experience, either in formal learning contexts or in everyday situations. We are continually being placed in situations where we have to revise, develop or discard ideas in the light of new evidence. The challenge this faces us with in science education is to present theories to pupils so that they can be understood and yet not be taken as immutable truths. There is an important distinction to be made here between understanding and belief: it is possible and important to be able to *understand* alternative interpretations, those suggested by other pupils or other scientists, without necessarily *believing* any of them.

THE 'EXPERIMENTAL METHOD' AND SCIENCE TEACHING

In appraising the role of practical work in secondary school science, a number of types of activity can be distinguished. There are those whose purpose is to extend pupils' knowledge of phenomena, others are used to illustrate and confirm 'accepted' principles. In addition, there is a case for including opportunities for pupils to undertake their own investigations, not in order to establish an important principle, but to gain some experience in planning an experiment using their own initiative. The focus of such activities is not the result obtained, but the steps along the way: the design of experiment, the choice and use of the apparatus, the careful recording and interpretation of the results. In order that children can undertake such investigations in as honest and thorough way as possible, time may have to be set aside from what is often the main orientation of the teaching programme.

These experimental exercises offer an opportunity to encourage individual initiative and imagination. They may be important in giving pupils experience of the rational – empirical approach to problem-solving. However, the skills they encourage, skills of careful observation, measurement and logical argument, are as relevant to the garage mechanic, electrician or dressmaker as they are to the scientist. The case for including exercises of this kind in science lessons is not to exemplify the way that science itself proceeds, but to encourage general rational thought, and to give pupils a sense of confidence in their own capabilities.

To illustrate the way science itself proceeds, the focus needs to be on competing conceptual systems. In a paper, 'Towards an integration of content and method in the science curriculum', Noretta Koertge states the following conclusion:

> To understand the growth of science and to get a balanced picture of both its fallibility and its claims to soundness, one must use a pluralistic approach and study at least two competing systems in detail.[8]

In reaching that conclusion, it is argued that science proceeds not by an inductivist approach of making generalizations about data, but that progress is made when an accepted theory competes with a new theory for the interpretation of data. Such a pursuit is very different from what has been characterized as the 'scientific method'.

Koertge proposes that case studies of competing theories from the history of science would be appropriate material for teaching the methodology of science. However, one need not search the literature on the history of science for examples of competing systems: pluralism in conceptual systems already exists among pupils in science classrooms.

Alternative frameworks suggested by pupils offer teachers readily available opportunities to illustrate characteristics of the scientific pursuit through the appraisal of competing interpretations or conceptions of events. Nor are new science teaching schemes necessary: as Baddeley[9] outlines, there are many opportunities within the current Nuffield science schemes to exemplify and test out competing theories which derive either from children's ideas or from the history of science.

A QUESTION OF TIME

Science is not just natural history, and education in science involves more than simply extending the range of children's sense experiences (though it may also do this). It is about introducing children to the conventional scientific interpretations of events and helping them to reorganize their ideas accordingly. Children need more than practical experiences for this reorganization in their thinking to take place. And yet, particularly in lower secondary school, it is the practical work, especially group practical work, which often occupies the greatest proportion of teaching time. Laboratory work is an important feature of science teaching, yet we may not be making the most of this important resource. In their survey of secondary schools,[10] the HMI report that

> [Science teachers] believed that pupils should have first-hand practical experience in laboratories in order to acquire skills in handling apparatus, to measure constants and to illustrate concepts and principles. Unfortunately, practical work often did not go further than this and few opportunities were provided for pupils to conduct challenging experimental investigations.

They suggest that an important reason for this is the constraint imposed by examination syllabuses.

Not only do pupils need time to undertake practical activities, but more time is needed to make the most of those that are undertaken. Where activities are intended to illustrate some concept or principle, then time is required for pupils to consider their results and generalize the findings to new situations.

In a study on group work in science, Sands[11] reports that a major omission in lessons was the necessary 'follow-up' relating to the group work. Many such practical lessons end abruptly when the prescribed task is complete and little, if any, time is given to the interpretation of the results obtained, although this is just as important as the activity itself. Pupils need time to think around and consolidate the new ideas presented to them. After all, they may have developed their own ideas as a result of many years of experience. It is unlikely that they will easily adopt new ways of thinking as a result of one or two science lessons. As was suggested in an earlier chapter, opportunities to apply new concepts or ideas in a range of situations are important in consolidating pupils' understanding and helping to build a bridge betweeen the presented theory and experience. Here there may be teaching techniques which can be borrowed from other school subjects. Just as science teachers have developed the necessary skills to organize group practical exercises, perhaps the time has come to consider the development of strategies to help children make more sense of those practical experiences. What is being suggested is not a return to a more didactic teaching, but an extension of the range of types of activities undertaken in science classes.

The suggestions made so far have one requirement in common, and that is *time*. It takes time to allow for speculative discussion in class, even more time is required if pupils are to follow up competing ideas or to undertake their own investigations. If the necessary time is to be allowed, then it appears inevitable that a careful appraisal of the content coverage of syllabuses is necessary. Of course, some hard decisions may have to be made as to which topics to include and which to leave out. But perhaps curtailing the syllabus is not too great a price to pay if as a result pupils gain greater confidence in their understanding of the ideas covered, and in addition have some time which can be specifically devoted to inquiries of their own, however simple.

The ideas suggested in this chapter indicate ways in which teachers can help pupils not simply to extend their sensory experiences through science lessons, but to understand the conventional theories and formalisms of the scientific community and to relate these to their experiences in a meaningful way. They suggest a role for teachers as mediators between the pupils' experiences and understandings and that of the scientific community.

The writers of the Bullock Report remind us of what this may involve in the following passage:

> What the teacher has in mind may be the desirable destination of a thinking process, but a learner needs to trace the steps from the familiar to the new, from the fact or idea he possesses to that which he is to acquire. In other words, the learner has to make a journey in thought for himself.[12]

REFERENCES

1. ASE policy statement, *Education Through Science* (1981).
2. Report of the Committee on the Position of Natural Science in the Educational System of Great Britain, in *Natural Science in Education*, HMSO (1918).
3. Science Masters Association, *The Teaching of General Science*, Murray (1936).
4. NSJA: National Science Teachers' Association Curriculum Committee, *Theory into Action* (1974).
5. *Harvard Project Physics*, Holt, Rinehart (1970).
6. M. Shayer and P. Adey, *Towards a Science of Science Teaching*, Heinemann (1981).
7. J. Bruner, *The Process of Education*, Harvard (1960).
8. N. Koertge, Towards an integration of content and method in the science curriculum, *Curriculum Theory Network*, **4**, 26–44 (1970).
9. J. Baddeley, Teaching the philosophy of science through Nuffield Schemes, *Sch. Sci. Rev.*, **62**, 154–9 (1980).
10. DES, *Aspects of Secondary Education in England*, HMSO (1979).
11. M. K. Sands, Group work in science: myth and reality, *Sch. Sci. Rev.*, **62**, 765–9 (1981).
12. The Bullock Report, *A Language for Life*, HMSO, 141–2 (1975).

24 Pupils' learning in science — issues in cognitive development

● J. Gilbert

Gilbert discusses the contribution that existing research into cognitive development can make to the identification of the nature, aims and scope of science education for the average citizen.

It begins by noting that 'Of the plethora of approaches available, only two seem to attract extensive attention in the UK: the ''Piaget-derived'' and the ''personal constructivist'''. After briefly explaining what these are, it considers how they relate to the aims of science education as recommended by the Association for Science Education (ASE) and how these aims can be implemented.

INTRODUCTION

My intention is to identify the nature, aims and scope of education for the average citizen, received in or through school science lessons and adult education and to consider these needs in relation to the strategies available to meet them. This chapter will discuss the contribution that existing research into cognitive development can make to this intention, and point to those issues that require further research and development. The treatment is not intended as an overall review of the literature, but rather to raise issues and provoke discussion. It is deliberately restricted in scope mainly to: the work of UK researchers; contributions that have already appeared in European journals; books published in Europe.

The Association For Science Education, the major UK forum for the discussion of issues by school science teachers, has recently produced a series of documents (ASE, 1979; ASE, 1981a) which are directly applicable to the theme of the seminar. This paper will consider such of the 'aims of science education' and 'summary of recommendations and proposals' (see: ASE, 1981b) which seems to require comments from a cognitive development viewpoint. Before that can be done, it is necessary to review the main orientations of cognitive development research within science education in the UK, so that the applicability of individual pieces of research to the solution of particular problems can be evaluated.

APPROACHES TO COGNITIVE DEVELOPMENT RESEARCH

Of the plethora of approaches available, only two seem to currently attract extensive attention in the UK: the 'Piaget-derived' and the 'personal constructivist'.

The first of these is centred on the work of Michael Shayer, and the now-dispersed CSMS team, at Chelsea College. In the book summarizing the work of the CSMS team (Shayer and Adey, 1981) they report that they sought to use

> . . . the promise offered by the Piagetian model: a promise that no other learning theory could offer, and one that was allowed to guide, but not to direct, the course of our investigations. . . . The scientist uses a theoretical model as a guide, that is, he goes along with it as long as it yields results which are useful, or as long as it continues to lead him into fruitful new areas of investigation.
>
> When the fruit dries up, or when the model has to be unreasonably strained to fit reality, then it must be abandoned or modified. Thus we accepted the model of Piaget, but with a measure of scepticism, and a willingness to use only those parts which could be validated to our own satisfaction.
>
> An aspect of the model that we certainly cannot ignore is the idea of stages of development. Stage theory is central to the Piagetian world view, and is its most distinctive feature.

They remained faithful to their intentions, but found little to disagree with in the Piagetian approach. Versions of Piaget's interview tasks were prepared for a 'demonstration plus paper-and-pencil test' format. These were applied, together with the original versions of the tasks, to a number of children. After satisfactory correlations had been obtained, the 'Shayer tests' were given to some 11,000 school children. The data obtained supported the presupposition of stages of development. Subsequently, common topics from the school curriculum e.g. 'floating and sinking density', 'solution', 'living things', were analysed to relate inferred 'levels of understanding', possible within them, to the Piagetian stages.

These ascriptions of 'cognitive demand' were supported, apparently after suitable training, by panels of judges. The Curriculum Analysis Taxonomy so produced was used to analyse pupils' science examination papers, and the outcome related to the CSMS test scores of the individuals concerned.

The work of the CSMS Project is open to all the criticisms that have been levelled against the Genevan School itself (see: Brown and Desforges, 1977). There are others, associated with the particular format of the tasks. It is therefore to be regretted that a critical review of the psychometric base of the project, and its particular design, has not been made, although useful qualitative comments have appeared (e.g. Sutton, 1981; Wood-Robinson, 1981). The issue is particularly important because teacher trainers are making extensive use of Shayer and Adey's book (op. cit.) and its conclusions may consequently become very influential in UK school science teaching.

The 'personal constructivist' approach is in the fortunate position of not being so open to detailed criticism. This is because its application has so far been uneven, its adherents dispersed and consequently its achievements fragmentary. Indeed, it is likely that many workers within this approach would not subscribe to the title 'personal constructivist'. The approach, which had 'the study of misconceptions' as its antecedent in science education (see, for example: Garforth, Johnstone, Lazonby, 1976: Johnstone and Mughol, 1978) was given considerable impetus by the particular emphasis contained in the appellation 'alternative frameworks' (Driver and Easley, 1978).

Personal constructivism is associated with the name of G. Kelly (see: Pope and Keen, 1981). It holds that an individual invariably approaches any situation in life with a personal theory of explanation. This theory is used to understand the situation, and is modified in the light of exploring its explanatory utility. One implication of constructivism is that individuals will have meaning for words, which are commonly used in academic subjects, before formal teaching is experienced. These 'alternative conceptions' are, for any individual, strongly held and extensively used. In formal teaching, these alternative conceptions interact with the teacher's views to produce a complex of understandings (see: Gilbert, Osborne, Fensham). A variety of approaches to the identification of conceptions have been developed, and some of them reviewed (see: Sutton, 1980).

Some workers have attempted to relate the Piagetian and 'alternative framework' approaches e.g. Archenhold (1980). There are many overlaps, as analyses of them into Lakatosian Programmes shows (see: Gilbert and Swift, 1981). The major parts of disagreement seem to be (i) the Piagetians see learning as essentially independent of content and context whilst the personal constructivists see it as content and context-dependent (ii) some Piagetians adhere to the concept of 'stages of development', with its overtones of predestination. Learning is seen as universal, and developing directionally with maturity. Personal constructivists see learning as a localised phenomenon, developing without a pre-ordained directionality and largely independent of age (iii) 'conceptual development', for a Piagetian, means 'progress through

Piaget's stages', whilst for a personal constructivist, it means 'developing one's conception of a phenomenon'. The resolution of these contradictions should lie in the applicability of the approaches to the design and conduct of school science for the average citizen.

THE AIMS OF SCIENCE EDUCATION

Looking now at the recommendations of the ASE (1981b):

> (i) The acquisition of a knowledge and understanding of a range of scientific concepts, generalisations, principles and laws through the systematic study and experience of aspects of the body of knowledge called science.

It is generally assumed that criteria should be produced for the selection of content for teaching 'from the body of knowledge called science'. At the moment, the basis too often seems to be 'because I was taught it'. Criteria should relate to 'the discipline of science', 'the students' personal future', 'the needs of society in the future', others or all of them.

Once selected, the 'logical structure' of the content needs to be established (see: Stewart and van Kirk, 1981). This procedure was followed in the Schools Council Integrated Science Project (see: Hall and Mowl, 1973) a curriculum development which made use of Gagné's ideas at that time. The issue for cognitive development will be: how does the apparent structure of the content relate to the psychological structure of the learner? Piagetians will seek an answer based on 'the perceived demands of stages', whilst the personal constructivists will use the existing knowledge of the learner as a basis.

Within either framework, the actual problems of presentation need attention. The role of models in teaching and learning is an under-researched area (see: Gilbert and Osborne, 1980). There is a clear need for a series of booklets for teachers addressing individual concepts from the viewpoint of a variety of psychological theories. Dierks (1981) has made a start here, but co-ordinated efforts by many researchers are needed.

> (ii) The acquisition of a range of cognitive and psycho-motor skills and processes as a result of direct involvement in scientific activities and procedures in the laboratory and the field.

Attention here centres on the role of laboratories in science education. Whilst many surveys have been made of *extent* of use, and in a few cases, the *reasons* for use (see, for example: Gonzalez and Gilbert 1980), the connections between 'purpose', 'activity' and 'learning achieved' has not been rigorously addressed. Whilst naturalistic studies may prove valuable here, psychometric studies of particular features (see: Heth, 1980) will be instructive. All schools of cognitive development agree on the importance of practical work. Given the expense of laboratories, and the current financial situation, more than belief and tradition are needed as justification.

Perhaps it is because Bloom's work on psycho-motor skills never reached fruition, but this field has been grievously neglected in school science education, and associated research. However the industrial training organisations have not neglected it, and insight may be obtained there.

(iii) The utilization of scientific knowledge and processes in the pursuit of further knowledge and deeper understanding, and the development of an ability to function autonomously in an area of science studies to solve practical problems and to communicate that experience to others.

This aim is so powerful as to constitute a cry for all the virtues in science education. West (1981) has called for

> a situation in which the majority of young people are made aware of, and become identified with, an approach to their education which uses scientific knowledge as freely and creatively as other forms of knowledge.

How is an 'ability to function autonomously to be achieved'? Piagetians might say that the cognitive demand of content should be matched to the cognitive level of individual students, although Shayer's current work on cognitive acceleration should open up this debate more widely. The personal constructivists might call for content to be selected from phenomena in which students have an interest, certainly that teaching should start from a student's current understanding base. It should seek to generate different perspectives, and not merely to promote algorithmic thinking.

On either approach, a greater emphasis on project work seems called for. This is an under-researched area at school level in the UK. If it is to be extended, greater attention will have to be paid to the development of student study skills. The issue being addressed in many schools is 'how best can this be done?' (see: Taberer and Allman, 1981).

The whole field of student learning styles and strategies is highly relevant to this aim. A recent book by Entwistle (1981) is based on Entwistle's own work, together with that of Pask and Marton. The central problems are: does an individual student have a distinctive and stable learning style which transcends content barriers? How can a student using a less productive style be educated towards a more valuable style? These exciting issues are central to the achievements on this aim.

(iv) The attainment of a perspective or way of looking at the world together with some understanding of how it complements and contrasts with other perspectives or ways of organizing knowledge and inquiry.

It is far from clear how scientists view the world – what 'scientists' science' is (see: Gilbert, Osborne, Fensham). Science educators are paying greater attention to philosophies of science: articles on Kuhn and Popper appear (see: for example, Cawthron and Rowell, 1978) whilst those on Lakatos and Feyerabend can be anticipated. The implications of philosophies of science for philosophers of science education need to be spelt out. Scientists don't seem to know what science is. Teachers aren't too sure what science education is. It seems unlikely that either group will have a strong grasp of how, for example, a historian sees the world. This calls for additional attention.

The implication so far has been that the acquisition by students of a world view, which can be called 'scientists' science' as it appears in textbooks, is the main aim of science education. The Piagetian approach seems to support this unquestioningly, seeing non-formal operators as partial failures. The personal constructivist approach includes an intrinsic valuation of students' 'alternative conceptions' and opens possible routes which build on these conceptions, in ways yet to be considered. A route for science education which does not necessarily lead to scientists' science seems open: the direction it leads, the distance that can be travelled, and the educational consequences of following this path, are not yet clear.

(v) The attainment of a basic understanding of the nature of advanced technological societies, the interaction between science and society, and the contribution science makes to our cultural heritage.

The approach taken by the ASE's 'Science and Society' course (ASE, 1980) seems to substitute different content for established content in science courses, leaving the acquisition of cognitive concepts as the main objective. As such, it is open to the same inspection as all other courses, as seen from the perspective of cognitive development. However, a more radical approach calls for a reappraisal by students of their value systems regarding the interaction of science and society (see: Ziman, 1980; Solomon, 1980). This latter approach must regard not only the cognitive development of students, but their affective development as well. The personal constructivist approach, by unifying the two, would seem to have a potentially powerful contribution to make.

(vi) The realization that scientific knowledge and experience is of some value in the process of establishing a sense of personal and social identity.

Personality development, which can be seen to be allied to attitude development, is at present an under-investigated field in UK science education to which Head (1979, 1980) has drawn attention. Head's approach, building on the work of Erikson and Loevinger, has considerable potential for outlining a workable developmental sequence, although any 'step-model' might meet the same objections as are levelled against Piaget's stages.

The 'personal and social identity' field seems certain to play a key role in the development of science education within systems where students have subject choice. If students perceive science to require world views which counter their own, they will reject science. This is particularly true of 'educational minorities', which I will carefully define as 'groups, of whatever size, whose interests are not actively considered in the design and implementation of science education'. Foremost in this category must be girls. Although, perhaps quite properly, much effort has been put into political rhetoric on girls in science education, systematic work is now looking into the psychological aspects of girls' low participation in science education (see: Kelly, 1981). Also within this group are blacks. This field has been apparently almost completely neglected, in the literature at least, although useful sociological perspectives are appearing (see: Stone, 1981). A third grouping is foreign language speakers. This group will possibly be quite small and diverse, but still deserving of attention (see: Strevens, 1976).

Educational minorities will bring to school personal and social identities, together with frameworks of conceptions, that differ widely from the 'norm of the supposed majority' which informs curriculum decisions. Their value, contribution and development are worthy of particular attention. Perhaps little will be achieved without 'affirmative action' programmes. The low priority of science for the physically and mentally disadvantaged in the UK calls for immediate remedy.

ASPECTS OF THE IMPLEMENTATION OF THESE AIMS

The ASE's document (ASE, 1981b) listed 35 recommendations and proposals. Only a few can be dealt with, however, briefly, in the space available.

> 1 Education through science is an important component of general education and as such could continue to be recognised as part of the core, or protected, element of the curriculum.
>
> and
>
> 2 All pupils should have the opportunity to benefit from a full and effective programme of science education throughout their period of compulsory schooling.

The statement is quite clear: all children should receive science education throughout their school lives.

The availability of science teachers may not be such a hindrance to the implementation of this policy, as once seemed to be the case. The problem now is finance. The point over core curricula seems to have been conceded (see: for example, Adkins, 1981). The issue for cognitive development may be: how to best describe a series of obtainable objectives within the contents presented, for this has been the approach to curriculum construction taken in many subjects.

> 3 All schools should have a strategy that enables aspects of the aims for science education to be achieved through appropriate work in science and other subject areas
>
> and
>
> 4 All schools should develop an approach to science studies based on the notion of science across the curriculum which sees science as essential in the development of a common or core curriculum at the primary and secondary levels of schooling.

The issue here is: how many of 'the processes that are found in science' are found throughout the school curriculum? Problem solving skills might be such a case (see: Larkin and Reif, 1979), as well 'as the components of scientific method' (see: Wild and Gilbert, 1977).

> 8 The Association remains fully committed to the development of effective provision of science education in the early years of schooling.

The contribution of the Schools Council Science 5–13 has been invaluable in this direction (see: Ennever and Harlen, 1972). The most significant problem lies in the education, training, deployment and support of suitable teachers in a shrinking resource sector.

> 10 A strong case exists for the redefinition and restructuring of introductory courses at the lower secondary level.

Brown (1977) has laid out the case over integrated science. The issue is how to implement such a policy. Cognitive development research contains the seeds of approaches built on the Piagetian view (see: Shayer and Adey, 1981) or the constructivist view (see, for example, Driver, 1981). However, their detailed working out will require much labour.

> 13 The Association supports the establishment of regular LEA reviews of curriculum provision at the secondary level and the provision of a national programme of research and development.

The latter part of this recommendation could readily be effected, if suitable finance were available. A rich diversity of approaches and skills exists (see: for example, Johnstone and Kellett, 1980; Bolton, 1977; Bliss, Ogborn and Grize, 1979). The issue is how could this diversity be orchestrated? The idea of a government controlled and directed research institution would strike at the heart of the tradition of 'teaching in an atmosphere of research' so valued in UK higher education. The discernible trend towards placing large blocks of finance with the bigger training units seems a move in that direction.

> 20 The Association accepts that a policy of science education for all has many pedagogic implications and strongly recommends increasing the levels of self-evaluation on the part of science teachers.

This policy seems admirable, and the seeds of its implementation are diverse (see: for example, Galton and Eggleston, 1979). However, applicable schemes will need further refinement. The main issue however remains: how best to involve teachers in this process of self-evaluation. A strategy of 'carrots not sticks' seems called for. 'Self-confrontation' techniques (see: Pope and Keen, 1981) seem especially valuable.

> 21 . . . the Association regards it as critical that teachers of science should adopt a wider and more flexible range of teaching styles in their science education programmes.

Operational guides on how teachers could implement a 'range of teaching styles' seem called for (see: Nussbaum and Novick, 1981; Osborne and Gilbert, 1980). However, more concentrated efforts are needed to relate 'teachers' styles' to 'students' learning'. This thorny issue may best be tackled through naturalistic enquiries i.e. case studies describing the learning found when particular teaching styles are used. However, the whole field remains fraught with difficulties (see: Delacote, 1980).

> 22 The Association attaches great importance to the role of written and spoken language in effective science teaching.

This recommendation underlies one of the major interest areas of science education research in the last few years (see, for example: Prestt, 1980; Sutton, 1980). The issue here is: what effect does an advocacy of student participation in speaking, reading and writing have on teachers' expectations and student learning?

> 23 The Association also attaches importance to the careful definition of the relationships between mathematics and science in the school curriculum.

Fensham (1979) has spelt out the scope and limitations to such relationships; Burghes (1980) has looked at its classroom implications from the mathematic side; Dudley (1977) has examined the use of mathematics in classroom biology teaching.

The issue now seems to be: how can mathematics educators and science educators best be brought together to produce classroom guides for teachers on 'using maths in science' and 'using science in maths'?

> 24 The Association welcomes the decision to implement a common system of examining at 16+ and attaches great importance to the creation of a

> system that increases educational opportunity and leaves schools free, within nationally agreed criteria and organisational frameworks, to measure student performance against their own detailed criteria and across the full ability range.

The discussions over a common system of examinations are well advanced (see: Dixon, 1979). Although this seems a wonderful opportunity to move towards criterion reference testing, the detailed resources to do so seem unlikely to be found. However, some innovatory ideas, useful within the 'personal constructivist' framework have been forthcoming (see: Friel and Johnstone, 1978). The major effort in the field is being made by the Assessment of Performance Unit (see: Driver and Worsley, 1979). The issue here: how far and in what manner, can the APU's reports have a supportive effect on UK science education?

Lastly,

> 19 The Association believes that greater resources should be allocated to science related courses in adult education.

In the UK at present, this is a pious hope. A survey has shown that only 16 per cent of all University Extra Mural Courses are science-related (Costell, 1977). Moreover, earmarked resources are not generally available and science tutors receive little institutional support. The immediate issue is: how far can adult education in science be built on the approaches used in schools?

CONCLUDING COMMENT

From this summary, the need for a co-ordinated approach to 'science for all', which crosses national boundaries, is apparent. Whilst allowance must be made for language and cultural differences, which will be considerable, the magnitude of the challenge presses greatly on the resources of any one nation.

REFERENCES

Adkins, C. J. (1981), A national core syllabus for A-level physics. *Phy. Educ., 16* (3) pp. 128–35.

Archenhold, W. F. (1980), An empirical study of the understanding by 16–19 year old students of the concepts of work and potential in physics. In Archenhold *et al*, (eds), *Cognitive development research in science and mathematics*. Leeds: University of Leeds.

ASE (1979), *Alternatives for Science Education: A Consultative Document*. Hatfield: ASE.

ASE (1980), *Science and Society*. Hatfield: ASE.

ASE (1981a), *Education through science*. Hatfield: ASE.

ASE (1981b), *Education through science: a policy statement of the Association for Science Education, 1981. School Science Review*, 63, pp. 5–52.

Bliss, J., Ogborn, J., Grize, F., (1979), The analysis of qualitative data. *Eur.J.Sci. Educ.* 1 (4), pp. 427–40.

Bolton, N. (1977), *Concept formation*. Oxford: Pergamon.

Brown, S. (1977), A review of the meanings of, and arguments for, integrated science. *Studies in Sci. Educ.* 4, pp. 31–62.

Brown, G., Desforges, C. (1979), *Piaget's theory: a psychological critique*. London: RKP.

Burghes, D. N. (1980), Teaching applications of mathematics: mathematical modelling in science and technology. *Eur. J. Sci. Educ.*, 2 (4), pp. 365–76.

Cawthron, E., Rowell, J. (1978), Epistemology and science education. *Studies in Science Education*. 5, pp. 31–59.

Costello, T. (1977), University extra-mural science. *Adult education*, 49 (5), pp. 285–89.

Delacote, G. (1980), Classroom based research in science and mathematics. In Archenhold *et al* (eds) *Cognitive Development research in science and mathematics*. Leeds: University of Leeds.

Dierks, W. (1981), Teaching the mole. *Eur. J. Sci. Educ.*, 3 (2), pp. 145–58.

Dixon, A. (1979), The proposed common system of examining at 16+ (GCSE): some implications for teachers of science in England and Wales. *School Science Review*, 61, pp. 247–53.

Driver, R. (1981), Pupils' alternative frameworks in science. *Eur. J. Sci. Educ.*, 3 (1), pp. 93–101.

Driver, R., Easley, J. (1978), Pupils and paradigms: a review of literature related to concept development in adolescent science students. *Studies in Science Education*, 5, pp. 61–84.

Driver, R., Worsley, C. (1979), The Assessment of Performance in Science Project. *Eur. J. Sci. Educ.*, 1 (4), pp. 441–7.

Dudley, B.A.C. (1977), *Mathematical and biological interrelations*. Chichester: Wiley.

Ennever, L., Harlen, W. (1972), *With objectives in mind*. Schools Council Science 5–13 Project. London: MacDonald.

Entwistle, N. (1981), *Styles of learning and teaching*, London: Wiley.

Fensham, P. J. (1979), Co-operation between cousins: science mathematical educators look at what is possible and when has proved not possible. *Eur. J. Sci. Educ., 1* (3), pp. 347–52.

Friel, S., Johnstone, A. H. (1978), Scoring systems which allow for partial knowledge. *J. Chem. Educ.*, 55, pp. 717–9.

Galton, M., Eggleston, J. (1979), Some characteristics of effective science teaching. *Eur. J. Sci. Educ.*, 1 (1) pp. 75–86.

Garforth, F. M., Johnstone, A. H., Lazonby, J. (1976), Ionic equations – difficulties in understanding and use. *Educ. in Chem.*, 13 (3), p. 72.

Gilbert, J. K., Osborne, R. J. (1980), The use of models in science and science teaching. *Eur. J. Sci. Educ.*, 2 (1), pp. 3 – 13.

Gilbert, J. K., Osborne, R. J., Fensham, P. J. (1982), Children's science and its consequences for teaching. *Science Education*.

Gilbert, J. K., Swift, D. (1981), Towards a Lakatosian programme of research into concept development. Presented at Oxford Science Education Conference, Sept. 1981.

Gonzales, G., Gilbert, J. K. (1980), A-level physics by the use of an independent learning approach: the role of the lab-work. *Brit. Ed. Res. J.*, 6, pp. 63–83.

Hall, W., Mowl, B. (1973), *Teacher's Guides 1 and 2* Schools Council Integrated Science Project. London: Longmans/Penguin.

Head, J. (1979), Personality and the pursuit of science. *Stud. in Sci. Ed.* 6, pp. 23–44.

Head, J. (1980), A model to link personality characteristics to a preference for science. *Eur. J. Sci. Educ.*, 2 (3), pp. 295–300.

Heath, T. (1980), Observation, perception and education. *Eur. J. Sci. Educ.*, 2 (2), pp. 155–60.

Johnstone, A. H., Kellett, N. C. (1980), Learning difficulties in school science – towards a working hypothesis. *Eur. J. Sci. Educ.*, 2 (2), pp. 175–81.

Johnstone, A. H., Mughol, A. R. (1978), The concept of electrical resistance. *Phy. Educ. 13* (1), pp. 46–9.

Kelly, A. (ed.) (1981), *The Missing Half*. Manchester: Manchester University Press.

Larkin, J. H., Reif, F. (1979), Understanding and teaching problem-solving in physics. *Eur. J. Sci. Educ.* 1 (2), pp. 191–203.

Nussbaum, J., Novick, S. (1981), Brainstorming in the classroom to invent a model: a case study. *School Science Review*. 62, pp. 771–8.

Osborne, R. J., Gilbert, J. K. (1980), A technique for exploring students' views of the world. *Phy. Educ.*, 15 (6), pp. 376–9.

Pope, M. L., Gilbert, J. K. (in press), Personal experience and the construction of knowledge in science. *Science Education*.

Pope, M. L., Keen, T. (1981), *Personal construct psychology and education*. London: Academic Press.

Prestt, B. (ed.) (1980), Language in Science. Study Series No. 16 Hatfield: ASE.

Shayer, M., Adey, P. (1981), *Towards a science of science teaching*. London: Heinemann.

Solomon, J. (1980), Science and society studies in the school curriculum. *School Science Review* 62, pp. 213–19.

Stewart, J., van Kirk, J. (1981), Content analysis in science education. *Eur. J. Sci. Educ.*, 3 (2) pp. 171–82.

Strevens, P. (1976), Problems of learning and teaching science through a foreign language. *Stud. in Sci. Educ.* 3, pp. 55–68.

Stone, M. (1981), *The education of the black child in Britain*. London: Fontana.

Sutton, C. (1980), Science, language and meaning. *School Science Review*, 62, pp. 47–56.

Sutton, C. R. (1980), The learner's prior knowledge: a critical review of techniques for probing its organisation. *Eur. J. Sci. Educ.* 2 (2), pp. 107–20.

Sutton, C. R. (1981), A system for curriculum analysis and matching. *J. Curr. Studies*, 13 (4), pp. 377–9.

Tabberer, R., Allman, J. (1981), *Study skills at 16 plus.* NFER Research in Progress No. 4. Slough: NFER.

West, R. W. (1981), Praxis and possibilities in school science education. *J. Biol. Educ.*, 15 (1), pp. 42–46.

Wild, K., Gilbert, J. K. (1977), The Nuffield 'Working with Science' Project. *School Science Review*, 58, pp. 560–6.

Wood-Robinson, C. (1981), Towards a science of science teaching: a book review. *J. Biol. Educ., 15.*

Ziman, J. (1980), *Teaching and learning about science and society.* Cambridge University Press.

25 Pupils' alternative frameworks in science

● R. Driver

The work of Jean Piaget and others on the development of children's thinking has indicated that, far from being the tabula rasa *of repute, pupils bring to their school learning in science those ideas, expectations and beliefs concerning natural phenomena that they have developed to make sense of their own past experiences. These alternative frameworks – in some cases strongly held* and *resistant to change, in others flexible and with many internal inconsistencies – have their influence on the effectiveness of formal school science programmes. Just as scientists in a period of 'revolution' in science have to make a paradigm shift, so pupils have to make a considerable journey in thought in moving from the ideas and beliefs with which they come to school to an understanding and acceptance of the explanatory systems being offered.*

Attention has been given recently in Britain and elsewhere to studies of children's thinking in science. The main focus of this research work has tended to be on the development of logical thought by children, based on Piagetian stage theory.

In this chapter I shall be considering a complementary aspect of children's thinking and learning: that is the sets of beliefs or expectations they hold about the way natural phenomena occur, and how they affect the sense pupils make of experiences we give them in science classes. I shall indicate that in some areas pupils hold beliefs which differ from the currently accepted view and from the intended outcome of learning experiences. Such beliefs I shall call 'alternative frameworks'.

In the first part of this chapter the status of alternative frameworks will be explored from a philosophical point of view. The second part gives further examples of pupils' frameworks and briefly comments on literature in this area. The last part addresses itself to the question of implications for classroom practice.

ALTERNATIVE FRAMEWORKS: A PHILOSOPHICAL PERSPECTIVE

We all have sets of beliefs about how things happen, and have expectations which enable us to predict future events. A piece of chalk rolls along the table and I know where to grasp for it to stop it falling. The fact that so many of us can drive around on our roads without more accidents occurring is possible because of the sets of expectations we have developed which enable us to predict the speed and movement of other vehicles on the road. Such sets of expectations enable us to operate in our daily lives without being constantly in a state of disorientation and shock. The children we teach also have built up sets of expectations and their own beliefs about a range of natural phenomena and these may differ from those the teacher wishes to develop.

Here is an example of the kind of situation to which I am referring. Two 11-year-old boys, Tim and Ricky, are doing simple experiments on the extension of springs when loaded. They have made their own springs by winding wire round a length of dowel and are now studying the way one of their springs extends as they add ball-bearings to a polystyrene cup hanging from it (Figure 1). Ricky is intent on adding ball-bearings one at a time and measuring the new length of the spring after each addition.

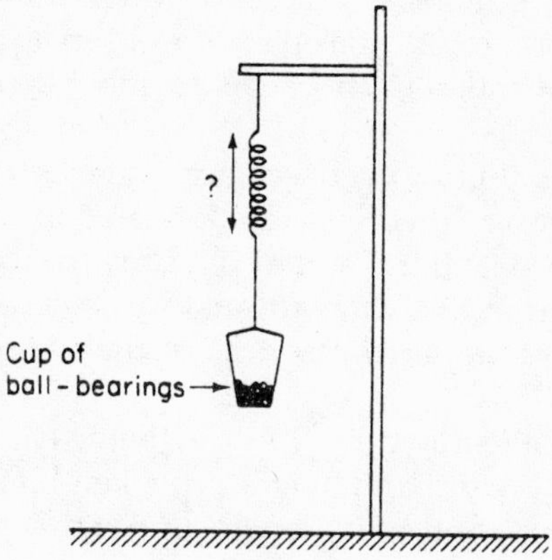

Figure 1

Tim is watching him, then interrupts: 'Wait. What happens if we lift it up?' He unclamps the spring, raises it higher up the stand, and measures its length again. Apparently satisfied that the length is the same he continues with the experiment.

Later, when he was asked the reason for doing this, Tim picks up two marbles, holds one up higher than the other and explains, 'this is farther up and gravity is pulling it down harder – I mean the gravity is still the same but it turns out it is pulling harder the farther away. The higher it gets the more effect gravity will have on it because if you just stood over there and someone dropped a pebble on him, it would just sting him, it wouldn't hurt him. But if I dropped it from an aeroplane it would be accelerating faster and faster and when it hit someone on the head it would kill him.'

Of course it should not be a surprise to us that children have developed expectations of common physical phenomena. Their experiences of pushing, pulling, lifting, throwing, feeling and seeing things contributes to these ideas, as does everyday language (as opposed to the specialist use of words in science). But we would be misled if we thought that these frameworks derived only from children's experiences, that they are arrived at through a process of induction. There is also a creative and imaginative element involved on the part of each child in constructing the meanings he imposes on events.

The example of Tim's idea about weight serves not only as an illustration of a pupil's alternative framework. It also indicates the poverty of an inductionist philosophy of science in adequately accounting for pupils' learning.

The empiricist's view of science suggests that scientific ideas and theories are reached by a process of induction. Investigators, whether pupils or practising scientists, proceed through a hierarchically organized sequence of processes, starting with observation of 'facts'. From such 'facts' generalizations can be made and hypotheses or theories induced.

However, current philosophy of science suggests that there is a fallacy here; that hypotheses or theories are not related in such a way with the so-called 'objective' data but that they are constructions, products of the human imagination. In this way of thinking, observations of events are not objective because they are influenced by the theoretical framework of the observer.

This was clearly illustrated by Tim's activity. His idea about the relationship between weight and height provoked him to raise the spring and make the observation of its length under this new condition. His observation in this sense was 'theory laden'.

Because any theory is not related in a deductive and hence unique way to observations, there can be multiple explanations of events. Pupils can and do bring alternative frameworks to explain observations which are in keeping with their experience and in this respect are not 'wrong'. However, we may recognize them as partial and limited in their scope.

Recently I visited a school in which the science for 11 to 13-year-old pupils was organized on an individualized basis. Pupils were programmed through a series of activities on work-cards. The teacher kindly let me audio-record some of the groups at work.

One group of girls was doing an experiment in which an immersion heater was placed in blocks of equal weight but made of different metals (Figure 2). The pupils had been instructed to draw a temperature-time graph as each block is heated. (The function of the experiment was to demonstrate variation in heat capacity.)

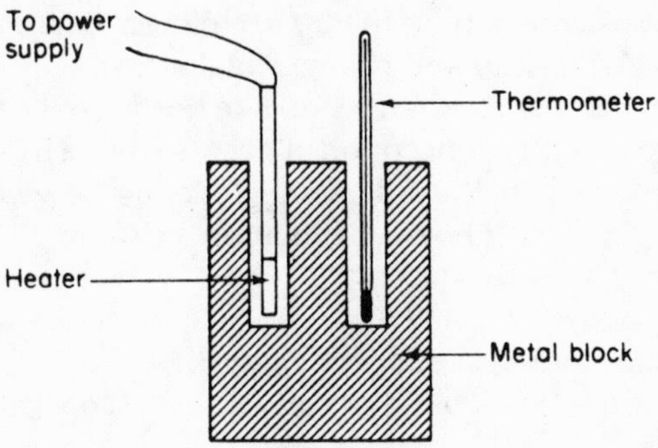

Figure 2

Towards the end of the lesson the girls were instructed to look at the graphs they had produced and compare them, suggesting an explanation. Here are their comments.

Pupil 1: 'We've got to do a graph for the aluminium.'
Pupil 2: 'Good. Aluminium isn't so – um – it.'
P1: 'Don't forget it has to go through doesn't it?'
'Through the thickness to reach there – the thermometer.'
P2: 'That was only thin to get to that.'
P1: 'Come on we've got to put it away now.'
The teacher (T) enters the discussion.
T: 'What has your experiment shown you?'
P2: 'That different – um – that different materials and that see how heat could travel through them.'
T: 'What did you find out?'
P1: 'Well – er – that heat went through the – the iron more easier than it did through the er . . . '.
P2: 'Aluminium.'

The pupils had had first-hand experiences – they had collected their data, but these had not been assimilated into the way of thinking that the teacher had expected. Later, we shall be returning to consider the implications of such a 'constructivist' philosophy of science in terms of classroom practice. First we will return to give further examples of pupils' alternative frameworks.

EXAMPLES AND CHARACTERISTICS OF ALTERNATIVE FRAMEWORKS

A common feature of new curriculum projects in science is the introduction of ideas of molecular kinetic theory to children to help them interpret phenomena involving heat and changes of state.

However, many of the children seem, like the ancient caloric theorists, to be much happier with a conception of heat as stuff, a fluid which flows. We see this reflected in the following dialogue between 12-year-old pupils who are explaining how a balloon on a tin-can gets bigger when the tin is heated.

P1: 'What do you think will happen, Kevin?'
P2: 'I think it will – er – blow up and – er – bop [smiles] with the force of the heat.'
P1: 'But where's the force coming from?'
P2: 'From bottom going through that [points to can] then – er . . . '.
P1: 'What do you think, Susan?'
P3: 'The heat's coming and it's collecting in that can and it's blowing the bubble up.'
P1: 'Well, there is air in there at first. And the heat gets into it and it's rising up and it's making the balloon bigger.'
T: 'So, what's pushing the balloon out?'
P1, 2 and 3: 'The air inside that can.'
T: 'How does the air do that?'
P1: 'The heats pushing the air so it blows the balloon up.'
T: 'What's this heat making the air do?'
P3: 'Rise.'
P1: 'Force up – it's forcing it up.'

Despite having been introduced to ideas of moving molecules these are not being used in the pupils' explanations. Instead we see evidence of ideas such as 'the force of the heat', 'the heat forcing the air to rise'.

The following example shows even more clearly the struggle that children have in using the kinetic-molecular model when it is presented to them. In this example, 13 and 14-year-old pupils have been presented with the elementary ideas of the molecular-kinetic theory of matter. They have then been asked to use those ideas to explain some simple observations. In this case, two pupils have observed a metal rod expand when it is heated (Figure 3).

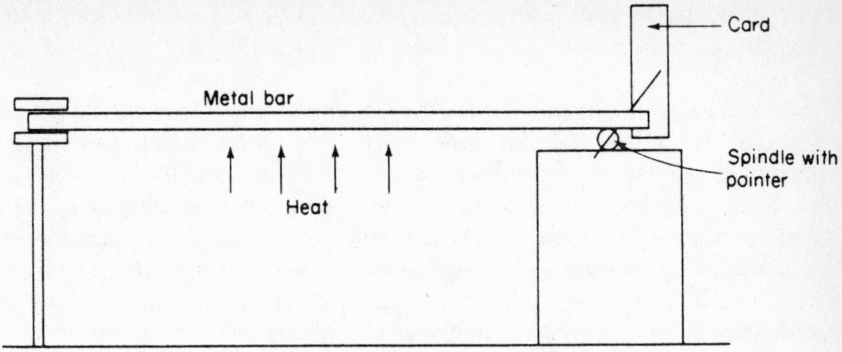

Figure 3

Here they are attempting to explain their observations.

P1: 'Yes, well that the – er – the heat molecules are pushing the . . . '.
P2: 'No, they're not.'
P1: 'Well, anyway, that thing is going down.'
P2: 'They're expanding. The – er – heat molecules are giving more energy, so they need more room to move about and so the bar needs to get longer, so it goes down, the needle.'
P1: 'If that's the heat, and molecules have to expand, right? [Yes] and you've got that thing like that, so when the molecules turn it round like that, and when that bar pushes it, it pushes the things round and that goes down.' (Transcript provided by M. Torbe.)

In this excerpt we see indications of how the notion of molecule is being assimilated by these pupils. For example, we see reference made to 'molecules of heat' and 'molecules expanding' on heating. The examples of alternative frameworks given here are only indications of the different ways pupils may interpret events. Little attention has been given to systematic studies of such alternative frameworks.

In general, of course, Piaget's work is a major source for studying children's ideas. But here I suggest his work should be read with more attention given to children's causal thinking than to the logical structures which Piaget postulates to explain them.

The way that younger children explain and interpret natural events was explored by Piaget in his well-known early works (Piaget 1929, 1930), in which he used verbal methods to explore pupils' explanations of questions such as: 'What causes night?' and 'How do clouds move?' These studies have been extensively replicated (see, for example, Laurendeau and Pinard 1962). The results of such studies are still worth scrutiny not in terms of the logical structures they reveal but in terms of the content of the responses of pupils of different ages. One might ask, for example, what implications it might have for introductory biology courses if you take seriously the finding that over 10% of 11 to 12-year-olds in Britain extend their concept of 'living things' to include the sun, wind and fire (King 1961).

Studies indicate that a similar problem exists with older pupils (Boyd 1966, Za'rour 1976), and that some alternative frameworks in the area of mechanics persist among university physics students (Viennot 1974). In Scotland, work by Johnstone and his students has illuminated problem areas in chemistry topics (Duncan and Johnstone 1973; Johnstone, MacDonald and Webb 1977). At Leeds, Lovell and his students have done studies to explore pupils' developing understanding of ideas of gravitational and potential energy (Archenhold 1975) and certain biological concepts (Okeke 1976). Of particular interest are the few studies which systematically attempt to trace the developmental path in understanding important scientific ideas. A recent study with American children, for example, traces the development of children's understanding of the 'earth concept' from that of a flat platform to a sphere in unlimited space (Nussbaum and Novak 1976).

Such studies indicate that although individual children will bring unique perspectives to learning there are enough common trends in their thinking to make a study of more common alternative frameworks worthwhile.

In the next section we will consider how such information may be used in curriculum design and in teaching.

IMPLICATIONS FOR CLASSROOM PRACTICE

One may well ask why attention should be paid to children's alternative frameworks. If such ideas are wrong, perhaps like the misdemeanours of a naughty child they are best extinguished by being ignored.

Over a decade ago, Ausubel commented on the importance of considering what he called children's preconceptions, suggesting that they are 'amazingly tenacious and resistant to extinction' and that 'unlearning of preconceptions might well prove to be the most determinative single factor in the acquisition and retention of subject matter knowledge' (Ausubel 1968). We have seen an indication of this problem in the case of pupils' understanding of the molecular-kinetic theory. Studies referred to in the previous section indicated the strength of Aristotelian ideas in pupils' understanding of mechanics.

If there is a problem in terms of the persistance of alternative frameworks, is it not important to be aware of these ideas in order to help pupils see their limitations and to develop their thinking? Let us now turn to look at how such information might be used and what implications it may have for classroom practice. Here I will suggest four points:

(1) Curriculum development in science needs to pay as much attention to the structure of thought of the child as it has recently paid to the structure of the disciplines in organizing learning experiences.

Currently our concern for the structure of thought of the child has been focused on Piagetian logical operations. I would argue that the content as much as the process of thought requires our attention.

(2) Teaching programmes may need to be structured so as to be more in keeping with the developmental path in understanding important scientific ideas. The logical order of teaching a topic may not correspond with the psychological order in learning.

This is a word of caution for those who are enthusiastic about structured learning programmes involving such hierarchies.

(3) Activities in science may need to include those which enable pupils to disprove alternative interpretations as well as affirm accepted ones. (This of course also has bearing on the shortcomings of learning hierarchies.) If we think back to the example discussed earlier of Tim's idea of weight related to height above the ground, we see an example of this kind of activity. Tim needed to explore that idea to disprove it to himself. Studies which indicate the possible importance of this are reported by Cole and Raven (1969), and Rowell and Dawson (1977).

(4) Lastly, if we are to take seriously the philosophical issues discussed earlier we need to include opportunities for pupils to think through the implications of observations and measurements made in science lessons. We must realize that our explanations do not spring clearly from the data.

As teachers we know how we expect an experiment to be interpreted. We have been along that route before. Our pupils perhaps have not – nor is it always an easy route to follow. Theory is not related in a unique deductive way to data; activities with apparatus in the laboratory and outside it are not enough to develop children's thinking.

Modern philosophers of science have indicated the limitations of rational empiricism, and yet I would hold that rational empiricism is still the view of science which predominates in our classrooms.

In England, the Nuffield O-level physics materials were launched on the slogan 'I do and I understand'. We now have classrooms in which activities play a central part. Pupils can spend a major portion of their time pushing trolleys up runways; gathering, cutting and sticking tangling metres of ticker-tape; marbles are rattled around in trays simulating solids, liquids and gases; batteries and bulbs are clicked in and out of specially designed circuit boards. To what end? Sometimes I suspect 'I do and I am even more confused'. Activity by itself is not enough. It is the sense we make of it that matters.

I am not here arguing for less practical work. What I am suggesting is that practical work by itself is not enough. Pupils need time both individually, in groups and with their teacher to think and talk through the implications and possible explanations of what they are observing – *and this takes time* – more time than often we see being given in classrooms. In the jargon of the philosophers of science, pupils' thinking may need to undergo a paradigm shift in learning science. A study of the history of science shows how difficult this can be for many scientists. In fact, Max Planck commented that 'New theories do not convert people; it is just that old men die.' If scientists have this difficulty in reformulating their conceptions of the world, is it a wonder that children sometimes have a struggle to do so?

REFERENCES

Archenhold, W. F. 1975, *A study of the understanding by sixth form students of the concept of potential in physics* (M. Phil. Thesis, University of Leeds).

Ausubel, D. 1968, *Educational Psychology: a Cognitive View* (Holt, Rinehart and Winston Inc.).

Barnes, D. 1976, *From Communication to Curriculum* (Penguin: Harmondsworth).

Boyd, C. A. 1966, A study of unfounded beliefs. *Science Education*, Vol. 50, pp. 396–398.

Cole, H. and Raven, R. 1969, Principle learning as a function of instruction on excluding irrelevant variables. *Journal of Research in Science Teaching*, Vol. 6, pp. 234–241.

Duncan, I. M. and Johnstone, A. H. 1973, The mole concept. *Education in Chemistry*, Vol. 10, No. 6, pp. 213–214.

Johnstone, A. H., MacDonald, J. J. and Webb, G. 1977, A thermodynamic approach to chemical equilibrium. *Physics Education*, Vol. 12, No. 4, pp. 248–251.

King, W. H. 1961, Studies of children's scientific concepts and interests. *British Journal of Educational Psychology*, Vol. 31, pp. 1–20.

Laurendeau, M. and Pinard, A. 1962, *Causal Thinking in the Child* (International University Press: New York).

Nussbaum, J. and Novak, J. D. 1976, An assessment of children's concepts of the earth utilizing structured interviews. *Science Education*, Vol. 60, No. 4, pp. 535–550.

Okeke, E. A. C. 1976, *A study of the understanding in Nigerian School Certificate Biology candidates of the concepts of reproduction, transportation and growth* (Ph.D. Thesis, University of Leeds).

Piaget, J. 1929, *The Child's Conception of the World* (Harcourt, Brace: New York).

Piaget, J. 1930, *The Child's Conception of Physical Causality* (Kegan Paul: London).

Rowell, J. A. and Dawson, C. J. 1977, Teaching about floating and sinking: an attempt to link cognitive psychology with classroom practice. *Science Education*, Vol. 61, No. 2, pp. 245–253.

Viennot, L. 1974, Sens physique et raisonnement formel en dynamique elementaire. *Encart Pedagogique*, Vol. II, pp. 34–46.

Za'rour, G. 1976, Interpretation of natural phenomena by Lebanese school children. *Science Education*, Vol. 60, pp. 277–287.

26 Children's science and its consequences for teaching

• J. K. Gilbert, R. J. Osborne and P. J. Fensham

As a consequence of their everyday experiences, children hold strong beliefs about how things happen. They also have clear understandings concerning the everyday meanings of words used in formal science. These beliefs and understandings constitute what the authors call 'children's science'. This children's science frequently conflicts with the teachers' science taught in schools. An approach to science teaching, based upon a much deeper understanding of children's science by teachers, is advocated.

Many research studies in recent years have shown that children have beliefs about how things happen and expectations which enable them to predict future events (Driver & Easley, 1978). Evidence is accumulating from a wide variety of sources (Clement, 1977; Nussbaum & Novak, 1976; Leboutet-Barrell, 1976; Stead & Osborne, 1980) to show that children, on the basis of their everyday experiences of the world, hold these beliefs and expectations very strongly. Moreover, children have clear meanings for words which are used both in everyday language and also in formal science (Gilbert & Osborne, 1980; Osborne & Gilbert, 1980a). Such views of the world, and meanings for words, held by children are not simply isolated ideas (Champagne, Klopfer, & Anderson, 1979) but rather they are part of conceptual structures which provide a sensible and coherent understanding of the world from the child's point of view. These structures may be termed children's science.

In the development of science curricula the existence of children's science has usually either been ignored or inadequately considered (Fensham, 1980). The two different assumptions on which science teaching has been based, and one on which it could be based, can be readily identified.

THE 'BLANK-MINDED' OR 'TABULA RASA' ASSUMPTION

This approach, which by implication underlies many modern curricula (Fensham, 1980), assumes that the learner has no knowledge of a topic before being formally taught it. The assumption is that the learner's 'blank mind' can be 'filled' with teacher's science (S_T). This is diagrammatically shown in Figure 1.

Figure 1 Science teaching in which it is assumed the learners have no theoretical view of the topics or phenomena under study.

Figure 2 Science teaching in which it is assumed that learners may have theoretical views but that these are easily displaced by the views presented by teachers.

Figure 3 Science teaching which recognizes that learners often do hold strongly entrenched theoretical views that persist in the face of teaching.

THE 'TEACHER DOMINANCE' ASSUMPTION

The assumption here is that, although learners may have some conceptual view of a new science topic before being taught it, this understanding has little significance for learning and can be directly and easily replaced. Thus, even if children's science views (S_{Ch}) exist, they are not strongly held in the face of science teaching. This is diagrammatically shown in Figure 2.

THE 'STUDENT DOMINANCE' ASSUMPTION

This assumption recognizes children's science views as sufficiently strong that they will persist and interact with science teaching. The interaction is diagrammatically shown in Figure 3.

There is growing evidence that the learned amalgam S_{CH} S_T of children's science and teachers' science can co-exist in varying proportions. 'Successful' learners use teachers' science when required in tests and examinations, but still retain children's science in dealing with many everyday situations.

If science curricula and teaching are to be based on the third assumption, rather than on either of the first two, it will be necessary for us to learn much more about children's science: to know how to explore it, to know about its nature, and to consider the various ways in which children's science may, or may not, be modified by learning experiences.

THE EXPLORATION OF CHILDREN'S SCIENCE

A variety of methods have recently been developed for use in investigating children's science. White (1979) has analyzed the similarities and differences of some of these methods. Most involve in-depth interviews with children (see, for example; Pines et al., 1978; Brumby, 1979; Tiberghien, 1980). This study used two such methods which we have called the Interview-about-Instances approach and the Interview-about-Events approach. The Interview-about-Instances approach (Osborne & Gilbert, 1980b; Gilbert, Watts, & Osborne, 1981) explores children's meanings for words by means of taped individual interviews. For a particular word, e.g., work, force, living, up to 20 familiar situations, depicted by line drawings on cards, are presented to the child. Some of the situations present an instance of the scientific concept embodied in the word and some do not. Children are asked, for each situation in turn, whether they consider it an instance or not. The children's reason for the choice is then elicited. The interview situation allows children to ask questions, to clarify perceived or actual ambiguities before answering, and also gives flexibility in discussing reasons or lack of reasons, for a particular answer. The method has been used to explore children's meanings for many words: for example, 'work' (Osborne & Gilbert, 1979); 'electric current' (Osborne & Gilbert, 1979; Osborne, 1981); 'force' (Osborne & Gilbert, 1980a; Watts, 1980), 'light' (Stead & Osborne, 1980), 'living' (Stead, 1980), 'friction' (Stead & Osborne, 1981a), 'gravity' (Stead & Osborne, 1981b), and 'animal' (Bell, 1981).

The Interview-about-Events approach (Osborne, 1980) places more emphasis on eliciting children's views of the world within the overall framework of children's science. It involves an individual discussion with an interviewee about an articulated series of demonstrations. This discussion is tape recorded, transcribed, and subsequently analyzed. The interview is built around a scientific concept, e.g., 'physical change'. The events are practical demonstrations of situations to which the concept may be applied. The demonstrations, performed by the interviewee with minimum assistance, are articulated to produce a smoothly linked conversation. The method has been used to explore children's views on 'physical change' (Cosgrove & Osborne, 1981), 'chemical change' (Schollum, 1981), and the 'particle nature of matter' (Happs, 1981). In the Appendix to this chapter a sequence of steps used to investigate children's views on physical change is provided.

PATTERNS IN CHILDREN'S SCIENCE

On the basis of the findings from research which has been carried out using the two investigatory techniques, referenced above, at least five different patterns of children's science can be described (Osborne & Gilbert, 1980a). These patterns will be illustrated from the sequence of discussions on physical change (Appendix A). These illustrations arise from interviews with 43 New Zealand school children spread evenly over the 10–17 year age range. (The 10–15 year olds were studying general science, the 16–17 year olds were studying physical science). The pupils were selected by their teachers as being of average attainment in science (Cosgrove & Osborne, 1981). Each quote given will be followed by the step in the discussion sequence to which it applied, and the age of the interviewee.

Everyday language

Many words in science are used in an alternative way in everyday language. Often a student can listen to, or read a statement in science and *make sense* of it by using the everyday interpretation of the word. The interpretation is not the one intended by the teacher or textbook writer. For example:

> The air is made up of small particles (is anything else made up of small particles?) glass . . . they are made out of small particles of sand which have been turned hot . . . turned clear and then sort of take them out . . . and put them between two pieces of metal when they have been hardened and when they take it off they find they have a clear surface called glass.
> (Step 7; age 11)

The word 'particle' is commonly used in science classes to mean atom, molecule or ion. In everyday use it refers to a small, but visible, piece of solid substance. The everyday meaning has been applied to air. The interviewee has apparently presumed that the 'particle' size in sand is retained in glass. A parallel has been drawn between glass and air based on appearance.

Self-centered and human-centered viewpoint

Many very young children have very egocentric views of the world. By age nine or ten most children no longer adopt this strictly egocentric view but they still interpret and consider things in terms of human experiences and commonly held values. For example:

> Ice is just frozen water (what's the difference between frozen water and ordinary water?) You can't drink it very good.
>
> (Step 7; age 10)

Properties as a drink govern the evaluation made by this child of ice and water. A second example is:

> I think I said it was oxygen in the bubbles . . . but if you put your face over (the steam) and breathe in . . . it doesn't seem you can breathe too well . . . so I don't think there is much oxygen . . . it be more hydrogen.
>
> (Step 2; age 17)

Steam has been evaluated here by its capacity to support breathing, oxygen being known to be effective. In both cases, simple human concerns have governed the interpretation made of phenomena.

This different focus on how and why things behave as they do can result in children viewing situations in quite a different way to the more analytical, and impersonal, view of science. Answers given by children in science classrooms are sometimes apparently 'off the track' hoped for by the teacher because of this difference in perspective of science teacher and student. The anthropocentric view often takes the form of some widely held beliefs – heavier objects do fall faster, things do get lighter when they are burnt, animals are things you take to the vet – and these human-centered views are reinforced by everyday language to some extent.

Nonobservables do not exist

To a number of children, and some learners despite formal teaching, a physical quantity is not present in a given situation unless the effects of that quantity or the quantity itself is observable. Some examples are: 'If you cannot feel an electric current it is not present' (Osborne & Gilbert, 1979); 'if the effects of the presence of light, for example, flickering on a wall, are not observable the light is not present' (Stead & Osborne, 1980).

> Oh, it has evaporated. (what does that mean?). Well it has not gone into the steam form because it doesn't look as if it has gone up in the water state . . . it must have split up because you couldn't sort of see steam or anything rising. (what do you mean split up?) The hydrogen and the oxygen molecules.
>
> (Step 5; age 16)

The student has presumed that, on all occasions, the visibility of water is maintained on the transition from the liquid state to the vapor state. When this visibility is not maintained, an explanation is presented in terms of elements known to be invisible and constituents of water, i.e., hydrogen and oxygen, commonly encountered in the gaseous form.

Endowing objects with the characteristics of humans and animals

Children often endow objects with a feeling, a will, or a purpose. This is partly related to children's view of living things being much broader than the biologists' viewpoint (Stead, 1980), but it is also reinforced by the use of metaphor in both common language and even in the teaching of science. Teachers make statements like 'the electric current chooses the path of least resistance,' 'the positive ion looks out for a negative ion.' However, it would appear that, not surprisingly, children do not always consider such statements to be metaphoric. For example:

> It's cold in there and the chill's coming to the outside . . . the coldness just . . . um . . . of, it's cold in there and it's just trying to get out . . . and it's somehow got out.
>
> (Step 6; age 13)

'Cold' is thought to move towards the outside of the jar under the effect of an implied will.

Endowing objects with a certain amount of a physical quantity

It is not uncommon for children to endow an object with a certain amount of a physical quantity and for this quantity (e.g., force, momentum, energy) to be given an unwarranted physical reality. For some physical quantities (e.g., force, coldness, etc.) this tendency of children leads to considerable difficulties in learning, particularly in appreciating the abstract nature of these quantities and their relationship to other quantities. For example:

> The heat makes the air bubble come out of the element.
>
> (Step 2; age 12)

The implication here is that heat is a physical entity. It is thought to physically force the air bubble to come out of the heating element in the kettle. Both the nature of heat and the source of air bubbles have been unconventionally understood. A second example is:

> The coldness of the ice could have brought the water . . . but that's a bit funny.
>
> (Step 7; age 12)

Here 'coldness' is thought to have a physical identity.

TEACHERS' VIEWS OF SCIENCE

Just as by *children's science* we mean those views of the natural world and the meanings for scientific words held by children before formal science teaching, so *scientists' science* (S_S) means the consensual scientific view of the world and meaning for words. Ideally the view of science presented to children by teachers, or directly through curriculum material, will closely relate to scientist's science. However this may not always be so. Teachers undoubtedly have a wide variety of viewpoints. S_{Ti}, ranging from almost children's science to scientists' science, but often differing from both these in distinguishing less clearly between the objects of science and the concepts that relate to them (Fensham, 1979). This teacher's view of science interacts with the science curriculum and its materials as he/she prepares for teaching. This may or may not modify this view in the direction of scientists' science as shown in Figure 4. The resultant is the *viewpoint presented* by the teacher to the pupils. It is the interaction of children's science and their teacher's science that will have profound implications for the outcomes of teaching.

Figure 4 Strongly held teachers' views of science may persist or interact with the views in science curricula.

THE CONSEQUENCES OF CHILDREN'S SCIENCE FOR TEACHING

A further consideration of the data collected using the Interview-about-Instances and Interview-about-Events techniques suggests that for children who have been taught science there are at least five patterns of outcomes from these interactions. The five outcome patterns will again be illustrated from protocols using the same Interview-about-Events sequence in Appendix A (Cosgrove and Osborne, 1981).

The undisturbed children's science outcome

Some children have an undisturbed viewpoint despite formal teaching. Reasonably common among this pattern of learners are those who now incorporate some language of science to describe the viewpoint, but whose viewpoint is essentially unaltered. The following is an example of undisturbed children's science despite teaching:

> (Where have you used the word particle?) In the science lab. (Are there particles in the jar of ice water?) Yes, I suppose so. (Which are the particles to you?) The ice blocks. (Has the water got anything to do with particles?) Oh, they melted into the water.
>
> (Step 7; age 13)

Figure 5 A prelearning or children's view of science can persist unchanged by science teaching.

The children's science view was that a visible piece of ice is a particle. The language of science, using 'particle' to mean molecule of water, has had little impact on this view. This type of interaction is presented in Figure 5. Similarly:

> The water has melted it . . . it has become part of the water . . . but there are parts of it left that you can't see . . . the taste of sugar.
>
> (Step 4; age 11)

The children's science view, that taste is separate from material substance, has not been modified by contact with the phenomenon of dissolving.

The two perspectives outcome

It is possible for the student to basically reject the teachers' science as something that can be accepted in terms of how to view the world, but to consider it as something that must be learned, e.g., for examination purposes. The student, therefore, has two views, but the learned science viewpoint is not one that has been adopted for use outside the formal learning situation. For example:

> It is dry . . . the water has evaporated . . . the water has gone (where to?) well . . . the teachers tell me that it has gone you know . . . that it makes up the clouds, you know in the sky and that sort of thing. (I see, it has gone up to the sky?) it is meant to have (where do you think the water that was on the saucer has gone?) I don't know . . . I don't think about it (it is not still on the plate dried up is it?) no, I don't think so . . . (how does it get from here to the clouds?) I don't know (magic?) no . . . it's sort of a gas there . . . not magic (where did you learn about clouds and evaporation?) in about fourth grade (9–10 years) . . . around there somewhere (oh, well they wouldn't have talked about it in much detail at that sort of level would

they?) no (and all that you can sort of remember is that when water evaporates it goes into the clouds?) yet (but you don't have a picture of how that goes on?) no, except for little arrows that point up (I see, what were those arrows do you think?) can't remember (so you have got this sort of picture of water, arrows and clouds?) yes, and it sort of comes down as rain.

(Step 3; age 14)

This student has the view that water disappears from a plate into the air. However, the standard explanation, concerning evaporation and using diagrams, has proved less than believable to the student. Nevertheless, it has been learned but is not used willingly to explain phenomena. This type of interaction is presented in Figure 6.

Figure 6 Science teaching can result in a second view being acquired for use in school but the original children's view persists elsewhere.

The reinforced outcome

The dominance of the students' prior understandings and meanings for words can, as suggested earlier, often lead to quite unintended uses of what is being taught. One common example of the outcomes of this is the confusion between physical quantities. Quantities defined in science in a particular way can be misinterpreted to mean something quite different.

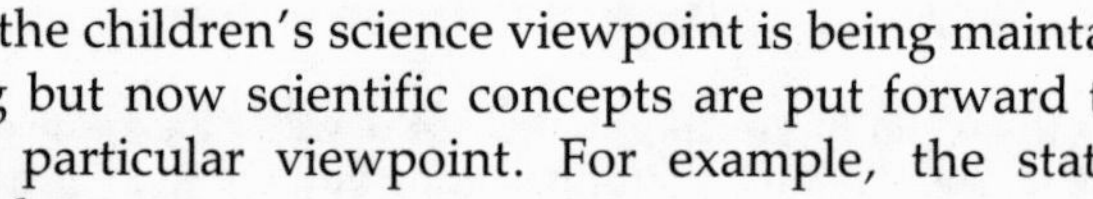

Figure 7 The original children's view is strengthened by science teaching which now is misapplied to support it.

In Figure 7, the children's science viewpoint is being maintained following teaching but now scientific concepts are put forward to explain or underpin a particular viewpoint. For example, the statement by a younger student:

It would come through glass

(Step 6; age 10)

becomes, for an older student

Through the glass . . . like diffusion through air and that . . . well it hasn't got there any other way (a lot of people I have talked to have been worried

> about this water . . . it troubles them) yes, because they haven't studied the things like we have studied (what have you studied which helps?) things that pass through air, and concentrations, and how things diffuse.
>
> (Step 6; age 15)

The notion of diffusion, learnt in connection with movement through air and water, has been applied to explain movement through glass. The children's science idea of 'movement through air' has been transformed into 'diffusion through glass.'

The mixed outcome

In many cases, scientific ideas are learned, understood, and appreciated by learners. However, the interrelationships of these ideas are manifold and at any one time only a limited amount can be learned. Often this results in students holding ideas that are not integrated and may be self-contradictory. In this outcome the learners' views are a mixture or amalgam of children's science views and teachers' views, Figure 8. For example:

> I think it is the same atoms in the ice before and now they are unfrozen in the water (what else is in there besides the atoms? the stuff that freezes?) no . . . I don't know . . . yes . . . no . . . it's all atoms but the atoms are just frozen.
>
> (Step 7; age 14)

Figure 8 Science teaching resulting in a mixed outcome where children's science and teachers' science now co-exist together

The idea of the conservation of matter between physical phases has been learned. However, the microscopic change in structure is being interpreted as a general change in the properties of microscopic components, i.e., atoms (sic).

The unified scientific outcome

The aim of all science education is that a learner should obtain a coherent scientific perspective (S_s) which he understands, appreciates, and can relate to the environment in which he lives and works. Students can be found who have this view in relation to specific words and viewpoints that we have investigated. In some of these cases, the learned viewpoint is in fact more closely aligned to scientists' science than to the teachers' views of the science. This outcome is represented in Figure 9. A typical example of the coherent scientific perspective:

> It is wet on the outside . . . 'cos the jar's cold . . . 'cos the ice is inside it and therefore the water molecules that are in the air moving around . . . although we can't see them . . . when they hit the cold jar . . . that makes them cold . . . and therefore they group together again in their groups of molecules and then they become water again because they've been cooled down.
>
> (Step 6; age 15)

Figure 9 Science teaching which extends children's science and teachers' science to a more unified science view

It is the outcome that all teachers would wish to arise from their interaction with students.

CONCLUSION

We have suggested, by argument and example, that the views which children bring with them to science lessons are, to them, logical and coherent and that these views have a considerable influence on how and what children learn from their classroom experiences. Our conclusions from a variety of studies support the view of Wittrock (1977) that people tend to generate perceptions and meanings that are consistent with prior learning. Learning can be anticipated and understood in terms of what the learners bring to the learning situation, how they relate the stimuli to their memories, and what they generate from their previous experiences.

We have also attempted to suggest, by argument and example, that the aim of science teaching and learning can be viewed as the development of children's science. Traditionally, the goal of the development is scientists' science. This has proved to be an immense task that is often very incomplete even among so-called successful learners. As happens in many present science classes, we may have to be satisfied with largely undisturbed children's science as our outcome. A more modest and manageable goal in these cases would be to make these learners aware that there *is* another viewpoint, the scientists' viewpoint, which is useful to scientists and may have more general use also. Only by adapting our teaching to make these two views explicit is this new goal likely to be achieved. This approach may also facilitate the development process on its way. Such a development will only occur in a genuine and non-superficial way if the scientific perspective appears to students to be at least as logical, coherent, useful, and versatile way of viewing the world than their present viewpoint.

Whatever the goal, it would seem that teachers need to be aware of children's science and to encourage students to express their views. We all need, as teachers, to listen to, be interested in, understand and value the views that children bring with them to science lessons. It is only against that background of sensitivity and perception that we can decide what to do, and how to do it. This is a major challenge for science teaching.

APPENDIX

Interview-about-events outline schedule for physical change

Step 1 The interviewee is presented with a screw-top jar containing ice and is invited to dry the jar thoroughly. The jar is then set aside.

Step 2 The interviewee is invited to observe the water coming up to, and boiling, in an electric kettle. Preliminary questions are 'What is happening?' and 'What are the bubbles made of?'

Step 3 The interviewee holds a saucer in the steam and is invited to comment on what is observed and why it has happened. After these questions, it is put, inverted, to one side.

Step 4 Some of the hot water (from step 2) is put in a cup. The interviewee puts some sugar in it and stirs the mixture. The preliminary question is again 'What is happening?.'

Step 5 The inverted saucer (see Step 3) is now reconsidered. The dryness is discussed through 'What has happened to it?' and 'Why is that?'

Step 6 The jar (see Step 1) is now reconsidered. It now has water on the outside. The interviewee is asked 'Is that different to when you had it before?' and 'Can you tell me about that?'

Step 7 The lid of the jar (see Step 6) is removed, and some water and ice extracted on a spoon. The questions begin with 'What is happening here?'

REFERENCES

Papers

Brumby, M. Students' perceptions and learning styles associated with the concept of evolution by natural selection. Unpublished doctoral dissertation. University of Surrey, U.K., 1979.

Champagne, A., Klopfer, L., & Anderson J. Factors influencing learning of classical mechanics. Paper presented at A.E.R.A. Meeting, San Francisco, April, 1979.

Clement, J. Catalogue of students' conceptual models in physics. Working Paper, Department of Physics and Astronomy, University of Massachusetts, 1977.

Cosgrove, M., & Osborne, R. Physical Change, L.I.S.P. Working Paper No. 26. Hamilton, New Zealand: University of Waikato, Science Education Research Unit, 1980.

Gilbert, J. K., Watts, D. M., & Osborne, R. Eliciting student views using an interview-about-instances technique. Symposium paper presented at the A.E.R.A. Conference, Los Angeles, April, 1981.

Happs, J. C. Particles, L.I.S.P. Working Paper No. 18. Hamilton, New Zealand: University of Waikato, Science Education Research Unit, 1981.

Osborne, R. J., & Gilbert, J. K. An approach to student understanding of basic concepts in science. Guildford, Surrey, U.K.: University of Surrey, Institute for Educational Technology, 1979.

Pines, A., Novak, J., Posner, G. & Van Kirk, J. The clinical interview: a method for evaluating cognitive structure. Ithaca, N.Y.: Department of Education, Cornell University, 1978.

Schollum, B. Chemical Change, L.I.S.P. Working Paper No. 27. Hamilton, New Zealand: University of Waikato, Science Education Research Unit, 1981.

Stead, B. E. The description and modification of some students' biological concepts. Unpublished M.Ed. thesis, University of Waikato, New Zealand, 1980.

Watts, D. M. An exploration of students' understanding of the concepts 'force' and 'energy'. Paper presented at the Conference on Education for Physics Teaching, Trieste, September, 1980.

White, R. Describing Cognitive Structure. Paper presented at the Australian Association for Research in Education Conference, Melbourne, Australia, November, 1979.

Publications

Bell, B. F. When is an animal not an animal? *J. Biol. Educ.*, 1981, *15*, 3.

Driver, R., & Easley, J. Pupils and paradigms: a review of the literature related to concept development in adolescent science students. *Stud. Sci. Educ.*, 1978, *5* 61–84.

Fensham, P. J. Conditions for Co-operation and Strategies for Innovation. In *Co-operation between Science Teachers and Mathematics Teachers*. H. G. Steiner (ed.). Institut für Didaktik den Mathematik der Universität Bielefeld, 1979, pp. 553–580.

Fensham, P. J. A. A research base for new objectives of science teaching. *Res. Sci. Educ.*, 1980, *10*, 23–33.

Gilbert, J., & Osborne, R. 'I understand, but I don't get it': some problems of learning science. *School Sci. Rev.*, 1980, *61*(218), 664–674.

Leboutet-Barrell, (1976) Concepts of mechanics among young people. *Phys. Educ.*; 1976, *11*(7), 462–466.

Nussbaum, J., & Novak, J. D. An assessment of children's concepts of the earth using structural interviews. *Sci. Educ.*, 1976, *60*, 535–550.

Osborne, R. Some aspects of students' views of the world. Res. Sci. Educ., 1980, *10*, 11–18.

Osborne, R. Children's views on electric current. *N.Z. Sci. Teach.*, 1981, 27, 12–19.

Osborne, R., & Gilbert, J. A technique for exploring students' views of the world. *Phys. Educ.*, 1980a, *15* (6), 376–379.

Osborne, R., & Gilbert, J. A method for the investigation of concept understanding in science. *Eur. J. Sci. Educ.*, 1980b, *2* (3), 311–321.

Stead, B. E., & Osborne, R. J. Exploring science students' concepts of light. *Aust. Sci. Teach. J.*, 1980, *26* (3), 84–90.

Stead, K. E., & Osborne, R. J. What is friction? Some children's ideas. *Aust. Sci. Teach. J.*, 1981a.

Stead, K. E., & Osborne, R. J. What is gravity? Some children's ideas. *N.Z. Sci. Teach.*, 1981b, *30* 5–12.

Tiberghien, A. Modes and conditions of learning. An example: the learning of some aspects of the concept of heat. In *Proceedings of Cognitive Development Research Seminar*, F. Archenhold et al. (eds.), Leeds, U.K.: University of Leeds Centre for Science Education, 1980, pp. 288–309.

Wittrock, M. C. Learning as a generative process. In *Learning and Instruction*, M. C. Wittrock, (ed.), Berkeley: McCutcheon, 1977, pp. 621–631.

27 Science teaching and children's views of the world

R. J. Osborne, B. F. Bell and J. K. Gilbert

INTRODUCTION

Approaches to education that emphasize the construction of meaning (e.g., Ausubel 1968, Kelly 1971) strongly suggest that, before any science teaching takes place, children have already acquired considerable knowledge about the natural and technological world. This knowledge has a number of characteristics which differentiate it from notions found in formal science and, more importantly, it can be amazingly tenacious and resistant to change. It is therefore essential for science education research to explore children's viewpoints, to study the impact of science teaching on these views, and to consider the implications for science teaching (ICPE 1976).

Researchers in science education have in recent years begun to take up this challenge by focusing their attention on children's misconceptions *(for example, Linke and Venz 1979, Helm 1980),* children's alternative frameworks *(for example, Driver 1981) and, as we increasingly realize how sensible and understandable children's views are in terms of their experience,* children's science *(for example, Osborne 1980; Gilbert, Osborne and Fensham 1982).*

In this paper we will clarify what we mean by children's science, and we will explore some of the differences between children's science and scientists' science. By scientists' science *we mean the generally-accepted scientific viewpoint regarding any particular aspect of science, e.g., the validity of Newtonian mechanics at non-relativistic velocities. In particular, we refer to* curricular science *(Sylbersztajn 1981), which is that version of scientists' science selected by curriculum planners for inclusion on a syllabus or textbook. We will also consider the implications of these differences for science teaching.*

CHILDREN'S SCIENCE

By children's science we mean the views of the world and meanings for words that children tend to acquire before they are formally taught science. Children's science develops as children attempt to make sense of the world in which they live in terms of their experiences, their current knowledge and their use of language. Kelly (1971) suggests we are all scientists of a sort from a young age.

Children, like scientists, use similarities and differences to organize facts and phenomena and, in the observation of facts and phenomena, search for elements, and relationships among elements, to build structures of relationships (Vicentini-Mossori 1980). In addition, children, like scientists, gather facts and build models to explain known facts and make predictions. However, there are at least three ways in which children's science differs from scientists' science, as summarized below.

(*a*) Young children seem to have difficulty with the kinds of abstract reasoning which scientists are capable of. They tend to view things from a self-centred or human-centred point of view, and they consider only those entities and constructs that follow directly from everyday experience.

(*b*) Children are interested in particular explanations for specific events. Unlike scientists they are not concerned with the need to have coherent and non-contradictory explanations for a variety of phenomena. With their limited experience and concern for a specific explanation only, children can latch on to any one of a number of possible explanations which are reasonable from their more restricted outlook.

(*c*) The everyday language of our society often leads children to have a view distinctly different to the scientists' law. Such views may not change as the child grows older, or they may even become, with time, *increasingly* different from scientists' science. In both cases it becomes *more* difficult to effect a change to the scientists' view as time passes (Osborne 1981a). For example, we have found (Bell 1981a) that young children often have a more scientific meaning for the word 'animal' than do older children. Older children often restrict their meaning of the word to large four-legged terrestrial creatures. Similarly younger children tend to have a more scientific meaning for the word 'living' than older children. Thus 'fire' tends to be non-living to young children, but many 11- and 12-year-olds consider fire to be living. These older pupils have had more exposure to the metaphoric view of 'living' both in, and outside, the classroom (Bell 1981b).

DISTINCTIONS BETWEEN CHILDREN'S SCIENCE AND SCIENTISTS' SCIENCE

Let us elaborate on the differences between children's science and scientists' science by considering the three aspects of children's science discussed above.

Firstly, as Layton (1973) has pointed out, the current scientific viewpoint has emerged in just the last 250 years. It has involved the introduction of conceptions for which there are no directly observable instances, e.g., atoms, electric fields, and conceptions which have no physical reality, e.g., potential energy. Such conceptions are outside the child's experience and can thus not be part of his or her scientific viewpoint.

Secondly, the abstract conceptions which have been created by scientists have not only enabled the explanatory and predictive power of science to increase, but have also led to a considerable coherence between scientific theories. However, unfortunately for the teaching of science, the abstract conceptions and coherent theories are connected to everyday observable phenomena by increasingly complex reasoning: for example, although Maxwell's equations do account for everyday electrical phenomena, e.g., lightning, they do not do so in a simple way. While scientists have become increasingly interested in coherent theories, children are much more interested in simple pragmatic explanations for things that occur in their familiar world and are not too concerned if two theories, each explaining a different situation, are mutually inconsistent.

Thirdly, in developing views of the world, scientists have found it necessary to develop a technical language where words have specific meanings and quantities have unambiguous definitions. This contrasts with the fact that children often do not appreciate the need for precision of language. Unfortunately, many of the words used in science have everyday meanings which are subtly different from their scientific meaning, e.g., work, force, power, friction, energy, animal, plant. This creates great problems for children learning about scientists' viewpoints.

In summary, children and scientists both have views about how and why things behave as they do and meanings for words used in science. However, children' views and meanings can be quite different to scientists' meanings. What needs to be remembered, from the point of view of science teaching, is that in terms of the child's mental maturity, experiences and language, the child's view of a particular phenomenon may appear far more sensible and logical to him or her than the scientists' viewpoint. For example, to a child heavy things fall faster than light objects whilst to the scientist they both fall at the same rate but air resistance slows some objects down depending on their shape. To a child a personal view seems much more direct and sensible.

During the last few years a variety of aspects of children's science has been investigated and contrasted with scientists' science. Where similar studies have been undertaken in different countries children's views have been found to be similar (see the Appendix). Perhaps this is not so surprising. As Vicentini-Mossori (1980) points out, there are many aspects of our natural and social environment which may result in many people of the world sharing similar experiences – the wind blows; the sun shines; the rain falls; there is dawn and dusk; there are things that appear continuous like water; and there are things like sand that seem discrete.

In Table 1 some specific examples of children's science, extracted from the work of the Learning in Science Project (Tasker *et al.* 1980, Osborne *et al.* 1981), are compared and contrasted with statements found in science textbooks. However, it must be remembered that children and adults hold a range of views of any one topic; young children can be found with views which are essentially the same as those of scientists whilst some, if not most, adults hold what we would call 'classic' children's science ideas.

Table 1 The contrast between children's science and statements in science textbooks: some specific examples

Children's science	*Curricular science*
Friction is rubbing and only happens between solid surfaces moving against each other.	The force of friction is the net tangential interaction between two substances in contact.
Gravity is something which holds us to the ground. If there was no air there would be no gravity.	Gravity is a force between any two masses. It depends on the size of the masses and the distance between their centres.
Electric current flows from battery to bulb and is used up.	Electric current is the flow of charge across a surface/second.
A body requires a force to keep it moving along.	A body remains at rest or in uniform motion unless acted on by a force.
The bubbles in boiling water are bubbles of air.	A change of state does not involve a chemical change.
In a gas burner, the flames are eating up the gas.	Burning involves rapid oxidization with the release of energy.

An animal is a furry four-legged creature. A spider is not an animal.	An animal is a consumer.
A plant is something growing in the garden. A carrot from the garden is not a plant.	A plant is a producer.
The light from a candle travels further at night than during the day.	Incoherent light does not effectively interact with other incoherent light rays.

IMPLICATIONS FOR SCIENCE TEACHING

What are the implications of the existence of children's science for science teaching? Firstly, we need to consider what impact science teaching has on children's viewpoints.

In our experience, based on a large number of studies (Osborne 1981a), children's viewpoints are largely uninfluenced, or influenced in unanticipated ways, by much of our present day teaching. Children often misinterpret, modify or reject the scientific viewpoint as it is presented to them (Freyberg and Osborne 1981, Gilbert, Osborne and Fensham 1982), using the way they *really* think about how and why things behave. The 'scientific viewpoint' might be regurgitated in an examination but it is not the way the pupil actually thinks about the world.

We consider that the above findings point to the need for a new view of science teaching. Science teaching, insofar as it is concerned with encouraging students to be aware of, and possibly even adopt, alternative views of the world and meanings for words, needs to build on or confront, but certainly not ignore, children's science. This aspect of science teaching should provide children with learning experiences which will broaden their experiences of the natural and technological world, encourage them to clarify the views that they already hold, challenge them with respect to the limitations of their viewpoints, enable them to appreciate the differences between their present views and those of others, and lead them to developing a personal perspective which is soundly based on their broader experiences and which is more useful than their earlier viewpoint. Where topics are appropriately chosen, it is likely that the viewpoint which emerges is closer to the accepted scientific viewpoint than the children's earlier viewpoint.

We suspect that what we have argued in relation to scientific knowledge, also applies to scientific skills and attitudes. Children bring to science lessons not only their views of the world and their meanings of words, but also their own methods of investigation, their own ideas about what constitutes adequate explanations, and their own outlook on science. All these profoundly influence learning, including the motivation to find out how and why things behave as they do (Tasker 1980 and 1981, Stead 1981).

CHANGING CHILDREN'S VIEWS OF THE WORLD

If an objective of science teaching is to help children to modify their views of the worlds and meanings of words, then we need to consider how we might encourage them to change their views. According to Hewson (1980), children must first find their present conceptions (for example, of how and why something behaves as it does) unsatisfactory. For this to occur, the child's present viewpoint has to be recognized by him or her as inadequate; this could happen if the viewpoint failed to anticipate correctly or to control events (Kelly 1971). The need is for well-chosen learning experiences, which will highlight to the child the inadequacies in a present view. However, dissatisfaction with a present viewpoint is not a sufficient reason for a child to change a viewpoint. What is also required if a child is to change a view, is access to a new and better idea with which to replace it. This new idea needs to be, according to Hewson (1980):

(*a*) *intelligible*, in that it appears coherent and internally consistent;
(*b*) *plausible*, in that it is reconcilable with other aspects of the child's view of the world;
(*c*) *fruitful*, in that it is preferable to the old viewpoint on the grounds of perceived elegance, parsimony and economy.

Hewson has also emphasized the dynamic nature of the views children hold, by indicating how dissatisfaction and the status of a particular viewpoint are linked and how these together change with time: 'dissatisfaction comes from loss of fruitfulness and plausibility and the reduction of dissatisfaction comes from increased plausibility and fruitfulness' (p. 10). Any change in viewpoint is generally a gradual process affecting different aspects of a changing viewpoint at different times. It needs to be appreciated that the reasons why a child changes a viewpoint are unlikely to be entirely on cognitive grounds: the cognitive and affective aspects of a person's thinking are not isolated. For example, if a child finds that other children do not think about something in the way that (s)he does, this may create social pressures which will support and legitimize a subsequent change of viewpoint.

As has already been implied, one of the problems of teaching science is that the scientists' viewpoint may appear to the child to be *less* intelligible, plausible and fruitful than the child's present view. In practice, what does all this imply for what and how we teach children in science classrooms? The following sections, based on recent work (LISP 1980), may offer some suggestions.

We need to identify, and be familiar with, children's current views

The Appendix provides references to some aspects of children's science that have already been established. Researchers have been using a variety of techniques for enquiry. Fensham *et al.* (1981), as well as White (1982), have considered the relevance of some of these to the classroom teacher. Unfortunately there is, as yet, no simple way for classroom teachers to establish children's views with respect to topics which have not been investigated by researchers. Most current research methods are time-consuming, e.g., clinical interviews, and teachers do not have the time to adopt them. Where children's views have been established, surveys can be used by the classroom teachers to establish the prevalence of aspects of these views within his or her class (for example, see Stead and Osborne 1981a and 1981b).

We need to design curricula which build on, rather than ignore, children's views

Some specific examples of attempts to design lessons, or sets of lessons, which build on 'children's science' have already been reported in the literature, e.g., by Nussbaum and Novick (1981), Bell (1981a) and Schollum *et al.* (1981). The work of Schollum *et al.* (1981), for example, is based on the fact that many children have a strongly-held view that objects move forward because there is a force in them keeping them moving (Osborne and Gilbert 1980). The lessons are designed to first modify this view by introducing the label 'momentum' for this aspect of the child's view of force. The concept of momentum is then refined, distinguished and isolated from the concept of force (i.e., push/pull). The results of this endeavour (Osborne 1981b) indicate it is not easy to modify children's science even when it is known! However, support for an emphasis on momentum in the teaching of dynamics has been given by Raven (1967–68) and also by di Sessa (1980).

Apart from a knowledge of children's views with respect to specific topics, what are the implications of our present knowledge of children's science for science curricula design in general? Let us return to the three major aspects of children's ideas identified earlier:

(i) If children's ideas tend to be based on concrete observables which follow directly from everyday experience, and if there is a tendency for children to view things from a human-centred point of view, it would appear desirable to plan the curricula to take this into account. For example, we may need to place increasing emphasis on *gradually* extending children's conceptions toward the non-personalized and more abstract view of the scientist. One possibility is that we should put greater emphasis on teaching about the senses, about the need to find ways to extend the senses, and about what we learn by doing this. For example, exploring with children ideas about how the eye 'sees' things, and exploring the idea that light may be incident on a wall even though the visible effects of this, e.g., reflection, are not apparent to the naked eye, may help to provide suitable extensions of pupils' ideas.

(ii) If children are interested in simple and pragmatic explanations for how and why things behave as they do, and show little interest in the mutual coherence of theories, it is not surprising that children do not find generalized laws and theories, with their complex relationships to the explanations of everyday phenomena, any more intelligible, plausible or fruitful than their own explanations. If an aim of science teaching is to move children's ideas towards those of scientists, this argues strongly for choosing topics, and providing pupils with experiences which are not only relatable to the child's everyday world but are also simply and effectively explained by aspects of scientists' science at a level understandable by the pupils. On the basis of some of our recent work (Osborne 1981a) we consider that the age at which these experiences and ideas are introduced may be critical. If introduced too early there are problems associated with the limited intellectual development of young children. On the other hand, we have some evidence to suggest that the ideas can be introduced too late; children's science can ossify into layman's science with children of 14 years of age and over showing little interest or motivation to change their present views.

(iii) If there are differences between everyday language and the specific technical meanings for words in science, then it is important to emphasize continually to children that words have multiple meanings and to identify clearly to children which meaning is being referred to in a particular science lesson. We have been surprised how frequently children bring the everyday meaning for a word into the science classroom and interpret much of what is taught from this perspective. For example, the everyday meaning of the word 'animal' relates, typically, to large four-legged terrestrial creatures that 'you take to the vet', and which are 'not allowed in shops'.

To be told that an 'ant is an insect', or 'a spider is an arachnid' reinforces the view that these are not animals. Perhaps therefore it is not surprising that children aged 12 tend to have less of a biological view of 'animal' than 5-year-olds (Osborne, 1981a). Other aspects of language use also need continual explicit clarification. The need to clearly distinguish the metaphoric and scientific meanings of certain words is a case in point, for example the word 'living' mentioned earlier.

In some of our recent research we have specifically designed lessons to attempt to overcome some of the problems associated with the multiple meanings of the words animal, plant and living (LISP 1982).

We must provide challenges and encouragement for children to change their views

If we are to follow the lead of Hewson (1980) we must provide learning experiences which will challenge the views children currently hold. Children need to be able to use their present views to make predictions and be led to explore the adequacy of their present viewpoints. For example, children hold a variety of different models about current flow in a simple bulb-battery circuit as demonstrated in Figure 1 (Osborne 1981c).

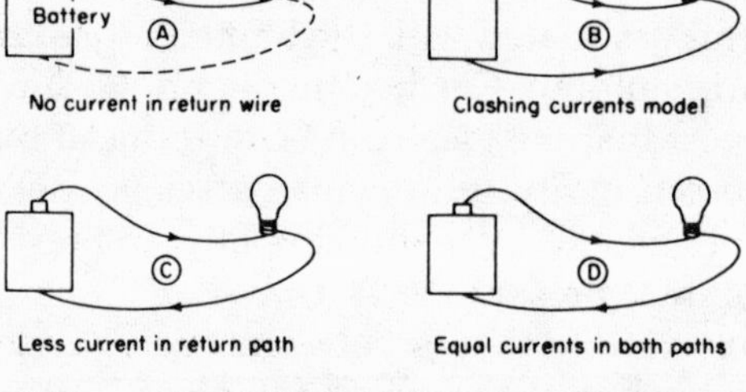

Figure 1 Various children's models for current in a simple electrical circuit

These views can be brought out in class discussion. Children can then use their individual views to predict the reading on an ammeter when placed in various parts of the circuit. The learning environment needs to be a supportive one where pupils are encouraged to put forward their viewpoints and where these viewpoints will be valued as worthwhile contributions to the learning experiences of the class. Where no pupil puts forward the accepted scientific viewpoint as a possibility, this alternative might be introduced by the teacher for pupils to consider.

The teacher therefore needs to develop an environment where children's views are accepted and where it is expected that these views will be brought out into the open, discussed, and challenged in the light of alternative viewpoints. Some pupils are often more influenced by views and explanations put forward by other pupils than by the teacher and this can often be used to advantage. Often it is the pupil whose views are respected who holds the scientific view. Opportunities must be provided for pupils to see why an alternative viewpoint may be more useful than the one presently held.

We must support pupils' attempts to rethink their ideas

Firstly we should not expect pupils to change their ideas immediately when new or contradictory evidence is provided. Any idea is linked in a complex way to many other ideas and changing one idea means that other ideas have to be rethought. This takes time and children consequently often change their viewpoint days after the teaching experience.

Secondly, pupils confronted with a better alternative than their present one may accept the new viewpoint, but this can result in confusion over other, associated ideas. The teacher's support and patience are important as these problems are thought through by pupils. For example, some 11-year-old children who held model *B* of figure 1 were shown the ammeter readings in various parts of the circuit. They accepted model *D* of figure 1 but that raised other problems, e.g., why, if there is as much current going into and out of the battery, does the battery not wear out?

Thirdly, one cannot assume that because of one experience, pupils' views related to analogous situations will also have changed. For example an 11-year-old pupil changed his view of electric current in a circuit, on ammeter evidence, from model *A* to model *D*. However, when asked about the electric current in a torch battery, he returned to his model *A* explanation. Challenged about this, he stated that as there appeared to be no return path, the current must be all just going from the batteries to the bulb! Many alternative situations, or instances and non-instances, must be considered to ensure the new view is fully appreciated and integrated into the child's view of the world. It is so easy for students to learn scientific information without linking it or relating it to their world.

We must be sensitive to the possible pupil outcomes of a teaching episode

Hewson (1980), in a more general context, and Gilbert, Osborne and Fensham (1982), in the science education context, have suggested a similar set of possible outcomes to a teaching episode. By being sensitive to these possible outcomes we may then be better able to appreciate the real effectiveness of our science teaching. These outcomes are summarized below.

(*a*) *The new view is simply rejected*: The child prefers his or her present view to the one being offered. The new view is rejected as not being plausible, intelligible, and/or fruitful. Alternatively the new idea is not even given serious consideration. As mentioned earlier, many young children have an Aristotelian view of motion. An object moves forward because of the force within it. This view is quite different to the view taught in secondary schools but some pupils, despite considerable exposure to physics teaching, retain their earlier intuitive ideas. An ex-pupil who had studied physics to 17 years expressed the following view when asked about the forces on a bike which was slowing down gradually, without brakes or pedalling.

> There is a force because of the bike's own mass . . . the mass of the bike has come to such a speed that it won't just stop straight away . . . the force is still in there . . . in the bike . . . the force was transferred from the person pedalling.

This view is really no different to the view of the following 11-year-old:

> It is just putting force on by itself from the force you gave it before (Osborne and Gilbert 1980).

(*b*) *The new view is misinterpreted to fit in with, or even support, present views*: The pupil incorporates the new ideas into his or her present views by misinterpreting the incoming message. Normally, and unfortunately, both the child and the teacher are quite unaware of the fact that the message is being misinterpreted. For example, consider the following sequence:

Child's view: bubbles in boiling water are bubbles of air.
Learnt ideas: water is made of oxygen and hydrogen, while air is made of oxygen and other gases.
Child's new view: water breaks up into oxygen and hydrogen on boiling.

This 'new' view is held by approximately 22 per cent of 12-year-olds *increasing* to some 45 per cent of 15-year-olds taking science for public examination at about 16-years-old. (Osborne and Cosgrove 1982). However, it is not the consensus scientific view nor is it a view taught by teachers.

(*c*) *The new view is accepted but in isolation from present views*: The child develops an isolated knowledge store of viewpoint rather than 'contaminate' an old and satisfactory viewpoint. This is done because the ideas cannot be related to the old ideas but it is considered advantageous by the child to have this new view, for example because of its acceptability by teacher or examiner.

Some 30% of 13-year-olds consider that gravity increases with height above the earth's surface. As stated by one pupil,

> The higher up you go, the stronger gravity is, until you get out of the atmosphere.

This view is retained by some 10 per cent of 16-year-old physics students, despite their familiarity with the inverse square law of gravitation. The two ideas are not related (Stead and Osborne 1981a).

(*d*) *The new view is accepted but leads to confusion*: The pupil attempts to reconcile a taught view with an old view, but these are not really reconciled into a satisfactory coherent whole. Thus when a 13-year-old pupil was asked what happens to the water which had disappeared from the surface of a wet plate, the discussion was as follows:

> [Where has the water gone?] I don't know . . . it's just the air . . . it's turned into a gas. [What's the gas?] I don't know. [What does gas mean to you?] A gas is a substance in the air . . . there's not just gas in the air . . . it's also underground . . . gas is just a thing you get in science . . . I don't know . . . it's hard to say (Osborne and Cosgrove 1982).

(*e*) *The new view is accepted and forms a coherent view of the world*: The child acquires a logical and coherent view which may or may not incorporate aspects of previously held views. However, the old view is relatable and related to the new view in a logical and coherent way. The following pupil was asked about melting. The pupil had a model which worked well in explaining the phenomena.

> [What happens when ice melts?] Temperature increases. It . . . water molecules get a greater kinetic energy? [So water molecules have got kinetic energy as well as gas ones?] Yes. [What about solid ones?] Um . . . yeah, they do but it's very, very, low, that's why they don't move around. [So how does this help you understand melting?] What . . . kinetic energy? Well, the lower the kinetic energy the less, the less if water molecules hit each other the less, the less the collisions going to be, it won't sort of bounce them off so much because it's got a low kinetic energy, and so

they'd be closer together, and when they get to a solid state they'd sort of form bonds between each other (Osborne and Cosgrove 1982).

IMPLICATIONS FOR TEACHER TRAINING

In this paper we have attempted to clarify ideas about children's science and to consider the implication of this knowledge for science teaching. One aspect of science teaching and learning which we have not considered is the views held by teachers. As Vicentini-Mossori (1980) points out, this is a particular problem with primary school teachers who normally have studied tertiary level subjects in the fields of education, humanities and social science, with some elementary mathematics and very little or nothing of natural sciences. In their professional activities as teachers they are continually confronted with samples of children's (or laymen's) science presented to them by pupils and parents. Scientific ideas, therefore, if they are acquired at all during school years, remain notions incompletely related to everyday experiences and are, therefore, soon forgotten. From our observations what is taught in the name of science is frequently a mixture of the teacher's own views (which may be largely children's science) and textbook quotations of scientists' science, or curricular science.

This has implications for the training of primary school teachers, and Vicentini-Mossori (1980) discusses attempts she is making to overcome this problem. Personally, we are optimistic that, if teachers college students are introduced to children's science first, they then might be easily encouraged to clarify the differences between these views, their own views and those of scientists. Many primary teachers trainees have a rather negative attitude to science based on their secondary school experiences. The suggested approach above attempts to build on students' interest in children and attempts to dissociate science at teachers college from negative secondary science experiences.

At the secondary level the situation is not so serious. Admittedly, secondary school teachers are often trained only in one scientific discipline. However this training at least introduces them to aspects of scientists' science: the rationale and purpose of science have often been understood. Such teachers usually appreciate that they have deficiencies in certain areas of their knowledge, and they have access to school colleagues who can help them with specific deficiencies. On the other hand, secondary school science teachers are largely unaware of children's science and are frequently not sensitive to the viewpoints children bring with them to science lessons.

It is therefore our view that both primary and secondary teachers need to be made aware of both children's science, and of scientists' science, and to clarify where their own views lie with respect to these two views. With respect to children's science, teachers in training can be made familiar with what is known about children's science to date (see the Appendix). Further they could use many of the techniques described by Fensham *et al.* (1981) to undertake small scale investigations of children's science in schools and the views of their teachers college peers.

In our experience this provides excellent opportunities for students to clarify their own ideas and to provide them with a sound orientation on which to base good science teaching. The following is an extract from the conclusion of a teachers' college student's report on her investigation of children's meanings for the word 'solution' using an approach suggested by Osborne and Gilbert (1980). While the comments might well have been more qualified, the student's enthusiasm and orientation is clearly apparent!

> The results of my investigations cannot be ignored by teachers. The children in this study do not appear to be aware of the appropriate use of both the common and scientific meanings of the word *solution*. Because children do seem to have their own concepts of the word [not necessarily a scientific one] it is the job of the teacher to clarify [various] meanings of the word and help children distinguish between them. Above all the teacher should not *assume* that children have a single scientific concept of words like solution but be aware that they may have their own meanings. Discrepancies in the meanings children and teachers have for words may occur in other areas of science. Wherever possible teachers should make an effort to investigate children's meanings for words and views of the world around them.

We have advocated that teachers should have a greater knowledge of, and respect for, children's science. What children think can be developed by causing them to reflect on, and discuss, its consequences. It follows naturally that teacher education can, and should, proceed in an analogous manner.

REFERENCES

Ausubel, D. 1968, *Educational Psychology* (Holt, Rinehart and Winston: New York), p. 685.

Bell, B. F. 1981a, When is an animal not an animal? *Journal of Biological Education*, Vol. 15, No. 3, pp. 213–218.

Bell, B. F. 1981b, Animal, plant and living – notes for teachers, Working Paper No. 30, Learning in Science Project, SERU, University of Waikato, Hamilton, NZ.

Driver, R. 1981, Pupils' alternative frameworks in science. *European Journal of Science Education*, Vol. 3, No. 1, pp. 93–101.

Fensham, P. J., Garrard, J. and West, L. 1981, The use of cognitive mapping in teaching and learning strategies. *Research in Science Education*, Vol. 11, pp. 121–129.

Freyberg, P. S. and Osborne, R. J. 1981, Who structures the curriculum: teacher or learner? *SET*, Vol. 2, Item 6. (Wellington: New Zealand Council for Educational Research).

Gilbert, J. K., Osborne, R. J. and Fensham, P. 1982, Children's science and its consequences for teaching. *Science Education*, Vol. 66, No. 4, pp. 623–633.

Helm, H. 1980, Misconceptions in Physics amongst South African students. *Physics Education*, Vol. 15, pp. 92–97.

Hewson, P. 1980, A case study of the effect of metaphysical commitments on the learning of complex scientific theory. Paper presented at AERA, Annual Meeting, Boston.

ICPE 1976, The effect on physics education of a better understanding of the psychological process of learning. In J. J. Lewis (editor), *New Trends in Physics Teaching* (UNESCO: Paris).

Kelly, G. A. 1971, Ontological acceleration. In B. Maher (editor), *Clinical Psychology and Personality: The selected papers of George Kelly* (John Wiley: London).

Layton, D. 1973, *Science for the People* (George Allen and Unwin: London).

LISP 1982, Towards Solutions: the Working Papers of the Action-Research Phase. Hamilton, NZ Learning in Science Project (University of Waikato: Hamilton, NZ).

Linke, R. D. and Venz, M. I. 1979, Misconceptions in Physical Science among non-science background students. *Research in Science Education*, Vol. 9, pp. 103–109.

Nussbaum, H. and Novick, S. 1981, Brainstorming in the classroom to invent a model: a case study. *School Science Review*, Vol. 62, pp. 771–778.

Osborne, R. J. 1980, Some aspects of the student's view of the world. *Research in Science Education*, Vol. 10, pp. 11–18.

Osborne, R. J. 1981a, Science Education: Where do we start? Keynote Lecture to the Conference of the Australian Science Teachers Association, Melbourne, August 1981.

Osborne, R. J. 1981b, Towards solutions: the work of the Physics Action Research Group. Working Paper No. 32, Learning in Science Project, SERU (University of Waikato: Hamilton, NZ).

Osborne, R. J. 1981c, Children's ideas about electric current. *NZ Science Teacher*, Vol. 29, pp. 12–19.

Osborne, R. J. and Gilbert, J. K. 1980, A technique for exploring students' views of the world. *Physical Education*, Vol. 15, pp. 376–379.

Osborne, R. J. and Cosgrove, M. 1982, Children's conception of the changes of state of water. *Journal of Research in Science Teaching* (in press).

Osborne, R. J., Freyberg, P., Tasker, R. and Stead, K. 1981, Description, Analysis and Action: Three Phases of a Research Project: *Research in Science Education*, Vol. 11, pp. 52–58.

Raven, R. J. 1967–8, The development of the concept of momentum in primary school children. *Journal of Research in Science Teaching*, Vol. 5, pp. 216–223.

Schollum, B., Hill, G. and Osborne, R. 1981, Teaching about force. Working Paper No. 34, LISP, SERU (University of Waikato: Hamilton, NZ).

Di Sessa, A. S. 1980, Momentum flow as an alternative perspective in elementary mechanics. *American Journal of Physics*, Vol. 48, No. 5, pp. 365–369.

Stead, B. and Osborne, R. 1980, Exploring students' concepts of light. *Australian Science Teachers Journal*, Vol. 26, No. 3, pp. 84–90.

Stead, K. E. 1981, My model or yours – exploring an individual's outlook on science with the repertory grid. Paper presented to the NZ Psychological Society Conference, Wellington, August, 1981.

Stead, K. E. and Osborne, R. J. 1981a, What is gravity? Some children's ideas. *NZ Science Teacher*, Vol. 30, pp. 5–12.

Stead, K. E. and Osborne, R. J. 1981b, What is friction? Some children's ideas. *Australian Science Teachers' Journal*, Vol. 27, No. 3, pp. 51–57.

Tasker, C. R. 1980, Some aspects of the students' view of doing science. *Research in Science Education*, Vol. 10, pp. 19–27.

Tasker, C. R. 1981, Children's views and classroom experiences. *Australian Science Teacher's Journal*, Vol. 27, No. 3, pp. 33–37.

Tasker, C. R., Osborne, R. J. and Freyberg, P. S. 1980, Learning in Science Project Considerations relating to approach and methods. *Australian Science Teachers' Journal*, Vol. 26, No. 3, pp. 79–84.

Vicentini-Mossori, M. 1980, Commonsense knowledge and scientific knowledge. In C. P. McFadden (editor), *World Trends in Science Education* (Atlantic Institute of Education: Halifax, Nova Scotia), pp. 276–81.

White, R. T. 1982, Probing techniques. SET, Vol. 1 item 7 (New Zealand Council for Educational Research: Wellington).

Zylbersztajn, A. 1981, Personal Communication. Institute for Educational Development, University of Surrey, UK.

APPENDIX: PAPERS WHICH INVESTIGATE CHILDREN'S IDEAS IN SCIENCE

In addition to Bell (1981a, 1981b); Gilbert, Osborne and Fensham (1982), Osborne (1980, 1981a, 1981b, 1981c) Osborne and Gilbert (1980), Stead and Osborne (1980); Stead and Osborne (1981a, 1981b) other papers include:

Anderson, B. 1980, Some aspects of children's understanding of boiling point. In W. F. Archenhold (editor), *Cognitive Development Research in Science and Mathematics*, (University of Leeds: Leeds).

Bell, B. F. 1981, What is a plant? Some children's ideas. *NZ Science Teacher*, Vol. 31, pp. 10–14.

Driver, R. 1980, The pupil as scientist. In U. Ganiel (editor), *Physics Teaching*, GIREP (Balaban International Science Services, Philadelphia), pp. 331–345.

Erikson, G. L. 1979, Children's conceptions of heat and temperature. *Science Education,* Vol. 63, No. 2, pp. 221–230.

Fredette, N. and Lochhead, J. 1980, Student conceptions of simple circuits. *The Physics Teacher,* Vol. 18, pp. 194–198.

Gunstone, R. F. and White, R. T. 1981, Understanding of gravity. *Science Education,* Vol. 65, pp. 291–299.

Guesne, E. 1978, Lumiere et vision des objects. In G. Delacôte *Physics Teaching in Schools* (Taylor and Francis: London).

Novick, S. and Nussbaum, J. 1981, Pupils' understanding of the Particulate Nature of Matter: A cross-age study. *Science Education,* Vol. 65, No. 2, pp. 187–196.

Nussbaum, J. and Novak, J. 1976, Children's concepts of the earth utilizing structured interviews. *Science Education,* Vol. 60, No. 4, pp. 535–550.

Stead, B. F. 1981, Ecology, Energy and Form 1–4 Science, *NZ Science Teacher,* Vol. 28, pp. 17–20.

Rodrigues, D. M. 1980, Notions of Physical Laws in Childhood. *Science Education,* Vol. 64, pp. 59–84.

Russell, T. J. 1980, Children's understanding of simple electric circuits. In T. J. Russell, and A. P. C. Sia, (editors), Science and Mathematics, Concept Learning of South East Asian Children: Second Report on Phase II, Glugar, Malaysia: SEAMEO-RECSAM, pp. 67–91.

Trowbridge, D. E. and McDermott, L. C. 1981, Investigation of student understanding of the concept of acceleration. *American Journal of Physics,* Vol. 49, No. 3, pp. 242–253.

Viennot, L. 1979, Spontaneous reasoning in elementary dynamics. *European Journal of Science Education,* Vol. 1, No. 2, pp. 205–221.

28 Teacher actions and student task involvement in high school science classrooms

● W. Beasley

The management behaviours of junior high school science teachers in classroom settings characterized by small group laboratory activities and individual problem-solving tasks were identified and described. Student attention to the task was recorded simultaneously. The relationships between the management behaviours of teachers and student task involvement are analysed.

INTRODUCTION

> 'Persons should be accustomed to the sight of experiments in early life and initiated in the theory and practice of investigation. Very young persons may be made so far acquainted with everything necessary to be previously known as to engage (which they will do with particular clarity) in pursuits truly original.
>
> Joseph Priestley, *Collected Works* (1790)

The virtues of laboratory-centred investigation have been with us for a long time. However the precise role and contribution of student laboratory activities to the goals of school science courses are not firmly established (Kreitler and Kreitler 1974, Anderson 1976, Tisher 1981).

During the 1970s the second generation curricula required a transformation of interaction patterns in science classrooms. Extensive studies of Australian Science Education Project classrooms (Tisher and Power 1973, 1975a and b; Fraser 1976) indicated that the new ASEP self-paced curriculum materials produced behaviour patterns in classrooms different from those occurring in conventional settings. Pupils perceived the new learning environment as different from the conventional learning environment but they did not always see the new environment as inquiry-centred, even though the new units were planned to foster inquiry. Students performed no better on tests of inquiry skills or on measures of understanding science (TOUS) than other students.

Here I describe the classroom management behaviours of junior high school science teachers in learning environments similar to those investigated by Tisher and Power (1973), in particular those classroom settings characterized by small group laboratory activities and individual problem-solving activities. This description includes an analysis of the relationship between teacher management behaviours and pupil task involvement in these settings.

Pupil task involvement and learning

A major goal is to identify management practices that maximize the time students were actively engaged in learning activities. Conceptual models developed progressively since 1963 have demonstrated links between the amount of time that students spend actually engaged with content and the level of achievement in that content area (Carroll 1963; Bloom 1973, 1976; Harnischfeger and Wiley 1975; Romberg 1976). Related research suggests that 'time on task' could be maximized through effective management behaviours (Kounin 1970; Brophy and Pitman 1979). Effective management criteria were a high degree of on-task involvement by students with a minimum degree of misbehaviour.

Science lessons as instructional settings

The science lesson possesses a number of distinctive properties. It usually occurs in a classroom, the physical features of which vary from rows of small portable independent desks to large fixed laboratory benches. The lesson has a definite time-span. The boundaries of the setting are variable for pupils and teacher, and may change as the lesson changes from one format to another. For example, in a demonstration lesson, pupils and teacher may be clustered around the front bench and thus the boundary is reduced from the four walls of the science classroom. Thus, the behaviours of the class and teacher and the objects in the room are internally organized and arranged to form a pattern. Demonstration lessons, chalk-and-talk lessons, small group experiment lessons all possess distinctive recognizable patterns. Each setting is also characterized by distinctive reciprocal teacher and pupil behaviours.

For the teacher at least, there are probably no global behaviours that can be demonstrated to be effective across a range of lesson settings (Brophy 1979a). However, Good (1979) and Brophy (1979b) have surveyed a number of studies and argued that taken together the studies support a number of generalizations including:

> effective teachers organize and maintain their classrooms so that maximum time is spent in productive [learning] activities and minimum time on transitions and disruptions.

Two distinct classroom settings within science lessons, individual activity and small group activity, are analysed in this paper. These settings are described in Table 1.

METHODOLOGY

All observations in the Science Classroom Management Project were made in a regular science classroom setting. The sample of teachers and their pupils came from 24 science classrooms in six Brisbane high schools. There were three Year 8 classes, twelve Year 9 classes and nine Year 10 classes with a median class size of 27 (range 20-36).

There were sixteen men and eight women teachers. The teachers volunteered to participate in the study after the project was described at meetings of the junior science teachers in each school.

It was planned that each teacher would be observed giving four science lessons, each about a month apart; from July to October 1979. Of the intended 96 lessons, 91 were recorded. Each lesson was recorded on to videotapes. One tape was made by a mobile camera with a zoom-lens that tracked the teacher from a position at the back of the classroom (Teacher Tape). The other tape was derived from a fixed camera with a wide-angle lens, in a corner at the front of the room facing the pupils (Pupil Tape). The teacher wore a cordless radio microphone, and there were two omnidirectional microphones on floor stands amongst the pupils, the total input from these three radio sources constituted the soundtrack on the videotapes.

Observing pupil behaviour

The 91 lessons were coded into distinct lesson segments. This was essential because it has been argued (McGaw *et al*. 1973; Medley 1979) that the 'whole lesson' is an inadequate unit for research under the 'mediating process' paradigm. These segments of lessons were defined as time periods of variable length which were characterized by distinct complementary sets of teacher/pupil behaviours. Those segments which possessed the characteristics of individual activity or small group activity (Table 1) are analysed in this paper.

Table 1 Classroom settings within science lessons

Type	*Function*	*Pupil-task structure*
Small Group Activity (SGA)	To present or illustrate new material which contributes to the cognitive or skill aim of the lesson.	Manipulate apparatus Take notes, collate data.
Individual Activity (IA)	To present, illustrate or give practice at new material which contributes to the cognitive or skill aim of the lesson.	Read Solve problems Summarize material
	To present students with information via notes on the board (written in silence) or by verbal dictation.	Write notes, listen

The 91 pupil tapes were coded for pupil task involvement (Kounin 1970; Butler *et al*. 1980). The categories for task involvement are given in Figure 1. Very full definitions and examples of the categories are given in Kounin (1970). Briefly, a pupil was scored 'definitely in' if he exhibited overt signs of direct compliance with the instructional or organizational task set by the teacher; 'probably in' if it could be reasonably inferred that

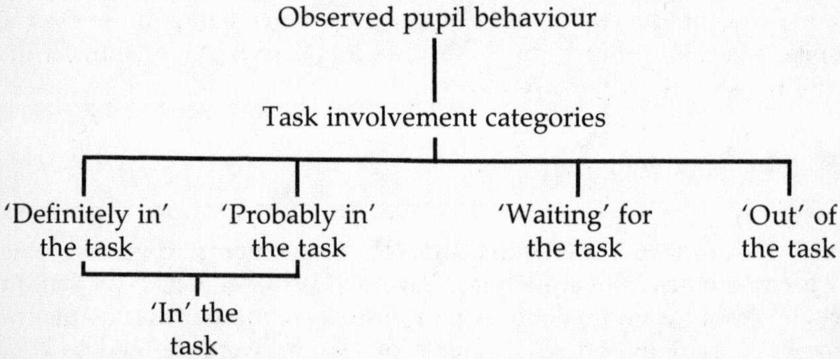

Figure 1 Pupil task involvement categories used to code the behaviour of the pupil in science lessons.

the pupil was engaged in the task; 'waiting' if he completed the teacher's task and there was no further task; 'definitely out' if he clearly showed signs that he was not engaged in the prescribed activity; 'in' is simply the sum of the 'definitely in' and 'probably in' scores.

Six pupils were selected for observation from the videotape (Pupil Tape) following a procedure that assured equal representation from all regions of the room. The behaviour of these pupils was coded by six trained coders whose observer agreement coefficients had a mean of 0.72 (Butler *et al.* 1980). Each of the six pupils was coded continuously throughout the observed lesson.

The reliability (Medley and Mitzel 1963, p. 309) with which task involvement was observed in the 24 classrooms was determined by calculating the intraclass correlation coefficient (Rowley 1976). The reliabilities of the mean task involvement scores for four observations in each classroom ranged from 0.63 ('probably in') to 0.82 ('waiting'). These high values indicate that the levels of task involvement in the 24 classrooms were observed to be reasonably stable across four observations (Butler *et al.* 1980).

Observing teacher behaviour

The overt low inference teacher behaviours which allowed the question 'What is the teacher doing now?' to be answered were categorized. These categories of behaviour are described in Table 2. The behaviours overlap consistently with those described in the Science Laboratory Interaction Categories instrument developed and validated by Kyle *et al.* (1979). An ongoing log was kept, on a time base, of the teacher overt management behaviours. This was achieved by utilizing observer controlled electronic button boxes which recorded each behaviour category as it occurred. The time each teacher spent in these operational modes listed in Table 2 was recorded continuously.

Although pupils were required to operate as members of a small group during laboratory investigations or alone during individual activity tasks, the science teacher's actions are directed either for whole class attention, or for small group attention or for an individual's sole attention.

Thus the first six categories of teacher management behaviours described in Table 2 (Organisation to Sociation) can be applied at three levels. These are teacher-whole group, teacher-small group or teacher-individual pupil. The final three teacher behaviour categories listed in Table 2 (walking, equipping, non-lesson related) are not directly intended for pupil attention.

The data were coded continuously and are representative of the proportion of time pupils were involved in the task (within Individual Ac-

Table 2 Categories of teacher management behaviours

Teacher overt behaviour	*Characteristics*
Organization	Gives special directions about the activity, group structure, location of equipment, etc.
Exposition	A teacher-initiated activity in which information is given to pupils either verbally (e.g., question/answer, statement, dictation) *or* written (e.g., blackboard summary) *or* by demonstration (e.g., techniques in setting up apparatus).
Explanation	A teacher response to an action initiated by a pupil (e.g., question answered, equipment demonstrated).
Order	Makes statement which changes behaviour of pupils or related to standard of behaviour expected.
Waiting	Teacher holding self in readiness while waiting for pupils to complete a task, or listening to students response or surveying whole class group.
Sociation	Discussion which is not relevant to the immediate classroom activity (e.g., results of school sporting events).
Walking	Teacher movement which is deliberate and with the purpose of simply moving from A to B.
Equipping	Getting equipment and materials which are not immediately available for pupil collection (e.g., ice from refrigerator, replacing faulty meter from storeroom supply).
Non-lesson related	Teacher presence is not directly related to classroom activity (e.g., answering inquiry at the door, gazing out of the window).

tivity or Small Group Activity settings) and the corresponding proportion of time teachers were involved in each of the management behaviours respectively. Pearson correlation coefficients were calculated for Pupil Task Involvement versus Teacher Management Behaviour.

Table 3 Correlation coefficients: small group setting. Whole class teacher management behaviour and pupil task involvement

		Teacher Management Behaviour					
		Organization	Explanation	Exposition	Waiting	Order	Sociation
Pupil Task Involvement	Definitely in	0.17	0.08	0.49	0.49	−0.25	—
	Probably in	−0.21	0.01	−0.27	−0.31	0.37	—
	In	0.08	0.10	0.45*	0.43*	−0.09	—
	Waiting	0.32	−0.09	−0.22	−0.27	−0.15	—
	Out	−0.10	−0.08	−0.41*	−0.39*	0.15	—

* $p<0.05$

Table 4 Correlation coefficients: small group setting. Small group teacher management behaviour and pupil task involvement

		Teacher Management Behaviour					
		Organization	Explanation	Exposition	Waiting	Order	Sociation
Pupil Task Involvement	Definitely in	−0.04	−0.47*	0.09	−0.04	−0.30	0.00
	Probably in	−0.25	0.17	−0.13	0.16	0.22	−0.26
	In	0.10	−0.49*	0.04	0.05	−0.24	−0.16
	Waiting	−0.17	−0.05	−0.04	−0.51*	−0.05	−0.08
	Out	−0.04	0.17*	−0.05	−0.23	0.29	0.21

* $p<0.05$

RESULTS

Teacher behaviour during small group laboratory activities and individual activities is presented under three headings:

(i) involvement with class as a whole;
(ii) involvement with a small group or individual within the class;
(iii) no involvement with any pupils.

Table 3 presents the correlation coefficients for the teacher management behaviour (directed for whole class attention) and the pupil task involvement during small group laboratory investigation settings. The significant correlations relate to those teacher-initiated actions of providing information or observed by students as being in a prominent position to monitor the class as a whole. Although the students were organized for small group activity, teacher actions directed for whole class attention maintained a higher degree of task involvement.

Table 4 presents the correlation between teacher management behaviour (directed for a small group's attention) and pupil task involvement during small group laboratory investigation settings. The significant correlations represent those teacher behaviours which are responding to a pupil-initiated inquiry. These teacher behaviours were associated with periods of lower pupil task involvement of the class overall.

Table 5 Correlation coefficients: small group setting. Teacher non-pupil related behaviour and pupil task involvement

		Teacher Behaviour		
		Walking	Equipping	Non-lesson Relate
Pupil Task	Definitely In	−0.17	−0.21	0.32
Involvement	Probably in	0.28	0.09	−0.17
	In	−0.04	−0.21	0.29
	Waiting	0.11	0.54*	−0.15
	Out	0.02	0.02	−0.29

* $p<0.01$

In Table 5, the teacher action of obtaining additional equipment for student use was associated with lower task involvement by group numbers. No other non-pupil related teacher behaviour was related to student task involvement.

Tables 6 to 8 present the correlation coefficients of teacher behaviour and task involvement during individual activity settings. The results in

Table 6 Correlation coefficients: individual activity setting. Whole class teacher management behaviour and pupil task involvement

		Teacher Management Behaviours Observed		
		Organisation	Explanation	Waiting
Pupil Task Involvement	Definitely In	0.22	−0.01	0.55**
	Probably in	−0.19	0.50*	−0.31*
	In	0.18	0.42*	0.51*
	Waiting	0.11	−0.17	0.08
	Out	−0.21	−0.37*	−0.54**

* $p<0.05$
** $p<0.001$

Table 6 relates to actions of the teacher directed at the whole class. The significant results, classified as explanation and waiting behaviour (Table 2), suggest that higher task involvement by pupils is related to those actions by teachers which are perceived by students to have a whole orientation.

These results in Table 6 are supported by the significant results presented in Table 7, where the teacher actions were directed at individual pupils. The consequence was an overall lower class task involvement.

Table 7 Correlation coefficients: individual activity setting. Individual pupil-teacher management behaviour and pupil task involvement

		Teacher Management Behaviours Observed				
		Organisation	Explanation	Exposition	Waiting	Order
Pupil Task Involvement	Definitely In	−0.15	−0.18	−0.21	−0.32*	0.02
	Probably in	−0.23	−0.01	0.19	−0.01	−0.21
	In	−0.31	−0.23	−0.13	−0.46*	−0.09
	Waiting	0.47	−0.19	−0.21	0.28	0.24
	Out	0.17	0.13	0.18	0.39*	0.05

* $p<0.05$

The correlation coefficients for teacher non-pupil related actions during individual activity settings are presented in Table 8. No significant relationships were observed.

Table 8 Correlation coefficient: individual activity setting. Teacher non-pupil related behaviour and pupil task involvement

		Teacher Behaviour Observed	
			Non lesson Related
Pupil Task Involvement	Definitely In	0.20	0.19
	Probably in	−0.23	−0.16
	In	0.07	0.14
	Waiting	0.29	0.26
	Out	−0.17	−0.23

DISCUSSION

The results given in Tables 3 and 4 raise issues concerning the nature of pupil learning in small group laboratory activities. If independent group investigation is to be valued then the involvement of the teacher at the whole class level seems hardly appropriate. Yet these results suggest higher student task involvement in small group activities is associated with a teacher whole class presence.

These findings are consistent with those reviewed by Power (1977). In the laboratory setting teacher talk remains a prevalent activity (30–50%).

Tisher and Power (1973, 1975) studied the relationships between measures of the educational values and preferred practices of teachers and their behaviour in ASEP classrooms. It was found that teachers foster activities in science lessons which are congruent with their beliefs about teaching. These teachers are what Eggleston and Galton (1976) would describe as having an 'actor-manager' style (enquiry-based lessons with transactions initiated by the teacher).

The teacher behaviour described as waiting (Table 2) was also significantly correlated with pupil task involvement. The teacher was seen to be in a position of being able to 'survey' or 'interact' with the class as a whole group. This behaviour could be classed as being similar to Kounin's (1970) description of 'withitness'. Pupils, perceiving that the teacher was in a position to know what was going on around the room and being able to interact with the whole class at that time, responded by undertaking the required task.

The significant correlation in Table 5 is predictable. Teacher time spent during the lesson in servicing the equipment needs of pupils will be associated with pupils' waiting (for the equipment) to complete the task.

In moving to individual activity settings, the results presented in Tables 6 and 7 are congruent with those presented in Tables 3 and 4. Those teacher management behaviours which portray a whole class presence are associated with higher task involvement. When the teacher acted at the individual student level, a lower overall class task involvement was evident.

These sets of results suggest that classes operating within small group or individual activity settings are effectively managed by teachers whose behaviour is more whole class centred. Those teachers who initiate interactions with pupils in these settings and are not 'trapped' by particular groups or individuals into spending a disproportionate amount of time in any one position are associated with classes with a higher pupil task involvement. It would seem that teachers observed in the Science Classroom Management Project believe and practise what Power (1977) reported about previous studies of science classroom interaction.

> A certain amount of structure in science lessons does seem to be essential for many pupils – if one is seeking to foster the meaningful acquisition of content.

These observations raise the question of what is meant by effective learning in small groups or individual activity settings. Effectiveness as measured in this study has been taken to be high levels of pupil task involvement. Those classes who attained high levels of task involvement were associated with teachers who managed the class through whole class surveillance, verbal interaction and by teacher initiated interaction.

Given that the mean level of task involvement for the category 'in the set task' was 82% with a standard deviation of 12, it would be possible to make a value judgement about teacher management practice, pupil task involvement and the nature of the learning setting. If one wished to manage science classrooms during laboratory activity periods in a way which allowed students to initiate more interactions and the teacher less, a lower level of pupil task involvement may be a consequence. This appears to be the trade-off for what self paced student activity curriculum projects must expect. It would be that teachers operating in small group or individual activity settings do not practice what Kounin (1970) would describe as 'overlapping' management techniques, i.e., the ability to interact at the level of pupil activity within the setting and maintain an effective management function with the remainder of the class.

REFERENCES

Anderson, O. R. 1976, *The Experience of Science* (Teachers College Press, New York).

Bloom, B. 1973, *Time and Learning*, Thorndike Address, 81st Annual Convention of the American Psychologist Association, Montreal.

Bloom, B. 1976, *Human Characteristics and School Learning* (McGraw Hill, New York).

Brophy, J. E. 1979a, Teacher behaviour and its effects. *Journal of Educational Psychology*, Vol. 17, pp. 733–750.

Brophy, J. E. 1979b, Advances in teacher research. *Journal of Classroom Interaction*, Vol. 15, pp. 1–7.

Brophy, J. E. and Pitman, J. 1979, *Classroom Management in the Elementary Grades: A Literature Review*. In Duke, O. D. (ed.), Classroom Management, The Twenty-eighth Yearbook of the National Society for the Study of Education, Chicago.

Butler, J. E., Beasley, W. F., Buckley, D. and Endean, L. 1980, Pupil task involvement in secondary science classrooms. *Research in Science Education*, Vol. 10, pp. 93–106.

Eggleston, J. F. and Galton, M. 1976, Curriculum evaluation and interaction analysis. *British Journal of Teacher Education*, Vol. 2, pp. 189–198.

Fraser, B. J. 1976, Classroom climate as predictor and criterion in science education research. *Research in Science Education*, Vol. 6, pp. 109–120.

Good, T. L. 1979, Teacher effectiveness in the elementary school. What we know about it now. *Journal of Teacher Education*, Vol. 30, pp. 52–64.

Harnischfeger, A., and Wiley, D. 1975, *Teaching-learning Processes in Elementary Schools: A Synoptic View*. University of Chicago: Studies of Educative Process, Report No. 9, February 1975.

Kounin, J. S. 1970, *Discipline and Group Management in Classrooms* (Holt, Rinehart and Winston, New York).

Kreitler, H. and Kreitler, S. 1974, The role of the experiment in science education. *Comparative Educational Review*, Vol. 3, pp. 75–88.

Kyle, W. C., Penick, J. E. and Shymansky, J. A. 1979, Assessing and analyzing the performance of students in college science laboratories. *Journal of Research in Science Teaching*, Vol. 16, 545–551.

McGaw, B., Wardrop, J. L. and Bunda, M. A. 1972, Classroom observation schemes: where are the errors? *American Educational Research Journal*, Vol. 9, pp. 13–27.

Medley, D. M. 1979, The effectiveness of teacher. *Research on Teaching: Concepts, Findings and Implications*, P. J. Peterson and H. J. Walberg, eds. (McCutchan, Buckley).

Medley, D. M. and Mitzel, H. E. 1963, Measuring classroom behaviour by systematic observation. N. L. Gage, ed., *Handbook of Research on Teaching* (Rand McNally, Chicago).

Power, C. N. 1977, A critical review of science classroom interaction studies. *Studies in Science Education*, Vol. 4, pp. 1–30.

Romberg, T. A. 1976, *IGE evaluation: Perspectives and Plan*, Working Paper No. 183. Wisconsin Research and Development Center, Madison W1.

Rowley, G. L. 1976, The reliability of observational measures. *American Educational Research Journal*, Vol. 13, pp. 15–59.

Tisher, R. 1981, *Teaching Strategies: a Study of Activities which Facilitate Learning in Science and Social Science Lessons where Self-paced Curricula are Used*. Final report, Education Research and Development Committee, Monash University.

Tisher, R. and Power, C. M. 1973, *The Effects of Teaching Strategies in Miniteaching and Microteaching Situations where Australian Science Education Projects Materials are used*. Report of AACRDE Project, University of Queensland.

Tisher, R. P. and Power, C. N. 1975, *The Effects of Classroom Activities, Pupils' Perceptions and Educational Values in Lessons where Self-paced Curricula are Used*. Report to AACRDE, Monash University.

Tisher, R. P. and Power, C. N. 1975b, A study of the effects of teaching strategies in ASEP classrooms. *Australian Journal of Education*, Vol. 19, pp. 127–145.

29 Personality and attitudes to science

• J. Head

The strong interest in science generally evident in boys aged eleven and twelve declines drastically during the next few years. This decline is usually discussed solely in terms of the content of science curricula. Head suggests that it may be explicable in terms of changes in the learners as they mature through adolescence. He illustrates his thesis by referring to two issues: what constructs adolescents hold about the world and themselves; how adolescents respond to challenges to current beliefs. He goes on to suggest changes in the way science is taught, which take account of what is known about the psychology of adolescents in relation to these issues.

1 INTRODUCTION: THE MISSING PERSON IN SCIENCE EDUCATION

In the last two decades we have witnessed the expenditure of considerable effort and money on science curriculum development in both countries, eg by the National Science Foundation in the US and the Nuffield Foundation in the UK. Despite such work there is little evidence of a positive effect on the average citizen, as distinct from the minority who opt for a career in science, in either country. Conventional science has a poor image being seen as difficult to study, to be scarcely relevant to the most crucial issues in contemporary society, or to be responsible for pollution, damage to the environment and introducing the threat of nuclear warfare. We might note, too, the growth in 'fringe science' in this era.

What went wrong? The answer lies at several levels, including the political and economic developments in the world in the period, but I want to concentrate on one perspective, that of talking about science education without taking into account the nature of the learners. Too often previous curriculum development was organised by eliciting from eminent professional scientists what they believed to be the key elements of their subject and then welding these together to produce the course. Inadequate attention was given to how actual students learn science in real schools. We would not try to teach the playing of the piano just by watching an eminent concert pianist, in fact we would probably suspect that good performers might not make good teachers, yet that was the basis of much science curriculum development.

We can still see in discussions of science education the ignoring of the person. There is ample evidence in the UK, to take one example, that boys aged 11 or 12 have a strong interest in science but that then drastically declines in the next few years (e.g. Whitfield, 1979). We often find, however, that situation solely being discussed in terms of the content of science curricula without reference to the learners and the fact that they are undergoing adolescence. Maybe that decline of interest can be attributed directly to the change in values as one matures in adolescence.

Similarly, the nature of adolescence is ignored in many discussions about school practical work. Common practice tends to make such work more closed and goal orientated as the learner matures, yet the psychological evidence is that it is only in later adolescence that the learner has the maturity to handle open-ended discovery exercises (Head and Shayer, 1980).

In the past decade or so there have been considerable advances in the study of individual psychology such that we can at the very least direct attention to the important questions and often provide some useful answers.

It might facilitate understanding to think of two issues: what are the constructs the individual learner holds about the world and himself; and how does the learner respond to challenge to his previously held beliefs. In a previous chapter John Gilbert has emphasised the importance of personal constructs and I am sure that we need to understand more fully what students actually think, and that a variety of techniques, including interviews about instances, repertory grids etc are relevant. When talking to students we ought to pay close attention to what they *actually say*, and not just assess their contributions in terms of being correct or wrong. One aspect of these individual belief systems is that of attitudes to science and that is one area, as we shall see in the next section, where the state of the art has now advanced so that we can make clear sense of the variety of evidence. With respect to the second factor, how individuals respond to the need to change their mind, one cannot yet provide such clear explanation but can perhaps detect the nature of the problem.

2 ADOLESCENTS AND SCIENCE

The survey by Head (1979) contains the full details about attitudes and personality related to science education. The evidence can be easily summarised. Attitude studies reveal that boys at the age of 10 or 12 tend to be very keen on science but after that age the interest steadily diminishes right through school and college years. Girls never show a lot of interest in science. A striking feature of the attitude studies is the widespread belief that science is not relevant to everyday life and is not therefore worth studying. Personality studies show that boys who choose science for a career tend to be rather more emotionally reticent, controlled and conservative. Girls who choose science show a totally different set of personality characteristics, being mature and balanced, without the emotional reticence of the boys. However, evidence like this is not usable until explained by a causal model.

Head (1980) has developed such a model which is based on the concept of adolescent ego identity achievement, originally postulated by Erikson, and later operationalised by Marcia (1966, 1976).

Erikson suggested that at different phases of life an individual faces a particular psycho-social problem which needs to be resolved before moving on to the next phase and for adolescents the acquisition of a clear ego-identity is the crucial task. At the beginning of adolescence, the individual is a dependant within the family and the school. By the end of adolescence, he needs to make choices about career, life-style, personal relationships and ideologies. The ego-identity of that person is shaped by these choices.

Marcia has put more detail onto the Erikson model and suggests that in going from the initial ego-diffusion condition to that of having achieved ego-identity, two processes are involved: *crisis* and *commitment*. Crisis in this context describes a period of intensive self-examination in which one's beliefs and values are re-examined. Commitment means that the individual has acquired clear and firm beliefs both about himself and the world. Figure 1 indicates a number of possible routes to ego-identity achievement. A person may undergo crisis and commitment simultaneously and progress by route A. An alternative is to undergo a period of considerable self-doubt and self-examination in which all one's beliefs tend to be very fluid, a period known as moratorium, before acquiring beliefs for oneself and ego-identity is achieved (Route B). A further possibility is that the individual may, at least for a time, hold onto beliefs and values taken without question from others, for example parents, teachers, peers. This condition is known as foreclosure. Eventually these persons might have to face up to a period of crisis, of self-examination, and so achieve ego-identity by route C. However, foreclosure does offer an escape route and an individual might postpone indefinitely any real self-examination by clinging rigidly to his beliefs and values (Route D). We can now make the link between this model of adolescent development and subject choice in schools.

For boys at the foreclosure stage, science is likely to be appealing. The

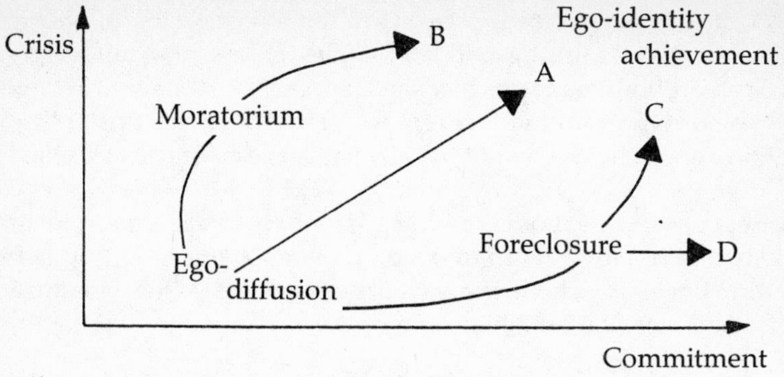

Figure 1

physical sciences in particular, offer a conventional career choice which is likely to win approval from parents, teachers and peers. They will tend to regard the overt expression of emotions, including much such expression in the arts, as being soft and feminine. Science, with its masculine image, makes little emotional demand on an individual and seems to offer clear, precise answers to problems. Opting for science will permit and possibly reinforce emotional reticence.

For a girl at the foreclosure stage the situation is very different. There is evidence that girls tend to be socialized into adult roles more through their potential of becoming a mother and housewife than through their career (Douvan and Adelson 1966). Furthermore, these girls will tend to go into a career with a feminine image, one which already attracts many girls. Consequently, very few girls at the foreclosure stage will enter science unless they receive considerable encouragement and a model to do so from their parents and their school.

Neither boys nor girls at the moratorium stage are likely to be attracted to the science that is usually presented in our schools. They are at a stage when they are likely to be concerned with a variety of complex issues; the meaning of life, the existence of God, ideologies, their emerging sexuality, their future career and life style. Too often science is seen as being purely instrumental with nothing to contribute to these debates. Science, somehow, seems to be scarcely relevant to the most important issues in our life.

A proportion of both boys and girls at ego-identity achievement stage will choose science. In fact, most girls entering science are probably at this stage as they will need some self-examination and sense of commitment to make this unconventional choice. However, only a minority of adolescents will have reached the ego-identity achievement stage at the age when most pupils have to make crucial decisions about subject choice at school.

This model seems to explain our observations. A large number of boys, particularly at the foreclosure stage, are initially attracted to science but there is a drift away throughout later adolescence as they undergo some crisis. The preponderance of boys at the foreclosure stage will yield the rigid, authoritarian attitudes often associated with scientists. The few girls who enter science will not usually show these foreclosure characteristics.

The real use of this model linking personality development to subject choice is that it allows us to make predictions about how pupils might react to changes in school science curriculum and school organization. We can consider two possible changes:

(1) *Giving science a more feminine image*: It is sometimes argued that science textbooks are sexist in showing illustrations of boys, rather than girls, doing practical work in the laboratory, and so forth. What effect would a deliberate attempt to change this image have? It might make it easier for girls at the foreclosure stage to accept science so recruitment might increase. Some of these girls might, however, drift away again when they reach their crisis period. Unless the change in image was immense, boys would probably not be affected, science would still be an obvious, acceptable choice for a boy. Overall there would be some increase in the recruitment of girls, but no qualitative improvement.

(2) *Emphasizing the applications and relevance of science*: To obtain a major qualitative improvement to recruitment in science with more girls and with students possessing imaginative, flexible minds it would be necessary to make science appealing to boys and girls at the moratorium stage.

In that event science must be seen to be relevant to the issues which concern them. The probable implication is that science would need to be presented in the context of the needs of society and individuals. Probably a case-study approach involving the application of science, and the interaction with other disciplines, would be needed. Our knowledge about the girls' concern with personal relationship suggests that the introduction of some elements of the social sciences into the case studies might prove attractive.

3 BLOCKS TO LEARNING SCIENCE

We can envisage many problems in learning science, eg the material may be too cognitively demanding (Shayer and Adey, 1981), and so forth, but I propose to mention only one of the possibilities, that of a resistance to changing one's mind, in other words to undergo learning.

It was reported in John Gilbert's paper that there has been considerable interest in recent years in the personal constructs the students possess. There is ample evidence, e.g. Archenhold *et al*. (1980), that students often hold ideas about science which are in conventional terms incorrect, and that they often tenaciously hang on to these prior beliefs and reject what the teacher tells them.

There are probably reasons for this clinging to former ideas. Sometimes they seem to make more sense in the everyday world, for example common experience might suggest that heavier objects fall faster under gravity than light objects. Another source of difficulty comes from the personality of the student and description of rigidity versus flexibility, conservatism, open versus closed minds, authoritarianism etc can be found in the literature on personality. Surely we should take these factors into account. Changing one's mind is not just a cognitive process. Consideration of the affective aspects hint at the pedagogic techniques which might be useful and possibly this resistance to new ideas is best overcome by getting the learner to articulate his explanatory model and then compare it with that of the teacher. In that way the nature of the change is defined so that the student is not being asked to abandon a former security and enter the unknown, but is being supported to make a step whose characteristics can be seen in advance.

4 A PERSONAL NOTE

In conclusion can I make a plea in considering the application of psychology to science education? It is characteristic of an immature discipline to think that if one explanatory model is correct then all others must be wrong. We have witnessed this in educational psychology in recent years with debates about the correctness of Piaget, and Bruner, and Ausubel, and so forth. Even in the more exact physical sciences we have eventually learnt to live in a pluralist world, eg with the dual nature of light, and surely we must do so in psychology. The real debate is not which theories are right or wrong but when are the insights of a particular theory useful and when are the limits of that usefulness met. Only by debating issues in those terms are we likely to progress.

REFERENCES

Archenhold, W. F. *et al.* (1980), *Cognitive Development Research in Science and Mathematics*. University of Leeds.

Douvan, E. and Adelson, J. (1966), *The Adolescent Experience*. Wiley.

Head, J. (1979), 'Personality and the Pursuit of Science'. *Studies in Science Education*, 6, 23–44.

Head, J. (1980), 'A Model to Link Personality Characteristics to a Preference for Science'. *European Journal of Science Education*, 2, 295–300.

Head, J. and Shayer, M. (1980), 'Loevinger's Ego Development Measures – A New Research Tool?' *British Educational Research Journal*, 6, 21–7.

Head, J. (1982), 'What Can Psychology Contribute to Science Education?' *School Science Review*, Forthcoming.

Marcia, J. E. (1966), 'Development and validation of ego identity status'. *Journal of Personality and Social Psychology*, 3, 551–8.

Marcia, J. E. (1976), *Studies in Ego Identity* (unpublished monograph).

Shayer, M. and Adey, P. (1981), *Towards a Science of Science Teaching*. Heinemann.

Whitfield, R. C. (1979), 'Educational Research and Science Teaching'. *School Science Review*, 60, 411–30.

30

Girls into science and technology: the first two years

● B. Smail, J. Whyte and A. Kelly

The purpose of the Girls into science and technology *(GIST) project is to help secondary schools to develop ways of encouraging more girls to study the physical sciences and crafts. The strategies being tried out are described in this article, and an early assessment of their success is given.*

INTRODUCTION

Girls into Science and Technology (GIST) is an action research project concerned with schoolgirl under-achievement. The project is based at Manchester Polytechnic and is jointly funded by the Equal Opportunities Commission and the Social Science Research Council with additional grants from the Department of Industry and Schools Council. Its purpose is to initiate and support school-based efforts to improve girls' attitudes to physical science and craft subjects, and to encourage more girls to study these subjects when they become optional. At present technical subjects, physics and to a lesser extent chemistry are dominated by boys from fourth year onwards.[1] This means that girls are cut off from most technical jobs by their lack of qualifications, with deleterious consequences both for themselves and for the country as a whole. It also means that many women are technologically illiterate and therefore at a distinct disadvantage in modern society. Schools will be failing girls if they allow this situation to continue. The GIST project is encouraging schools to take practical action to remedy the situation.

By 'action research' we mean that action and evaluation are proceeding simultaneously. GIST is not a traditional research project where the design is thought out at the beginning by the research team, implemented in a carefully controlled way in the schools and finally evaluated. On the contrary many of the interventions will arise from teachers' ideas developed during the course of the project. The research design is fluid and constantly changing. If something does not seem to be working it is dropped. Conversely we are prepared to capitalize on any fortuitously presented opportunity. Many variables are changing at once. This is not a neat experimental situation, but it does approximate to everyday life in a school. We hope to show that, under normal school conditions, teachers can bring about changes in girls' attitudes and achievements. Our main outcome measure is the proportion of girls choosing to study physical science and technology in fourth year in the action schools; if this proportion increases, relative to the control schools, we shall have succeeded.

Ten co-educational comprehensive schools in Greater Manchester are involved in the GIST project. Two of these are control schools, where attitude and achievement tests are being completed but no intervention is taking place. Although not a random sample, the schools serve a wide variety of socio-economic catchment areas. We decided to restrict the project to co-educational comprehensive schools because the majority of schoolchildren in the country are in such schools, and because previous research has shown that the problem of girls' under-achievement in science may be most serious there.[2] Moreover, ten schools is too few to introduce additional variables such as single-sex or selective education. We are mainly interested in the group of children, some 2,000 in all, who entered these ten schools in September 1980. This cohort is being followed from their entry to secondary education at age eleven until the end of their third year in July 1983.

We have chosen to concentrate on these first three years of secondary school for several reasons. At the end of third year, when the children are fourteen, they usually have to choose their subjects for O level or CSE. If they drop physical science or technology at this time it is difficult if not impossible to take it up again later on. Yet previous research has shown that girls' attitudes to science frequently decline sharply over these first three years.[3,4] By intervening at this stage we hope to arrest this decline and encourage more girls to continue physical science and technology into fourth and fifth year.

It is frequently suggested that it is too late to do much by the time the girls get to secondary school, and that we should really be working with parents or primary school teachers. While not denying the importance of these other influences we think this is unduly pessimistic. We do not want to write children off as beyond redemption at the age of eleven! Most pupils now coming into secondary school have had little or no formal science or technology teaching, and this new experience must surely have a strong influence on them. On a practical level we feel that our very limited resources can be most effectively used in working with a group of professional science and craft teachers in secondary schools, many of whom are already aware of and worried about girls' under-achievement in their subject.

The GIST project is funded for four years. The first year was preparatory, and was spent recruiting the schools, making contact with local employers to ensure that they would accept girls in technical jobs, piloting our attitude and achievement tests and recruiting women for the VISTA programme. We have now completed one intervention year in the schools, with two more to go. We have already learned a lot and at this halfway stage in the project it seemed appropriate to share our insight and invite feedback from people not directly involved. Our work so far has been concentrated in three main areas: raising teachers' awareness of girls' under-achievement and helping them to realize that they can do something about it; initial testing of children's attitudes and knowledge in science and technology for comparison with their later performance and choice; and arranging a series of visits to schools by women working in scientific and technological jobs who could act as role models for the girls. These are described in turn.

WORKING WITH TEACHERS

The success or failure of the GIST project will largely depend on the attitude and response of teachers in the action schools. From the beginning we have recognized that intervention strategies are more likely to work if the teachers believe them to be effective and, preferably, have chosen them themselves. We do not expect teachers to solve the problem of girls' under-achievement as seen from the researcher's perspective, but to take up questions of interest to themselves as professionals, with the GIST team in a supportive role.

Ideally, awareness of girls' under-representation in physical science and technical subjects would be a focus of spontaneously occurring discussions among staff in schools. In practice, patterns of sex difference in classroom behaviour, subject choice and academic achievement are frequently accepted as a customary and unquestioned feature of school life. We therefore had to stimulate the sort of discussion which would lead teachers to recognize sex-stereotyping as an educational problem, capable of being tackled in the school context. This is not to say that every teacher would come to view the problem in the same way. But some questioning of the existing patterns was necessary so that the strategies adopted would be in line with teachers' own perceptions and definitions of the problem.

Our approach to potential action schools stressed that all teachers, including the most junior (who frequently carry the main responsibility for teaching younger pupils) should be involved right from the start. Rather than merely negotiating with the head teacher or head of science/crafts, we asked each school we approached if we could talk to the whole department about our plans. At these meetings we presented some information on the extent of girls' under-achievement in science/technology and briefly described the theories put forward to account for the situation. We described some of the strategies which had been suggested to counter this situation, emphasizing that it would be up to the teachers to decide which strategies they implemented if they decided to take part in the project. We then left the staff to discuss our proposals among themselves and let us know over the next week or so whether they wanted to be involved.

In fact none of the schools where we gave this preliminary talk turned us down. All agreed to the next stage, a series of three two-hour workshop meetings where science and craft teachers would meet with the GIST team to discuss the 'problems' of getting girls into science and technology, and develop their own ideas for intervention strategies suitable for their school. The commitment of staff was mixed. In some cases we felt the decision to go ahead had been carried by the obvious enthusiasm of senior staff and that some teachers remained sceptical. It was not always easy to overcome a tendency for GIST to be cast in the role of outside researchers proffering solutions. The sessions were held in school time so as to give staff the opportunity to voice their doubts and discuss their reactions in a relaxed atmosphere. And by meeting on teachers' home ground, we hoped to underline the importance of their own expertise in designing interventions.

Previous work with student teachers and on in-service training courses had convinced us that, as professionals, most teachers are genuinely interested in fostering the development of all their pupils and so resent any suggestion that they treat either sex unfairly. At the same time they are prepared to voice highly stereotyped opinions about the behaviour and abilities of girls and boys. Sex differences are often felt to be natural and unchangeable, in line with their own self-concepts as a man or woman, father or mother, son or daughter. Because of this contradiction between a professional commitment to equality and a personal belief in the natural inequality of the sexes, the workshops had two main elements. We provided a good deal of information about sex differences in the classroom, and the research that has been done into the origins of these differences. We also used a number of games and exercises designed to make people conscious of their own sex-stereotypes and of the way social roles and expectations operate in the classroom. The final session was devoted to detailed planning of interventions for that particular school.

In general this combination worked quite well, but there were occasional problems. Some schools found it difficult to get all the relevant members of staff together and we were faced with a different group of teachers at each meeting. In one or two cases there have been such large staff changes that few if any of the teachers who attended the workshops are still teaching lower school science. Some groups were impatient with the 'airy-fairy' theorizing and de-stereotyping exercises and wanted to get on to concrete proposals. It was noticeable that science and technical staff tended to value research-based factual knowledge highly and were frequently suspicious of psychological or sociological theories about behaviour. However, when pastoral staff, who often taught English or Humanities, were present, their response to 'de-stereotyping' discussions was much more enthusiastic. We also had the impression that younger female science teachers were less likely to dismiss personal experience as irrelevant than older male scientists. There was some concern that boys might be disadvantaged by our interventions and we found it important to stress that all we wanted was a fair distribution of examples, teaching strategies, role models, etc. between the sexes, rather than the present overemphasis on boys.

As a follow-up to the workshops, broader staff meetings were held in action schools with representatives from all departments. The point to be made here was that sex-role stereotyping pervades all aspects of life, and that notions such as 'science is for boys' or 'girls can't be engineers' are not exclusively picked up in science and craft departments. Expressions of support for what we were saying about informal learning or the 'hidden curriculum' then helped to create an atmosphere in the school of general belief in the value of trying to change children's sex-typed attitudes and choices. In such an atmosphere, science and craft teachers can receive constant support for their efforts from staff with other subject backgrounds. Moreover, since the large staff meetings were arranged with the help of the schools' senior management they signify that the idea of positive intervention has received an official seal of approval.

The extent to which schools have implemented the interventions we suggested varies considerably. Some teachers have realized the importance of classroom interactions and have begun to make small but significant changes in their classroom management techniques. We are now trying to establish a scheme whereby teachers can monitor interactions in their own and others' classrooms. Other schools have merely accepted the offer of VISTA visits and agreed to administer attitude and achievement tests. Teachers' willingness to commit themselves further seems to depend to some extent, on how much time we can spend with them. With a small research team (one full-time and two part-time researchers) special efforts have to be made to visit schools frequently enough for a relationship of mutual trust to develop. In the remaining two years of the project we will continue to work closely with teachers and we hope to reach the stage where every school is using a unique set of strategies developed by teachers for the children and environment they know, which is capable of running quite independently of GIST.

ATTITUDE AND ACHIEVEMENT TESTING

Our major presence in the schools during the pupils' first term was as piles of questionnaires and brown envelopes. In the preparatory year we had developed a number of tests designed to measure the children's attitudes towards science and technology, their preliminary knowledge of these subjects, and their attitudes towards sex roles. Since most of these tests had no right or wrong answers they were generally enjoyed by the children. The results will be used to assess the effectiveness of the interventions. We intend to test the children again in their third year and compare the change in attitudes and achievements in control and action schools. We also hope to be able to see which groups of girls have responded best to the interventions – for example, girls with positive initial attitudes to science or weak sex-stereotypes might be more receptive than girls who are less well motivated initially or more strongly stereotyped.

The tests are also an intervention strategy in their own right. We suggested to the action schools (but not the control schools) that they might discuss each test with the children after they had completed the schedules. In practice this was seldom done. Now that the data have been analysed we are taking the results back to the schools and again suggesting that they be discussed with the children concerned. It is generally easiest to do this in English or Social Studies classes where sex-stereotyping can be examined. But pupils' attitudes to science and crafts, and the reasons for any sex differences found, can also form the basis of a discussion. We have prepared a booklet explaining what we have found and the possible implications of these results, which we are distributing to all teachers involved in the project. And we are visiting each action school to explain what was found in that particular institution (although to maintain confidentiality we are not giving teachers any information on individual pupils).

During the first week of the first term the children were given two science tests, to assess the knowledge and attitudes which they brought with them to the secondary school. The differences between the sexes in science knowledge were very small (see Figure 1). Boys did slightly better than girls on the physics items, particularly when they were written in multiple choice form, but other sex differences were negligible. The most striking differentiation came on the essay part of the test, where children had a choice of subjects to write about. Most of the boys chose 'how cars

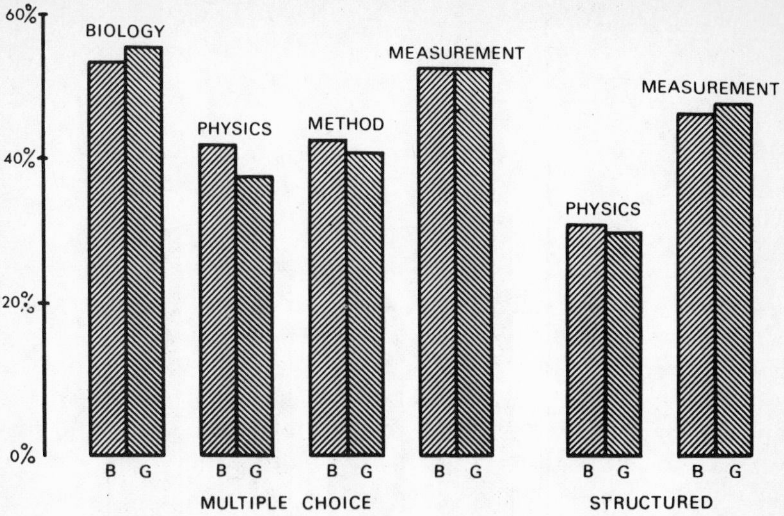

Figure 1 Boys' and girls' mean scores on different parts of the Science Knowledge test

work' or 'rockets and space travel', but these topics were very unpopular with the girls. Girls predominantly chose 'the human body', 'birds near my home,' 'seeds', or 'pond life'.

This suggests that sex differences in interests among 11–12-year-olds are much stronger than sex differences in knowledge, and this was borne out by the attitude scales. One of these asked the children to indicate which scientific topics they would like to learn more about and which they were not interested in. Most of the pupils were interested in most bits of science, but there were quite marked sex differences (see Figure 2). Boys were much more interested than girls in learning about physical science, and girls were much more interested than boys in learning about animals and plants. The most popular topic overall was human biology, followed by 'spectacular' or 'TV' science. We are therefore suggesting to schools that one way to interest both girls and boys in physical science might be to approach it through its links with the human body (e.g. forces via muscles, light via eyes, air pressure via lungs), so emphasizing its relevance to ourselves. However, our results suggest that attempts to interest girls in physics via its domestic applications would not be so successful. Neither girls nor boys were very enthusiastic about learning 'how a vacuum cleaner works' and girls were even less interested than boys!

It is generally assumed that boys have greater experience in technical matters outside school than do girls, but this has seldom been investigated. However, one of our tests asked children about the sort of activi-

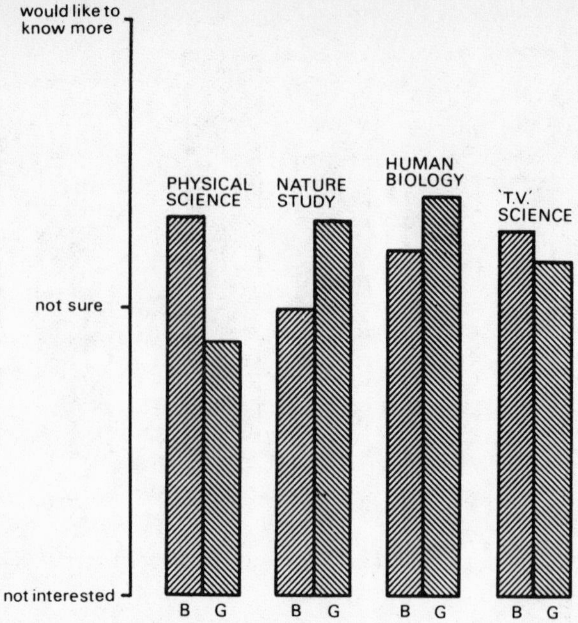

Figure 2 Boys' and girls' mean scores on different parts of the Science Curiosity test

ties they participated in outside school which might develop skills and knowledge relevant to science and technology. As expected we found that boys had a lot more experience of tinkering activities – using tools, taking things apart and mending them, playing with constructional toys – and girls had a lot more biological experience of things like planting seeds, watching birds and collecting flowers.

The importance of tinkering experience, particularly for technical subjects, is evident from the result of two other cognitive tests. There was a mechanical reasoning test, with questions on gears, pulleys, screws, etc. And a spatial test involving the ability to visualize and mentally manipulate objects in three dimensions. On both of these boys did better than girls. In this context a natural experiment in one of the schools is interesting. Because of the way the craft 'circus' in the first year was organized there, some children spent twelve weeks on technical crafts while others spent the same twelve weeks on domestic crafts. Both groups completed the spatial and mechanical tests before and after these twelve-week periods. The groups that had been doing technical crafts for the intervening weeks improved their scores on the spatial test significantly more than the group which had been doing domestic crafts. This suggests that boys' greater prior experience in technical matters outside school may have caused their better initial scores on this test.

Another of our tests looked at the image of science and scientists held by these pupils. Overall both girls and boys had quite favourable impressions. They thought the social effects of science were mainly good, that scientists were quite normal people and that they themselves would enjoy learning science. But boys were far more likely than girls to see science as a masculine subject. Girls mostly disagreed with statements such as 'girls who want to do science are a bit peculiar' or 'girls don't need to know about electricity and light', but boys were much more likely to agree or be unsure. Boys who think like this probably transmit their attitudes to the girls and make them feel out of place in the science laboratory. So it is as important to work with boys in changing the masculine image of science as it is to work with girls.

Our tests included several measures of sex-typing, and they all showed much the same thing. Boys are more strongly sex-typed than girls at age eleven. They have more definite ideas about what boys should do and what girls should do. In general the pressures on boys seem to be stronger than those on girls – it is worse for a boy to be a sissy than for a girl to be a tomboy – and the strongest disapproval was reserved for feminine behaviour in boys. This again emphasizes the importance of working with boys to relax their stereotypes rather than concentrating all our efforts on girls.

We also examined the children's attitudes to school, their home background and their parents' attitudes. Although these questionnaires have not yet been fully analysed, they have revealed some interesting trends. More girls than boys in first year named maths as their favourite subject, and nearly as many girls as boys named science. However boys were much more likely than girls to give technical crafts. Girls were more enthusiastic about school than boys were and seemed to be quite confident of their own abilities. Both girls and boys tended to value their own sex and rather despise the opposite sex. Parents were just as ambitious for their daughters and their sons to do well in school and equally keen for all their children to study science (including physics). Contrary to what some teachers believe, the vast majority of parents were happy with mixed craft 'taster' courses. But they were not so sure about children pursuing non-traditional craft options after third year and seemed to expect very different things of their daughters and sons out of school. Parents had quite traditional occupational aspirations for their children, and they expected girls to do a lot more housework than boys.

THE VISTA PROGRAMME

The chief intervention strategy in the first year was the VISTA programme, a series of visits to schools by women working as scientists or technologists. The aim of the visits was to provide the children with role models of women working in 'masculine' occupations who enjoyed their work and were successful at it. Ideally they should have an attractive and vivacious personality and be leading active personal and family lives. In this way we hoped to counter the image of the woman scientist as an oddity and reassure the girls that studying science did not mean abandoning all their existing dreams of adult life. We also wanted to de-stereotype the remote impersonal image of science and technology by stressing the links between the work the VISTA visitors were doing and what the children were learning in class.

Women were recruited for the programme by advertisements in the national press, visits to local industry, the 'Women in Manual Trades' group and personal contacts. Some 90–100 volunteers were obtained and they were invited to an afternoon briefing session in groups of 8–10. The letter of invitation asked each woman to think about some aspect of her work which could be linked to the science and crafts curriculum in the lower secondary school and to prepare a talk lasting a few minutes to perform at the meeting. An American project similar to VISTA found that girls were particularly interested in ways of combining paid work with family life, but were often shy about discussing this with boys present[5] so we encouraged the women to mention this in their talks.

About fifty women attended briefing meetings. During the afternoon we tried to give the women information about the GIST project, its progress so far, and the aims of the VISTA intervention. The majority of women responded warmly and gave accounts of their personal experience at this stage. Next we tried to give the women a picture of the 11-year-olds they would be talking to in terms of their interests, language level and their image of science and scientists. In doing this we used some essays written by 11-year-olds in the GIST pilot study, on the theme of an interview with a famous woman scientist. The essays were effective in revealing both the stereotyped ideas of the children about women scientists and the vast difference between the language level of a typical first year and that of an adult as evidenced by the handwriting, spelling, grammar and sentence construction of the essays. In one briefing we used a videotaped classroom discussion on sex stereotyping with a mixed class of 11-year-olds but this was not so successful.

Each woman was then invited to give a short extract from her talk in front of the group and a television camera. It was explained that this micro-teaching was a confidence-building technique often used in teacher training. Each talk was replayed and discussed, pointing out as sensitively as we could, the good things to build on. The women were generally sufficiently aware to pick out for themselves the parts which would not work with the 11-year-olds we had described. The final stage of the briefing was to discuss with each woman the parts of her job we thought would be particularly interesting to children and to think of ways to link the talks with topics on the science and crafts syllabus. Each woman left with a number of ideas which could be developed and promised to send us a short paragraph about her revised talk. Some 25–30 paragraphs were received.

In January 1981 these women began visiting schools. Visits are arranged to fit in with the work the children are doing in class and take place in normal science or craft lessons. Over thirty visits have been arranged so far, and each woman has seen three or four first-year classes for half an hour each in the course of a morning or afternoon. They are usually accompanied by a member of the GIST team so that we can provide the women with some feedback on how their talk went and how it could be improved.

A few examples will illustrate the type of topics that have been covered and the links with the pupils' normal school work. When children are working on forces we have a lecturer in anatomy who can talk about the forces in the human arm. When they are learning about acids and alkalis there is a food technologist who brings cakes made from cake mixes and incorrectly balanced baking powder to show the use of pH measurements in the food industry. Learning to use a thermometer is linked to a gas engineer who talks about the different ways of measuring temperature she uses in her work, including a demonstration of heat-sensitive crayons. In craft there is a supervisor in a small brass-foundry who brings rough castings of brass 'tortoise' doorstops and other decorative articles and demonstrates the finishing processes used.

The response to the talks by the teachers and children has been quite positive. Some teachers complain that, despite our efforts, the language used by the women is still too difficult. Most of the women have improved their performance in this respect after meeting their first class. The impact of the talks on the children seems to increase as they become familiar with the situation. Some classes have had visits by three different women and during the third session questions showed that the children were understanding the underlying purpose and implications of the visits, e.g. children asked about the attitudes of male colleagues and family members. In some groups the boys have dominated the questioning and we have had to coach the women in strategies for getting girls to participate too. The number of each sex in the group and whether a girl or boy asks the first question seem to have an effect on the girls in the group. The level of interest and participation of the teacher also seems to have an effect. The teacher can often put into words something which she knows would interest or puzzle the children and this can produce follow-up questions from the class which they may have been reluctant to voice without the teacher's support. Our main problem has been recruiting women technicians and crafts-people doing jobs requiring only CSE or O-level qualifications. Not only are there fewer women working in trades than in professional jobs, but they are less likely to be able to get time off with pay to take part in the VISTA programme, and less likely to have the verbal skills and self-confidence to face a school class.

THE NEXT TWO YEARS

Work with teachers, analysis of the test results and the VISTA programme will all continue over the next two years. In addition we hope to develop interventions in three other main areas: crafts, curriculum and careers.

So far most of our work has been in science. This is largely due to our own backgrounds in science teaching and ignorance of craft and technology. However we have now appointed a former head of department in craft, design technology to work with craft departments. His main task will be to develop CDT syllabuses which appeal to both sexes equally to replace traditional skills-based education in woodwork and metalwork which has little attraction for girls.

We have always seen curriculum development as one of our major concerns. Several pieces of research have shown the way in which science textbooks are biased towards boys in terms in their illustrations and examples.[6] However, we believe the problem goes deeper than this. The way that science is approached as an abstract, ahistorical, impersonal subject may fit boys' interests better than girls'. Beginning with electricity, a topic which often seems particularly unattractive to girls, we want to try to develop some alternative approaches. We have already set up a teachers' group to work on this, in cooperation with the Girls and Physical Science group of the Association for Science Education. But it is difficult for practising teachers to find time to work out materials in detail. So far we have only been able to respond to teachers' requests for materials on a particular topic but in future we hope to be able to devote more time to systematic curriculum development.

As the pupils enter third year and approach their option choices, careers advice will become increasingly important. It has already been shown that girls can be encouraged to study physics if its career implications are clearly spelt out.[7,8] We hope to develop this approach to include technical subjects. In addition to film and tape-slide shows, the VISTA visits will be slanted more towards careers advice and less towards lesson content in third year. We also hope to arrange individual counselling of girls who have shown scientific or technical aptitude, and consultations with their parents.

This list of interventions is by no means exhaustive. We are cooperating with the Equal Opportunities Commission to produce a series of posters about women's achievements in science and we have developed some worksheets on this topic. We arrange occasional conferences with outside speakers to provide an intellectual stimulus for the project. Several teachers are planning to implement 'girls only' clubs in science or technology where girls can gain confidence in handling tools away from any possible ridicule from the boys. This can be seen as compensating for boys' greater experience with tinkering activities outside school. And the list is not definitive. Ideas are coming forward all the time and the next two years may turn out quite differently from the way we currently envisage them.

REFERENCES

1. Kelly, A., 'Girls and science education: is there a problem', in Kelly, A. (ed.), *The Missing Half* (Manchester University Press, 1981).
2. Harding, J., 'Sex differences in science examinations', in Kelly, A. (ed.), *The Missing Half* (Manchester University Press, 1981).
3. Brown, S. A. and T. N. Davies, 'The development of an "attitude to science" scale for 2–14 year olds', *Scottish Educational Studies*, 1973, Vol. 5, 85.
4. Goodwin, A. J., B. Hardiman and V. Rees, 'An investigation of the attitudes to school, science and science lessons of 10–13 year old children', *Mimeo* (Manchester Polytechnic, 1981).
5. Weiss, Iris, Carol Pace and Larry E. Conaway, 'The Visiting Woman Scientists Pilot Program 1978', *Highlights Report*, Research Triangle Institute, North Carolina, USA.
6. e.g. Walford, Geoffrey, 'Sex bias in physics textbooks', *S.S.R.*, 1980, 219, **62**, 220–7.
7. Hearn, Michael, 'Girls for physical science: a school based strategy for encouraging girls to opt for the physical sciences', *Education in Science*, April 1979, 14–16.
8. Patterson, Angela F., 'You want physics for everything', *Education in Science*, April 1980, 14–15.

VI REVIEW AND EVALUATION: SCIENCE IN SCHOOLS

The simple scale of science activity in secondary schools means that assessing its organization and the process of science teaching sets formidable tasks. Science has a relatively assured position in any core curriculum. Further, although science teaching has changed radically (as earlier articles make clear) its image, even within the profession, is as a constant and untroubled area of knowledge for student study. Science departments tend to have the collective loyalty of a substantial proportion of the whole school staff who, given the nature of the activity, require a major share of school resources. For these reasons it may be felt necessary to use different approaches to the review of school science as compared to other types of activity — particularly where the curriculum is highly differentiated. Even *within* science teaching, the faculty or department is, in effect, a 'holding company' for teaching which is very diverse in content and pedagogy. The extent to which those examining science activity need to reformulate accepted review procedures depends on the degree to which science is integrated across the full curriculum, the scale of the science department and the utilization of science resources.

The two articles in this section offer a contrast in forms of evaluation. Prickett provides a self-evaluation exercise, appropriate particularly to heads of departments. It lays stress on aspects of communication, the gathering of opinions and views, and the dissemination of information and decisions. Brown and McIntyre assess the experiences of schools in implementing innovations. Their review of these processes highlights the significance of teacher-attitudes towards 'organizational' and 'pedagogical' features of the curriculum change envisaged.

31 Departmental self-evaluation in practice

● G. J. Prickett

Prickett describes the use made of a published scheme for self-evaluation in secondary school science departments. The author discusses the unforeseen problems which the use of this scheme revealed, and the actions proposed in order to overcome them.

THE SCHOOL AND THE DEPARTMENT

Wilsthorpe Comprehensive School is an eight-form entry, 11 to 18 comprehensive school. The science department has nine modern laboratories, five preparation rooms and a lecture theatre, all situated in a centralized area. There are ten full-time teaching staff and two laboratory technicians. The department offers physics, chemistry and biology to O and A level (plus one electronics option at A level) and physics, chemistry, biology, engineering science and general science to CSE level. A form of Nuffield Combined Science is taught in years one and two and a physical/biological science course in year three.

THE SELF EVALUATION EXERCISE

I started the exercise by reading through the whole of the self-evaluation guide in the book, in an attempt to establish which areas of the science department required attention, and produced the following list of things to be done or questions to be answered. I have grouped the points under the headings laid out in the guide.

1 Communications

(a) Are communications within the department satisfactory? A questionnaire could be used to establish staff opinion.

(b) Do I know my department well enough? An interview with each member of staff may help.
(c) Produce a science department booklet containing aims, objectives, job specifications, policy on use of language, diagrams, apparatus, safety, breakages, discipline, marking, assessment and possibly other topics. (Most of these items already exist separately.)

2 Organization and management
(a) The technicians were sometimes unsure when dealing with physics equipment. Could some form of in-service training help?
(b) How can breakages be reduced?
(c) Is the allocation of money to each sub-department fair, since it is, at present, unrelated to the number of pupils taking that subject.
(d) The creation of a central science resource bank (reference books, video cassettes, computer tape or cassettes) seems like a good idea.

3 Curriculum (General)
(a) Produce an overall curriculum flow diagram and look for important areas of omission, overlap or repetition within the science department. (Also possibly consult other departments.)

4 Curriculum (specific)
(a) A more detailed syllabus/scheme of work is required for years 1 and 2. Worksheets need reviewing. What about: sets of books, 'Insight to Science' materials, remedial texts, library books, kits for extension work for pupils, trips out, films?
(b) Project work by pupils in the general science course requires more rigid structuring to make it more educationally beneficial. Some resources for this work are inadequate.
(c) Check the departmental situation regarding schemes of work.
(d) The department needs more resource 'packages' of a general scientific nature which can be used in the event of staff absence or as extension work for the pupils.
(e) Staff teaching the remedial pupils in the department are non-specialists and tend to 'do their own thing'. Special guidance, texts or syllabuses are desirable.

5 Liaison outside the Department
(a) Could some of the problems encountered with the mathematical aspects of science be reduced by further negotiation with the mathematics department?
(b) No member of the science department has ever visited any of our feeder junior schools.

COMMUNICATIONS WITHIN THE SCIENCE DEPARTMENT

I decided finally to choose communications for the initial self-evaluation exercise because it is an aspect which affects all other aspects of the department and because, although I thought communications were adequate, there had been odd signs in the past that all was not well – in a large department there are bound to be problems with communications at times.

The present situation within the science department

All the department (teachers and laboratory technicians), with the exception of people on duty or with the occasional other commitment, meet for refreshments every morning break (15 minutes) in the main science preparation room. The main lines of communication within the department are by word of mouth or by notices placed on the departmental notice-board situated in the main prep room. Heads of department and the technicians have pigeon-holes in the main prep room which are labelled Resources Directory, Safety File, Head of Science, Laboratory Technicians, Physics, Chemistry, Biology. There is also a wall diary and two notice-boards.

Means of disseminating information

1 By word of mouth to the group as a whole or to individuals; announcements at break or at departmental meetings.
2 Notices on the day notice-board in the main prep room.
3 Memos from head(s) of department, with a staff tick list.
4 Duplicated handouts for each member of the department.
5 Messages in pigeon-holes.
6 Other notice-board in prep room.

Types of information to be communicated within the department (outside of departmental meetings)

1 Description of departmental organization, job specifications, aims, objectives, syllabuses, schemes of work, policy documents.
2 Day-to-day information concerning the general running of the school. (The head of science collects a copy of a 'day sheet' every break from main school and displays it on the science department notice-board. He also clears the departmental pigeon-hole and checks on the substitution list.)

3 Notices specific to the science department (meetings, appointments, dates, progress reports, information on all aspects) are displayed on the main science notice-board and filed after use.
4 Substitution timetable – in main staff room.
5 Dates – year planner in main prep room.
6 Course details, meetings.
7 Science newsletter, bulletins, circulars.
8 Additions to the resource centre/library texts in science.
9 Bookings for science lecture theatre.
10 Science department timetable.
11 Safety file.
12 Resources directory.
13 Ordering of apparatus.
14 Location of apparatus and resources
15 Minutes of meetings
16 Correspondence
17 Ideas.

Departmental meetings

Full departmental meetings are held on average about once a term with individual sub-departments or sections of the science department meeting occasionally throughout the year. The full departmental meetings are always arranged on the same day of the week at the same time in the same place. The members of the department are asked at the beginning of the year to leave Friday clear of other commitments at lunchtime, e.g. duties or clubs.

There is always a notice in the main prep room inviting items for a meeting agenda. When the agenda is sufficient to fill the time available a meeting is called. The agenda is usually filled by items from the Head of Science. The agenda is printed and a week's notice given of the meeting. The meetings are chaired by the Head of Science. Minutes are recorded by him and filed. The minutes are not circulated or published but are available for departmental reference. The minutes are sometimes shown to the Headmaster. The Headmaster, Deputy Head and Director of Studies have been invited when appropriate. Papers are sometimes circulated for discussion before meetings.

Some problems of communication which had arisen

1 Agenda is usually filled by the Head of Science.
2 Some staff have not read items on a notice-board, although they have been published for several days.

3 Decisions made at departmental meetings have been forgotten or not implemented by certain staff.
4 Department as a whole has not met very often in a formal situation. Much discussion has taken place in an informal way, but were all relevant staff present?
5 Some schemes of work for some courses are lacking in clarity and direction.

ACTION

Departmental survey

A questionnaire on communications within the science department was produced and circulated, and nine staff and two technicians responded. The general conclusions which could be drawn from the survey were:

1 Many staff thought communications were poor and that the department as a whole, and certain sections of the department, did not meet often enough.
2 Lunchtime meetings were preferred but the preferred days were spread throughout the week, only two preferring Friday.
3 The meetings were usually of sufficient length.
4 Most of the department did not want meetings on a regular basis.
5 Several staff felt that they had not been informed of an important issue at times and several thought that they could have been informed of an issue earlier.

There were very few problems with information regarding INSET courses. The results of the questionnaire were published on the science department notice-board.

Departmental meeting to discuss the implications of the survey

A tick list was circulated to the whole department to establish when, within the next fortnight, staff would be available for a meeting to discuss the implications of the survey. A meeting of nine science staff and both technicians was held one lunchtime. Everyone present was invited, in turn, to state what they thought the problems were, a simple organization development technique. A summary of the points made is as follows:

1 Because of the geography of the department, the physics department staff are remote from the rest of the department and therefore less available for discussion than others.

2 There is a lack of structure and direction for the lower school syllabuses. More detailed schemes of work are necessary. Some worksheets are missing, some need updating. Good worksheets should be located in the main science prep room and individual copies circulated to staff. Regular communications between staff teaching the same class is absolutely essential.
3 There are problems of repetition of work for pupils who are transferred from one group to another. Some overlap occurs between syllabuses anyway.
4 Staff would prefer to know in advance, if possible, if any member of the science department is going to be absent.
5 Work set by absent staff often lacks structure. It is necessary to structure the existing 'packages' e.g. 'Safety', 'Milk', 'Teeth', 'Energy' to clarify what pupils are expected to do. More 'packages' would be useful.

It was agreed to hold a further meeting in the near future in order to attempt to sort out the problems in the lower school. The minutes of the first meeting were published on the science notice-board and staff invited to add or comment.

Follow-up action

Blank papers were circulated to the department inviting them to make suggestions for (a) improving communications within the science department and (b) making any necessary changes in the organization of the lower school science courses. The responses from the staff regarding (a) (which is the subject of this self-evaluation exercise) were naturally a repetition of much of what was said in the meeting and they are not included here.

The proposed actions to be taken in order to attempt to resolve the communication problems are as follows.

1 The whole department is to be invited to meet more often.
2 Meetings are to be held in the near future to try to sort out the problems in the lower school science courses.
3 The date/time of meetings is in future going to be decided by consulting the departmental staff as to their availability, as opposed to the same day/time procedure adopted in the past.
4 The notice-board in the main prep room is to be increased in size and split into more definite areas of communication.
5 The appropriate people are to be asked to produce more detailed schemes of work for the lower school science courses.

6 Staff absence (if known in advance) is to be advertised.
7 A departmental booklet containing the items listed earlier in this report is to be produced.
8 The Head of Science is to attempt to improve contact with the members of the biology and chemistry sub-departments by attempting to contact them informally on a more regular basis – as a matter of policy.
9 The Head of Science is to interview each member of the science department in order to establish opinion, attitudes, problems, etc.
10 Science department minutes are to be published.

32 Influences upon teachers' attitudes to different types of innovation: a study of Scottish integrated science

● S. Brown and D. McIntyre

It is generally recognized that successful innovation depends substantially on teacher attitudes towards proposed curricular alterations. Brown and McIntyre propose that the relationship between views and implementation relate directly to the nature of the innovation itself. They characterize innovation as either 'organizational' or 'pedagogical', drawing upon typifications provided by teachers. They made a survey of science teachers in eight Scottish secondary schools, who were introducing a new integrated science scheme. Their results suggest that whether innovations, not dependent on collegial action, are implemented depends upon the individual teacher's attitudes and beliefs. Yet, for organizational innovation, dependent on collective changes, teacher attitudes and responses are significantly related to the views of heads of departments.

INTRODUCTION

Over the last few years numerous studies have recorded the meager level at which the intentions of curriculum developers have been reflected in classroom implementation of innovations (see, e.g., reviews of such work by Fullan, 1972, and Fullan and Pomfret, 1977). It is clear that teachers exert considerable power over such implementation but that this power has been, up until now, very largely of a negative kind. Teachers can and do effectively prevent the introduction of innovations which they see as impracticable or to which they are not committed.

More recently, there has been increased emphasis on analysis of the features of innovations that determine whether teachers see them as 'practical' and desirable (e.g., Doyle and Ponder, 1977; Brown and McIntyre, 1978). However, although a fair amount has been learned about the general sorts of things that present barriers to innovations and put limitations on their success, our understanding of the crucial factors that influence teachers' views of the suggestions for change is at a very primitive level.

In this article, we assume, with Clark and Yinger (1977), that 'what teachers do is affected by what they think,' and that teachers' attitudes toward an innovation are an important factor in its implementation. Furthermore, we assume that in trying to conceptualize the attitude changes that arise from the influence of potentially relevant social groups and cognitions, the theories of social psychology and, in particular, those of cognitive consistency are likely to be helpful. We are not attempting, within the confines of this article, to conceptualize the curriculum problems faced by teachers, nor shall we explore the relationships between attitudes and teaching behaviors (see, e.g., Kremer, 1978; Kremer and Ben Peretz, 1980). We shall suggest, however, that the nature of the relationship between the attitudes and the implementation will depend on the nature of the innovation itself. The attitudes of science teachers to four different innovations and the influences on those attitudes of the school and of the views of other teachers within the same department (and in particular those of the head of the department) will be explored. We shall argue that the patterns of attitudes that emerge reflect a distinction that can be made between those innovations that call for changes to be made in the way that the teaching is *organized* and those that relate to some new feature in the *pedagogy*; and that this distinction is related to the conceptual and procedural clarity with which innovations are presented, to the amount of control that science departments and school administrators have over the implementation of innovations, and to the aspects of their work for which teachers are accountable to their departments and to the wider public.

The four innovations that we studied were aspects of the Scottish Integrated Science scheme that is intended for the first two years of secondary school and was published in *Curriculum Paper 7* (Scottish Education Department, 1969). This scheme was developed by a central Working Party of science teachers, inspectors, and local authority advisers over a period of five years. In addition to *Curriculum Paper 7*, the Working Party produced a set of worksheets (Heinemann, 1969, 1974). In the centralized education system of Scotland there is no legal requirement for schools to adopt particular courses but the public examinations of the Scottish Certificate of Education ensure a high degree of uniformity among schools in the later years of secondary education. The pressure of national examinations is less urgent in the early years but the system is such that the official publication by the Scottish Education department of a detailed course will ensure widespread adoption in schools. Within 18 months of the publication of *Curriculum Paper 7* over 80% of Scottish secondary schools were following the Integrated Science Scheme with their first- and second-year pupils (aged 12-14 years) and this level has been sustained over the last decade.

Projects carried out by teams of professional curriculum developers are rarely promoted by the Scottish Education Department, and ideas of producing finalized 'curriculum packages' are normally eschewed. Innovatory schemes, therefore, are seldom tightly defined and are subject to continual development. Integrated science has been no exception and new Working Parties were formed during the 1970s to produce new materials (Scottish Central Committee on Science, 1977a, 1977b). It is in this evolving context (not necessarily accompanied by corresponding evolution in the patterns of science teaching) that we have been carrying out research on the factors that influence the effectiveness of innovations. That research has been directed toward four innovations intended by the original Working Party: (1) the integration of previously separate subjects, (2) grouping pupils in mixed-ability classes and taking account of differences among them, (3) new teaching methods (guided discovery), and (4) teaching toward specific objectives as laid down for the course.

Our research approach has been multifaceted and has included studies of teacher's commentaries on their own teaching, of pupils' attainments and attitudes, of teachers' attitudes and understandings, of systematic classroom observation, and of the effects of subject departments on implementation. Within the last of these strands of our own work (see Brown, McIntyre, and Impey, 1979), we explored the relationships among the attitudes to innovations of individual teachers and those of the colleagues. It is these findings that we use in this article to develop our theoretical ideas about how teachers' attitudes are influenced by those with whom they work.

TYPES OF INNOVATIONS

It is possible to categorize innovations in a wide variety of ways. This arises, in part, from the multiple ramifications and implications of most innovations, (e.g., changes in teaching aims, social practices, materials, and relationships among individuals or groups) and, in part, because emphasis may be put either on the changes that occur or on the changes that were intended. In talking about 'implementation' or 'adoption' of innovations one is necessarily focusing on ideas (although the ideas may have some clear concrete referent such as curriculum materials). But whose ideas? Typologies of innovations have tended to concentrate on the ideas of curriculum planners. If we are trying to understand the process of change, then it is likely that it will be more useful to focus on the ideas of those who are most involved in such processes, i.e., the teachers.

In this article, we make a distinction between 'organizational' and 'pedagogical'. This typification is ours, not the teachers, but it is a second-order concept that we have derived from teachers' talk about the four proposed innovations that we have been concerned with. Each of these innovations could be interpreted in a variety of ways, and there was considerable ambiguity about what was intended by the curriculum developers. Teachers, however, when asked directly about what they took to be the meanings of the innovations (Brown et al., 1976) and when giving commentaries on recordings of their own lessons (McIntyre and Brown, 1979), showed a strong tendency to limit the range of interpretations they offered and in so doing to reveal, in our view, quite clear differences among innovations in the kinds of interpretation they were making. It is on the basis of these differences in teachers' interpretations that we have made our distinction between two types, i.e., *organizational* and *pedagogical*.

ORGANIZATIONAL INNOVATIONS

From our earlier work (Brown *et al.*, 1976), in which we used group interviews to collect the views of about 500 science teachers from 50 comprehensive schools in Scotland, it emerged that there was general agreement among the profession that 'integration' of science meant that *all the science should be taught by one teacher*. Beyond this there were only infrequent references to other interpretations of integration such as those relating to the unified nature of the structures of scientific knowledge and enquiry. It appeared that 'integrated science' was primarily seen as a way of *organizing* the allocation of teachers to classes, and there was little evidence to suggest that it was viewed as having any implication for the kinds of knowledge imparted or for the teaching methods to be used. This was not surprising since the content of the course did not put emphasis on the unified nature of science; indeed the major constraint on the construction of the syllabus was the requirement that it be seen as including all the material of the alternative biology, chemistry, and physics courses.

It seemed, therefore, that the teachers perceived the change that was being mooted as a new arrangement or way of *organizing* the teaching so that the teacher takes on the responsibility for three separate sciences (biology, chemistry, and physics) instead of one. But there was no conception of any new 'integrated' form for the science to be taught.

Statements about the introduction of mixed-ability teaching were also collected and were about equally divided between those for and those against. The concerns shown were not, however, with such things as the details of teaching strategies to be adopted or with the problems of assigning differentiated work in this new context; instead, the teachers saw the advent of heterogeneous classes as an *organizational* change arising from new political beliefs and pressures of which they might or might not approve. A need for individualization of work was recognized by some, but the curriculum developers were seen as not having provided materials[1] or adequate suggestions for procedures that might be used in the classroom in order to take account of differences among pupils. The teachers' response to this shortfall was to continue to teach the classes in much the same way that they had always taught groups with more homogeneous distributions of ability. This was reflected in their answers to general questions about differentiation of tasks set for pupils and in the findings of a later study of teachers' commentaries on specific lessons they had taught (McIntyre and Brown, 1979).

It seems plausible then to suggest that the teachers' attitudes to mixed-ability teaching reflected how they felt about the new ways in which science classes were *organized* in relation to the abilities of the pupils. There was little evidence, however, to suggest that they perceived the innovations as implying fundamental changes in their own classroom behavior.

It is, therefore, our conjecture that these two innovations were seen by the teachers as *organizational* in nature; by organizational we mean that their implementation required some sort of corporate action of adjustment (e.g., new patterns of cooperation among teachers, organizational changes in departments, redistribution of resources), but that this was not necessarily accompanied by any change in the content or method of teaching. In conventional size classrooms, integrated science interpreted as 'all the science taught by one teacher' and mixed-ability teaching interpreted as 'grouping pupils in classes without reference to ability' may be seen as examples of organizational innovations.

Organizational innovations tend to be distinctive in the clarity with which they are presented and understood, in the lack of control which individual teachers can exercise over whether they are adopted, in the extent to which teachers are held accountable for implementing them and consequently, we will argue, in the extent to which they are in fact implemented. These characteristics are displayed by the two innovations discussed here.

First, the innovations are presented very clearly. There is no confusion about what is meant by 'all science to be taught by one teacher,' and the way to go about achieving this in the Scottish system is for the head-teacher to schedule teachers and classes in that way. There is some variation in the operationalization of 'mixed-ability grouping' (it may include the whole range of abilities or a small group at the lower and/or upper end of the range may be omitted), but within any school the interpretation is normally quite clear. There is, therefore, little potential for disagreement or confusion about what the innovation means or about what procedures are appropriate for implementation.

Second, the individual teacher has little control over the decisions to integrate the science teaching or to abandon the grouping of pupils by ability. In our centralized educational system, the important factors that influence those decisions are the constraints that are imposed by nationally determined curricula, the time and resources that are made available to support their favored science programs, the current dominant political ideology with regard to whether pupils should be grouped by ability, pressure on schools from science advisers and inspectors, and the extent to which a headteacher prefers to conform to officially sanctioned changes. In some cases, science departments[2] with strong views may be in a position to decide the issue for themselves, but in general, influences external to the department are very strong indeed in comparison with the individual teacher.

Third, in schools where the decision has been made to schedule pupils in mixed-ability classes and to organize science as an integrated subject (as it has in each of the schools used in this study) there is little alternative for the individual teacher but to comply with the arrangements. Teachers are accountable to departments and to headteachers for taking charge of whatever groups of pupils are allocated to them and for covering more or less the same content in the course as do the other teachers. Failure (or refusal) to accept mixed-ability groups or to teach science (as opposed to biology or chemistry or physics) would lead to early confrontation with the department head, headteacher, local authority, or parents.

Finally, the implementation of these organizational innovations has had striking success in Scottish schools. Within two years of the official publication of the integrated science scheme more than 80% of secondary schools had organized their first-year science teaching so that each class was taught all their science by one teacher; by 1974, 87% of first-year classes were arranged as mixed-ability groups. Our contention is that this widespread implementation follows from the characteristics of these organizational innovations that we have described above: The nature of the innovations and the procedures necessary for their implementation are clear; pressure for that implementation in this centralized system is effectively channeled through the Scottish Education Department, local authority advisers, and headteachers to school departments leaving little opportunity for teachers with adverse views to control the decisions;

and, since the ways in which teachers are held accountable to their colleagues and the wider public relate closely to these organizational features of their teaching, the innovations have been effectively introduced.

This account of how implementation is achieved has not involved discussion of the attitudes of individual teachers. In each of the schools in our sample we would expect that the decision to implement the innovations would be in line with the current views of some teachers but not of others; consequently, there would be individuals who will have to work in a way prescribed by the system that they would not choose if left to their own devices. Our hypotheses about how and by what teachers' attitudes to the innovations will be influenced in this sort of situation arise from psychological theories of cognitive consistency [e.g., Festinger's (1957), theory of cognitive dissonance] and from the pressures for attitude change that groups exert on their members.

Where there is inconsistency between the way individuals are predisposed by their attitudes to behave and the way in which they find themselves behaving, all cognitive consistency models suggest that there will be a tendency to try to reduce that inconsistency; whether that will involve an attitude change will depend on the availability and salience of other mechanisms for decreasing the inconsistency.

Teachers tend to be members of groups that comprise some or all of the staff of their departments. These social groups may have certain attitudinal norms relevant to innovations, in which case there will be group pressures on individuals to conform to these norms. Where a department has a high level of social cohesiveness, its members will probably make considerable efforts to influence each others' attitudes; less cohesive departments, however, are more likely to depend on bureaucratic structures and procedures to achieve compliance among their members.

Teachers who are obliged to conform to a school's decision to implement mixed-ability grouping or integrated science are likely to experience pressures from two main sources: from the 'authority' (school, local authority, or national system) that asserts this is the way things are to be and applies sanctions through arrangements for distribution of resources, regulations on pupil testing, and opportunities for promotion; and from their departmental colleagues insofar as they are dependent on them for cooperation, companionship, encouragement, and status. Whether an individual's attitude toward these innovations will change is likely to depend, we suggest, on the relationships of these pressures to one another and to the individual's initial attitude.

If teachers have negative attitudes toward an innovation which they are obliged to implement, one might hypothesize that they will experience dissonance between their attitudes and their behavior. Such dissonance will not be experienced, however, if they can convince themselves that they have been *coerced* into behaving in ways which are inconsistent with their attitudes. We suggest that whether teachers will be able to convince themselves will tend to depend on the attitudes of their colleagues to the innovation. If most other teachers in a department share a negative attitude toward the innovation, or if there are a wide variety of views within the department, the individual will probably find sufficient social support to be able to maintain this interpretation and therefore his or her negative attitude. On the other hand, the more generally the various others affected by the innovation accept it as a proper and reasonable, or even desirable, aspect of the job of being a science teacher, the more difficult it will be to sustain the perception of being coerced (unless one can perceive oneself as being coerced into being a science teacher) and therefore the more likely that one will experience dissonance and consequently modify one's attitude.

Thus, since all science teachers will be affected by the innovations of mixed-ability grouping and of integration (the latter being particularly salient for the heads of the biology, physics, and chemistry departments, since it implies some surrender of their personal power) their attitudes to the innovation will be important determinants of whether an individual's negative attitude is changed. If there is a majority view in favor of the innovation, there will be a tendency for a move towards this becoming a consensus view within the department.

This hypothetical tendency towards consensus is not so likely to occur if the majority departmental attitude toward an innovation is negative. In such circumstances, if an individual's initial attitude is favorable to the innovation, it will be consonant with the 'authority' view and also with the required behavior. This will exert a pressure which will support the individual in withstanding any group pressure for a change in attitude. While the relative influence of such opposing pressures is likely to vary with the cohesiveness of departments, it is not possible to hypothesize any general tendency for attitudes to change in one direction or the other.

The conclusion that we are led to is that individual teachers' attitudes to organizational innovations will tend to be correlated with the majority attitudes of their departments, but that these relationships will be asymmetric, with greater tendencies toward consensus in departments which are generally favorable toward an innovation than in those which are generally unfavorable.

PEDAGOGICAL INNOVATIONS

We have argued that the teacher's concerns with integration and mixed-ability teaching were primarily concentrated on the *organizational* features of the innovations. When we turned our attention to the other two innovations, however, we found no evidence of interpretations of 'guided discovery' or of 'teaching toward specified course objectives' that appeared to view the proposed changes as *organizational* in the sense that we have been using the word. In contrast, the interpretations reflected the *pedagogical* nature of the innovations, and by *pedagogical* innovations we mean those for which teachers are asked to change the behavior (their own or their pupils), the lesson content or the organization that goes on *in the privacy of their own classrooms*.

The earlier studies of teachers' perceptions of their own general patterns of teaching (Brown *et al.*, 1976) and of teachers' commentaries on specified lessons that they had just taught (McIntyre and Brown, 1979) identified a variety of ways in which guided discovery was being interpreted. Comments on the method were largely concerned with questions of sustaining pupils' interest and attention in class, of getting through the content in the given time, of ensuring that pupils learned what they were supposed to learn, and of teachers acquiring the skills necessary for new classroom strategies and the anticipated discipline problems. Thus, while there was clearly some variation among teachers in the ways that they conceptualized the characteristics of guided-discovery methods, they consistently viewed it as a classroom phenomenon that related to fundamental features of the teaching and teacher-pupil interaction rather than to any administrative arrangements.

Similarly, the question of whether to teach toward the objectives specified for the course was seen as a matter that the individual teacher would decide for himself or herself in the planning and evaluation of their own teaching. It was not felt that it should, or could, be imposed by the science department or wider authority.

Pedagogical innovations generally lack each of those several characteristics of organizational innovations which, we argued, lead to their widespread implementation.

First, the meaning of pedagogical innovations and procedures appropriate for their implementation is by no means always clear. In this case, the curriculum writers ascribed a variety of interpretations to guided discovery. They used 'discovery' in the sense of scientific discovery, pupils' abilities to discover, the process of learning by discovery, and discovery teaching methods; and 'guidance' was seen, on the one hand, as a *limitation* and, on the other hand, as a *support* for pupils' own discovery. Unlike the two organizational innovations, the practitioner was not provided with a clear unambiguous conception of what was meant by this pedagogical innovation. Closely allied to conceptual clarity is the issue of procedural clarity. It might be possible to clarify what was meant by guided discovery by suggesting how teachers could set about providing guidance conducive to pupils learning by discovery. However, that was not done and the teachers were left to provide their own interpretations of the innovation and their own ideas about how to go about its implementation. The teachers were left in a similar situation with regard to the other pedagogical innovation: while course content and objectives had been specified, no linkage between recommended classroom activities, specific objectives for sections of work, and general objectives for the course had been made explicit; there were no explicit criteria for pupil performance in relation to content that would enable the teacher to develop readily or select either formal or informal assessment procedures relevant to the attainment of the objectives.

Second, the choice between implementation or not belongs primarily to the individual teacher. Unlike the organizational innovations where the pressure is on the teacher to conform with an administrative decision, usually made by others, pedagogical innovations depend on the teacher's willingness to introduce change. Even at the department level, the evidence (Brown, McIntyre, and Impey, 1979) suggests that the methods to be used and the planning of the teaching are seen as matters for the individual teacher and not as appropriate candidates for departmental policies that are to be adhered to by everyone. (If the context were such that team teaching were used in open-plan laboratories this autonomy might well be modified.)

Third, although teachers in Scotland are accountable to their departments and to the wider public for the implementation of various organizational innovations, this is not the case for the teaching methods they use or for their planning and evaluation in terms of objectives. As long as the pupils are not so disruptive as to disturb others, and provided the class gets through the content of the course required for the examination, the teacher can structure and execute his or her teaching as he or she wishes.

Finally, the most striking difference between organizational and pedagogical innovations lies in the evidence available on instances of their effective implementation. The impressive record of organizational change contrasts with the depressing series of studies that report little change at the classroom level despite money spent on extensive developments and equipment of schools. For the change in pedagogy there is no coercive thrust from national, local, or school authority that demands that the teacher be accountable for what goes on behind the classroom door. The innovation will be implemented in any classroom only insofar as the individual teacher has a favorable attitude toward it, has the motivation, skills, and resources to modify his current patterns of teaching, and understands what is meant by the innovation and how to go about introducing it.

In these circumstances, where teachers are not forced to implement the innovation, attitude-behavior inconsistency is unlikely, departments see the decision to implement as the responsibility of the individual teacher, and different teachers may interpret the innovation in different ways, we would not expect to find any systematic relationship between the attitudes of teachers and those of their departments. The individual's attitude will be an important factor in determining implementation and may or may not relate closely to that of the peer group; other factors such as previous training, perceptions of pupils' abilities and interests, time constraints, and confidence in teaching skills will all contribute to the way in which a teacher views an innovation.

The following three sections describe a study of teachers' attitudes to the four innovations and the extent to which the findings of that study provide support for our hypotheses about the relationships between the attitudes of the individual teachers and those of their colleagues.

DEVELOPMENT OF THE ATTITUDE SCALE

Four Likert-type attitude scales corresponding to the four innovations were developed. They were based on 'position statements' for each innovation that were derived from the views expressed by teachers in the earlier stages of the work and are exemplified by the following:

(a) Attitude favorable to working toward specified objectives

It is the teacher's job in teaching S1 and S2 classes to ensure that, in general, pupils attain the various general objectives specified for them in CP7. One should plan one's teaching of each section, and of each lesson, to motivate and enable pupils to attain these objectives. Through tests and classroom observation one should assess the progress of pupils toward each of these objectives and evaluate one's teaching largely in terms of the degree to which each is being attained. In so far as a class, or an individual pupil, is not progressing toward the attainment of one of the specified objectives, one should be aware of this and should take some deliberate remedial action.

(b) Attitude unfavorable to mixed-ability teaching in S1

One needs to take a different approach to science teaching with pupils of differing abilities. A common course is undesirable because it holds back the more able and leaves the less able lost. In a common course it is not possible to give pupils an adequate grounding for the certificate course which follows. In mixed-ability classes it isn't feasible adequately to differentiate the work for the more able and less able. Effective teaching depends on assessing pupils' abilities early and on grouping and teaching them according to their abilities. It is unrealistic to expect pupils of the whole ability range to achieve the same objectives.

'Items' for the attitude scales were collected from teachers' statements; some 100 of these items, which in the view of four judges reflected one or other of the position statements, were used in a pilot study. Selections of items for the final versions of the scales were based on the correlations of the scores on each individual item with the total scores for the appropriate scale ($p<0.001$). The final version of the questionnaire with 46 items making up the four attitude scales was completed by the 86 science teachers from the science departments of 8 comprehensive schools.

The 8 schools were all situated in the central belt of Scotland and within the conurbations of either Glasgow or Edinburgh. Each had a comprehensive intake of pupils, taught integrated science to mixed sex and ability groups in the first and second years, and was large enough to have separate biology, chemistry, and physics departments. The science teachers were all graduates with teaching qualifications in at least one of the three sciences, and while everyone was attached and displayed loyalty to one of the single-subject departments, for the purposes of integrated science there was a collaborative arrangement. Our work in these schools involved an extensive exploration of the effectiveness of the innovations including a detailed classroom observation study, an examination of the policies and practices of the departments, and a program of interviews with teachers as well as the attitude study that is reported here.

THE STRUCTURE OF TEACHERS' ATTITUDES TO INNOVATIONS

In addition to demonstrating that the items were working satisfactorily in the attitude scales, we felt it necessary to show that the four distinct attitudes that we were assuming teachers would display toward the innovations were indeed exhibited in their responses to the questionnaire. Teachers' responses might, for example, have tended to reflect one or more overarching attitude dimensions not related closely to the specific innovations with which we were concerned. We carried out a Principal Components Analysis on the teachers' responses to the items and extracted six factors (using a screen test) which were then subjected to a Varimax rotation. These factors accounted for just over 50% of the variance.

The first four factors reflected the four attitudes: 10 of the 12 'guided discovery' items had loadings of 0.30 or better on factor 1, all the 'integration' items had similar loadings on factor 2, all the 'mixed-ability' items on factor 3 and all but 2 of the 'specified objectives' items on factor 4. Neither factor 5 nor factor 6 displayed loadings of 0.30 or better on more than three items of any one scale.

FINDINGS

The mean attitude scale scores and standard deviations were computed for various groups of teachers: the science staff of each school, teachers of biology, of chemistry, of physics, and heads of department (see Table 1). The great majority of these group mean scores expressed attitudes favorable to the four innovations. The three exceptions were scores from three schools on the mixed-ability teaching scale. (We are taking the simplistic view that the 'favorable'/'unfavorable' boundary occurs at the midpoint of a Likert scale.)

Table 1 Mean attitude scores + standard deviations[a]

	Attitude scale			
	Integration	*Guided discovery*	*Mixed-ability teaching*	*Specified objectives*
Total Population	5.2	6.6	−1.7	3.0
n = 86	(8.8)	(6.3)	(7.6)	(5.2)
Schools:	7.5	4.0	0.25	−1.4
1. n=8	(8.0)	(6.7)	(8.1)	(3.2)
2.	2.3	5.6	−6.3	5.4
n=11	(11.7)	(4.7)	(6.1)	(4.2)
3.	3.6	6.3	1.6	4.4
n=10	(9.0)	(5.5)	(6.1)	(5.5)
4.	12.0	10.1	2.1	2.9
n=13	(6.3)	(4.8)	(5.8)	(4.8)
5.	9.7	7.4	−0.9	2.6
n=10	(6.1)	(6.2)	(6.6)	(6.3)
6.	3.2	7.9	3.6	4.0
n=10	(6.8)	(6.1)	(5.6)	(6.0)
7.	1.8	5.5	−6.0	1.4
n=16	(7.1)	(7.3)	(7.4)	(6.7)
8.	1.5	5.1	−7.0	5.4
n=8	(10.4)	(8.6)	(7.7)	(3.0)
Biology teachers	6.4	5.4	−1.8	3.9
n=27	(8.7)	(7.1)	(8.2)	(6.2)
Chemistry teachers	5.1	6.5	−2.9	3.2
n=31	(7.2)	(5.2)	(6.9)	(4.1)

Physics teachers $n=25$	2.8 (10.2)	7.2 (6.3)	−1.5 (7.3)	1.9 (6.0)
Department heads $n=21$	2.7 (8.9)	5.3 (6.0)	−2.1 (6.2)	2.1 (4.6)
N.B. range	−24 to +24	−24 to +24	−25 to +19	−25 to +19
Neutral point	0	0	−3	−3

[a]Standard deviation given in parentheses.

An analysis of variance comparing the differences in attitudes among the different specialist subject areas (biology, chemistry, and physics) with the differences among teachers within those areas indicated that on none of the four attitude scales were the subject differences insignificant at the 0.05 level. A further series of one-way analyses of variance revealed statistically significant differences among schools in their attitudes toward integration (at the 0.05 level) and toward mixed-ability teaching (at the 0.001 level), but showed no significant differences among schools on scores relating to guided discovery or specified objectives.

An examination of the relationship between mean departmental attitude scores and standard deviations (Table 1) shows that those schools

Table 2 Correlations between individual teacher's attitude scores and those of other groups of teachers in the science department

	Integration	*Guided discovery*	*Mixed-ability teaching*	*Specified objectives*
1 Mean attitude score of all other science teachers ($n=65$)	0.26	−0.10	0.45	−0.19
2 Mean attitude score of other teachers within specialism ($n=65$)	0.24	0.24	0.33	0.27
3 Department head attitude score ($n=53$)	0.33	0.14	0.21	−0.25
4 Mean attitude score of 3 science heads ($n=47$)	0.45	−0.02	0.16	−0.29
5 Attitude score of A.P.T. ($n=28$)	−0.18	10.28	−0.21	−0.05
6 % of variance accounted for by other teachers' scores (1-4 above)	60	9	26	14

with the most positive attitudes toward integration (i.e., schools 4, 5, and 1) have relatively low standard deviations and high consensus (S.D. 6.1-8.0). A similar effect is apparent for attitudes towards mixed-ability teaching (schools 6, 4 and 3; S.D. 5.6-6.1). Schools with more neutral or negative attitudes, however, have much greater variation in their standard deviations and, therefore, in their levels of departmental consensus. Inspection of the corresponding figures for guided discovery and specified objectives suggests that the relationships between the mean departmental scores and the departmental consensus levels are much weaker.

Table 2 shows the correlations between the attitude scores of non-promoted science teachers and (1) the mean of the other science teachers in the school, (2) the mean of the other teachers within that teacher's specialty (biology, chemistry, or physics), (3) the head of that teacher's special department, (4) the mean of the three heads of science in that school. In addition, for four schools with an assistant principal teacher with special responsibility for S1 and S2 science the extra correlation is given. Finally, the percentage of the variance in teachers' attitude scores accounted for by all these various measures of other science teachers' scores are shown.

In relation to all four innovations, there is a slight tendency for teacher's attitudes to be correlated with those of other teachers in their own subject specialty. In the cases of guided discovery and specified objectives, however, these were much the highest correlations found and in no case did the correlation coefficient between teachers' attitude scores relating to these two innovations and those of other groups of teachers reach 0.3. Moreover, the common variance in scores was only 9 and 14%, respectively. This suggests that attitudes toward these innovations were for the most part personal matters for individual teachers, and insofar as they related to those of the other science teachers, they did so in idiosyncratic ways.

However, some of the correlations for integration were more substantial, particularly those between teachers and heads of department. The highest coefficient ($r=0.45$) related teachers' attitudes to the consensus attitude of the heads of the three departments. The departmental nature of this attitude was further reflected in the relatively high proportion of the variance (60%) in teachers' scores that could be accounted for by the scores of these various other groups within the science department.

In the case of mixed ability teaching there was a correlation of 0.45 with the mean attitude scores of all the other science teachers. Correlations with the other smaller groups within the science departments were lower, and the variance in teachers' attitudes accounted for by attitudes expressed by the rest of the department was substantial but not high (26%).

DISCUSSION

We have distinguished between two types of innovation. One of these (pedagogical) we have exemplified by guided discovery and specified objectives. We have argued that the decision to implement these sorts of innovation lies with the individual teacher, the innovations relate to aspects of the teaching for which the teacher is not accountable to the department or wider public, departments do not impose policies or pressures on teachers to conform on these matters, teachers interpret the innovations and devise procedures for their implementation in idiosyncratic ways, and there is little reason to expect a clear relationship between the attitudes of individuals and those of their colleagues.

This prediction was supported by the absence of any significant differences among schools in their attitudes toward the innovations (i.e., variations among departments are not significantly greater than variations among individuals within departments) or of substantial correlations between the attitudes of individuals and those of other teachers in their departments, and by the wide variety of levels of consensus, unrelated to mean attitude scores, to be found in different departments.

The second type of innovation, we have suggested, is organizational in the sense that it will involve organizational changes in departments and new patterns of cooperation among teachers. Our examples of mixed-ability teaching and integration do not require the teachers to implement any particular change within the privacy of their classrooms, but they do hold teachers accountable for complying with new administrative arrangements. The nature of the innovations and procedures for their implementation are normally quite clear, but the decision to implement, unlike the case of pedagogical innovations, is not the responsibility of the individual teacher. Instead, it rests with the school and will depend on factors such as external political pressures, available resources, the head-teacher's views, the attitude of the science department, and encouragement from local authorities. Some of these factors are characteristics of the school and it seems likely that there will be differences in attitudes among schools that reflect differences in amenities, social organization, relationships within the school, and susceptibility to external pressures. The significant differences found among schools in their science departments' attitudes toward these two innovations are consistent with this prediction.

We have also argued that because the implementation of organizational innovations is not an autonomous act on the part of each teacher, we would expect the attitudes of individuals to be influenced by others in the same department in a more systematic way than is the case for pedagogical innovations. In particular, we have predicted that departments with clear positive attitudes toward the innovations will have high levels of consensus among their members, and that in departments with neutral or negative attitudes consensus may be high or low. That sort of relationship should lead to a positive, but only moderate, correlation between individual's attitudes and those of their departments. Furthermore, for one of the innovations, integration, we have suggested that the attitudes of heads of departments will provide a particularly salient influence on teachers' attitudes; the success of integrated science depends on the three department heads valuing the idea, cooperating among themselves, and providing the resources, support, and rewards conducive to the development of favorable attitudes on the part of teachers.

Our findings give some support to these arguments: there were some moderate correlations between the attitudes of individuals and those of their colleagues (in particular, the correlations with all other science teachers for mixed ability teaching and with the three department heads for integration reached 0.45); and departments with the most favorable attitudes displayed a high level of consensus (low standard deviations) while those with neutral or negative attitudes displayed a variety of different consensus levels.

These results, we believe, give us some slightly greater insight into the gradual and uneven way in which the teaching profession adapts to institutional change. For those who are concerned above all with the effective implementation of innovations in schools, ours may be somewhat depressing results: they suggest that in certain circumstances it may be possible to create organizational conditions through which teachers may be influenced to adopt more favorable attitudes to specific innovations, but that this is so only for innovations which may be implemented virtually without reference to teachers' attitudes. For those classroom innovations which depend crucially for their implementation on the attitudes of individual teachers, it seems that professional colleagues are almost as powerless as administrative authorities to exert effective pressure on the individual to change his attitudes. Such an interpretation of our results may, on the other hand, be reassuring to those who value the autonomy of individual teachers and who trust their rationality: it may even be that to persuade teachers to change their classroom practices one has to give them convincing reasons for doing so.

Our arguments, and the evidence we have presented to support them, do not lead us to conclude, however, that the most appropriate strategies for curriculum change relating to the pedagogical process would be those that do not rely on teachers' mutual influences upon each other. On the contrary, our interpretation of the available evidence (e.g., Fullan and Pomfret, 1977) is that little change is likely when individuals are expected to sustain their understanding, enthusiasm, and effort in isolation from others concerned to introduce such changes. But to achieve the necessary corporate approach to innovative teaching it would be necessary for changes in patterns of working in Scottish schools to be made which would be much more fundamental than those involved in any particular curriculum innovation. Possibilities for pedagogical change depend on making it rewarding, rather than threatening, for teachers to engage in rational ongoing debate on their day-to-day practices. If aspects of classroom activity that have traditionally been the exclusive concern of the individual teacher are to become matters for departmental discussion, then the cost of the sacrifice of personal autonomy would have to be balanced by substantial benefits. These benefits might be of a material sort or might be such as to make the teacher's job easier or more satisfying.

One way in which teachers' work could become more satisfying might be through them having greater independence in deciding on the content and structure of courses. Although teachers in Scotland have been represented on the Working Parties that develop national courses, circumstances are such that their freedom to decide, to choose, or to create curriculum elements is very limited. In contrast, Ben Peretz (1980) reports an Israeli project on teacher-centered curriculum planning where the status and centrality of the teachers was assured by using nonteacher 'experts' as external advisers rather than as members of the planning groups; in Scotland Her Majesty's Inspectors and local authority advisers play dominant roles in the groups (sometimes with paralyzing effects on teacher members). The Israeli teachers received official recognition of their contributions in the tangible form of extra payment, and their remit called for the development of alternative forms of a course (varying according to teachers' different orientations, environments, and preferred practices). In Scotland there has been no extra financial remuneration for teachers and developments have been committed to the provision of a single orthodox course plan that denies the possibility of alternatives among which teachers may choose according to their own circumstances.

The existing arrangements for the professional training of Scottish teachers are not conducive to the fostering of the reflective stance that would be necessary for teachers to engage actively and effectively in policymaking. Elsewhere, Connelly and Ben Peretz (1980) have argued for enquiry-oriented teacher education programs and have suggested several ways in which this might be achieved through the involvement of teachers in research and development as consumers, participants, partners, or planners. They have no doubt that teachers are willing to participate in research and development in Israel and North America, and we suspect the same would be true of Scotland if teachers were encouraged to take the initiative in planning innovations. But many are currently unprepared for such an active role in the control and introduction of change; their preservice training consists largely of separate theoretical and practical programs while in-service training is primarily directed toward informing teachers about government and local authority initiatives or providing technical information about practical matters. Teacher educators might contribute to the development among teachers of the necessary critical consciousness of their working lives and of the conditions which shape them, if they were to place much more emphasis on reflection in practice. This might well be done through the introduction of enquiry-oriented programs of the type proposed by Connelly and Ben Peretz.

NOTES

1 More recently (Scottish Central Committee on Science, 1977a) differentiated worksheets for pupils of various abilities have been developed.
2 In Scottish secondary schools it is normal for there to be three separate departments of biology, chemistry, and physics; but for some purposes, and in particular for the teaching of integrated science, they are treated and act as if they were one department. There are generally three department heads of equal status with at most an informal understanding that one of these is the 'senior' head who speaks on behalf of all science teachers.

REFERENCES

Brown, S., and McIntyre, D. 'Factors influencing teachers' responses to curricular innovations.' *Research Intelligence* 4, no. 1 (1978): 19–23.

Brown, S., McIntyre, D., Drever, E., and Davies, J. K. *Innovations: Teachers' Views*, Stirling Educational Monographs No. 2. Stirling, Scotland: Department of Education, University of Stirling, 1976.

Brown, S., McIntyre, D., and Impey, R. 'The evaluation of school science departments.' *Studies in Educational Evaluation* 5 (1979): 175–186.

Ben Peretz, M. 'Teachers' role in curriculum development: an alternative approach.' *Canadian Journal of Education* 5, No. 2 (1980): 52–62.

Clark, C. M., and Yinger, R. J. 'Research on teacher thinking.' *Curriculum Inquiry* 7, No. 4 (1977): 279–304.

Connelly, M., and Ben Peretz, M. 'Teachers' role in the using and doing of curriculum development.' *Journal of Curriculum Studies*, 12, No. 2 (1980): 95–107.

Doyle, W., and Ponder, G. A. *The Practicality Ethic in Teacher Decision Making* (in mimeo), University of North Texas, Denton, 1977.

Festinger, L., *A Theory of Cognitive Dissonance*. Evanston, IL: Row, Peterson, 1957.

Fullan, M. 'Overview of the innovative process and the user.' *Interchange* 3 (1972): 1–46.

Fullan, M., and Pomfret, A. 'Research on curriculum and instruction implementation.' *Review of Educational Research* 47, No. 1 (1977): 335–397.

Heinemann. *Integrated Science Worksheets.* Edinburgh: Heinemann Educational Books; 1969.

Heinemann. *Integrated Science Worksheets.* Edinburgh: Heinemann Educational Books; 1974.

Kremer, L. 'Attitudes towards educational goals and their reflection in teaching behaviors.' *Journal of Educational Psychology* 70, No. 6 (1978).

Kremer, L., and Ben Peretz, M. 'Teachers' characteristics and their reflection in curriculum implementation.' *Studies in Educational Evaluation* 6 (1980): 73–82.

McIntyre, D., and Brown, S. 'Science teachers' implementation of two intended innovations.' *Scottish Educational Review* 11, No. 1 (1979): 42–57.

Scottish Central Committee on Science. *New Science Worksheets.* Edinburgh: Heinemann Educational Books, 1977a.

Scottish Central Committee on Science. *Teachers' Guides.* Edinburgh: Heinemann Educational Books, 1977b.

Scottish Education Department. *Curriculum Paper 7: Science for General Education.* Edinburgh: H.M.S.O., 1969.

Index